GEOSCIENCE

Understanding Geological Processes

DEE EDWARDS AND CHRIS KING

One Week Loan

One Week Loan

Hodder & Stoughton

A MEMBER OF THE HODDER HEADLINE GROUP

Note from the editors:

We would like to thank all the following people, for without their help and contributions this book would not have been possible: The other authors, for their original contributions. In alphabetical order, they are: Alastair and Zoë Fleming, Education Department, Keele University (Chapter 10); Colin Dickinson, Widnes Sixth Form College (Chapter 3); Dave Williams, Department of Earth Sciences, The Open University (Chapter 12); Maggie Williams, Birkenhead Sixth Form College (Chapter 8); Mike Tuke, Cambridge Regional College (Chapter 6); Pete Loader, St Bede's College, Manchester (Chapter 2); Peter Kennett, High Storrs School, Sheffield (Chapter 11); Tony Shelton, Stoke Sixth Form College, Stoke on Trent (Chapter 7).

We have had invaluable help from members of the Earth Science Teachers' Association (ESTA), through whom the team of authors was assembled and who encouraged the development of this book, but holds no responsibility for its contents. Colleagues in the Department of Earth Sciences at the Open University have provided comments at all stages. Friends and colleagues have loaned us transparencies, provided images of crystal structures and reconstructions of past environments which have enhanced the book immeasurably.

We would like to acknowledge the advice of, in alphabetical order: Diana Smith, Jane Wares, Mike Brooks, Ian Thomas, Val Russell. The authors and advisors made invaluable contributions to the text and to overall accuracy; however, any errors remain the responsibility of the editors.

Most thanks go to Phoebe and Dave who have put up with us during the long gestation of this book.

Dee Edwards, Department of Earth Sciences, Open University
Chris King, Department of Education, Keele University

Orders: please contact Bookpoint Ltd, 39 Milton Park, Abingdon, Oxon OX14 4TD. Telephone: (44) 01235 400414, Fax: (44) 01235 400454. Lines are open from 9.00–6.00, Monday to Saturday, with a 24 hour message answering service. Email address: orders@bookpoint.co.uk

British Library Cataloguing in Publication Data
A catalogue record for this title is available from The British Library

ISBN 0 340 68843 2

First published 1999
Impression number   10 9 8 7 6 5 4 3 2 1
Year   2005 2004 2003 2002 2001 2000 1999

Typeset by Wearset, Boldon, Tyne and Wear.
Printed in Great Britain for Hodder & Stoughton Educational, a division of Hodder Headline Plc, 338 Euston Road, London NW1 3BH by Redwood Books Ltd

Contents

Introduction: about Geoscience

About the book

This book is aimed at a wide audience: including students in their final years of school and first year at college or university, their teachers and also adults who want to learn more about the science behind current environmental concerns or have a general interest in Earth Sciences. As an introductory book that aims to be accessible to the general reader, none of the topics is covered at the depth appropriate for a more specialist audience, so a list of further reading has been provided.

Geoscience and its study

We recognise that the Earth is a complex, active natural phenomenon that has been the site of physical and chemical processes since its formation 4600 million years ago and biological processes for at least 3500 million years. In more recent times, systematic study of the Earth and atmosphere is an activity that has accelerated and now there is a wide range of specialisms focusing on different aspects of the Earth sciences that together can be called geoscience. Geoscience is a relatively new term; it encompasses sciences rooted in the solid Earth, such as geology, and also newer areas of study such as oceanography. One book cannot cover the breadth of the subject and we have focused, as the subtitle suggests, on geological processes.

Throughout the centuries there has been growth in scientific knowledge and understanding of the air we breathe and the land that supports us. However, the 21st century will see science that is more structured and organised than formerly. Scientists observe, explain, predict, and construct hypotheses to formalise this activity. Scientific advances occur when observations, measurements or other data cannot be explained by current theory. The advances usually involve increasing the complexity of the ideas (and the accompanying equations) to incorporate these 'exceptional' events. The

physicist Richard Feynman likened this process to trying to work out the rules of chess, from a small number of snapshots of the game. Despite this complexity, advances have been made, through thousands of individuals and teams observing, attempting to explain patterns, hypothesis-constructing, predicting, experimenting, data collecting and publishing in the areas of science where their natural curiosity and training have led them. In the future, it is likely that large teams with experts in different fields will collaborate to understand the complex interactions of Earth systems. Already there are cross-discipline international projects, for example the International Geosphere-Biosphere Programme: a Study of Global Change (IGBP) of the International Council of Scientific Unions. This is an umbrella for many other international, interdisciplinary studies, of gas fluxes in the atmosphere, ocean ecosystems and terrestrial ecosystems.

Grand ideas

Occasionally 'grand' ideas arise that bring together observational data and the understanding of phenomena, or simplify existing models. Galileo, for example, accounted for the apparent motion across the sky of planets, while stars remained stationary, using a heliocentric (i.e. seeing the sun as the centre) model (though, at the time, this explanatory theory was not universally welcomed). Mendeleev's periodic table of elements provided both an organising structure and a spur to further work, to discover the elements that the model predicted must exist. Mendel's work on variation led to plant and animal breeding programmes which are the basis of modern genetics.

The developments in instrumentation and mathematics since the seventeenth century have enabled physical, chemical and biological laws and principles to be investigated, quantified and refined. During these advances, however, our knowledge of the oceans, 70% of the surface area of the Earth, has been negligible until this century. During the Cold War of the 1950s and 1960s it was the military need for basic information about the shape (bathymetry) of the ocean basins that led the US Navy to the discovery of ocean ridges and basalt pillow lavas, the magnetic stripes (the so called 'ocean-floor tape recorder') and by the mid 1960s to the development of the theory of plate tectonics. This provided an integrating explanation of many physical features of the Earth's surface and processes within the lithosphere. At this stage the contributions of the oceans and the atmosphere were often ignored as component parts of the Earth system. We can speculate on reasons for this: at the end of the 1960s, more was known about the surface of the Moon than the nature of the ocean floor; atmospheric systems develop and move very quickly and, for both areas, data were sparse and the need was always to 'simplify the variables' (sometimes interpreted as – ignore them).

It is now clear that we need to know much more about the oceans in order to fully understand how the surface of the Earth works, as their contribution to moderating climates and buffering the interactions of the atmosphere and lithosphere begins to become apparent. Perhaps life began in the oceans; it seems that the future of life may well depend upon the oceans and our knowledge of their role.

Interactions

Since the publication of Rachel Carson's book *Silent Spring* there have been voices raised in concern at the damage to our environment, through pesticides that persist in the food chain and, more recently, fertilisers that pollute underground water supplies and consequently our drinking water. Issues such as ozone depletion in the atmosphere because of the release of CFCs, the environmental effects of increasing carbon dioxide through burning fossil fuels, the threat of global warming, accompanied by sea-level rise and desertification all feature in the media.

The study of the interactions between the oceans, weather systems and climate have come to the fore in the 1980s and 1990s, with the realisation that human effects on these natural systems need to be monitored. Recently, for example, we have begun to realise the scale of the cooling effect on climate when dust is thrown into the atmosphere by volcanic eruptions. These processes have been active throughout the geological past and their size and influence cannot be ignored. What we are working towards is a better understanding of how all these processes, and hence the Earth, works.

We especially need to know when positive feedback loops are in operation. Positive feedback occurs when small changes amplify each other, resulting in much larger effects. In other words: how much exploitation and pollution can be tolerated by Earth systems before the damage is irreparable?

The geological record shows that surface conditions on the Earth have not always been as we experience them now. The evidence indicates that the amount of oxygen in the atmosphere has been at its present level only since the Carboniferous Period, the last 350 million years; days have lengthened as the Earth slows in its orbit; the Sun's luminosity has increased 25% since the formation of the Earth; there have been periods when the mean temperature was much lower than at present (during Ice Ages and glaciations) and the sea level has moved up and down by hundreds of metres. The life-cycles of planets and solar systems take us out of the Earth sciences into astronomy and cosmology and the question arises as whether the human intervention can affect planetary evolution. The importance of biological processes in these global changes must be recognised, such as the formation of oxygen in the atmosphere, the soil of the continents and the effects of organisms on the development of the chemistry of the oceans. Armed with a biological, chemical and physical perspective we can assess the likely future evolution of the Earth and the impact of human activity and pollution on the whole system.

The rock record

Geologists seek to understand the remote past by studying fossils and other traces of past conditions which they find preserved in ancient rocks. We assume that 'cause and effect' were the same in the past as they are today, so that, for example, animals living today only on the seashore, indicate a seashore environment when they are found as fossils in rocks a 100 million years old. This is usually called 'uniformitarianism', the central idea of which is that 'the present is the key to the past'. Most geological processes that we can see operating today at the Earth's surface seem very slow, in terms of human lifetimes. A seashore has sand which moves up and down the beach with each tide and the cliffs behind may be battered by winter storms each year, causing rock falls, but in most of Britain the overall shape of the beach is the same today as 30 years ago. However, if you were able to return in a few million years, the sea may have 'eaten away' several cubic kilometres of the land, so the new beach is now many kilometres 'inland' from where it used to be. This central idea can be thought of as given enough time, very slow or irregular present-day processes can bring about huge geological changes.

me geological processes are, however, violent or
n catastrophic: an erupting volcano, for example, can
pill out many cubic kilometres of molten rock or ash in a
few days, devastating huge areas of land, killing all living
things. An earthquake can so violently shake the ground
surface that most buildings can be reduced to rubble in a
few moments. Water from a broken dam, or a freak
rainstorm can do more erosion down a valley in a day
than will happen in a hundred years of gradual wearing
away of the land by 'normal' erosion. A meteorite may
strike the Earth causing regional devastation that also has
global effects.

This is a third central idea:

- 'some geological processes whose record is preserved
  in the rocks represent single catastrophic events'.

When geologists try to work out a record of the events of
past times from the evidence preserved in the rock, they
have to be like detectives, and use these three ideas, with
a heavy dose of insight, and common sense.

Think of the geological events of each year as stories
'written' on sheets of newspaper, land ones to your right,
sea stories on the left. Most of the 'land stories' soon get
obliterated by normal geological erosion, and every 100
years or so a major flood will violently remove any
remaining traces. All that we can hope to find are a few
scraps of paper (the odd half headline, fragment of a
picture or few incomplete lines of print) in sediments laid
down in the seas around our shores. In a similar way your
stone might reach the sea still bearing your initials, to
form a 'trace' fossil of your life.

'Sea stories' have a better chance of survival, especially
if they are 'written' in the sedimentary layers far from
destruction by burrowing animals or violent storms: this
means well away from the land, and best of all on the
deep ocean floor where it is too dark and inhospitable for
scavenging animals, and far below wave and storm
disturbance. Anything which is not dissolved or
chemically attacked by conditions on the ocean floor will
eventually be covered by fine muddy layers, and
fossilised for posterity. There is an additional bonus,
geologists of the future could date the 'fossil' because they
could identify the age of the layer of mud immediately
below your stone, just as we can today. The deep oceans
carry a complete sedimentary record since their
formation. Sometimes different coloured layers of
sediment record single events like major volcanic
eruptions (e.g. Krakatao) which put enough ash into the
atmosphere to send clouds around the whole Earth
several times, before they fall back to Earth and became
part of the sediment on the ocean floor.

Although many geological processes can be
understood by studying today's processes and the
evidence they leave behind, others are clearly
characterised by sudden catastrophic events, for example,
a crater and the spherical glassy particles (tektites) caused
by the impact of an asteroid. Most geological events occur
at rates between these extremes, and the classification of
the type of event depends on the view of the observer. A
one metre sand deposit, the product of a single storm,
might be a catastrophe if it happened in a Saharan oasis
now, but will appear as one layer if seen in a cliff face
showing a sequence of sandstones 100 million years old.

Evidence and hypotheses to explain catastrophic
events, such as craters on the surface of the Earth, or the
mass extinctions of many species at the end of the
Cretaceous Period, provide a framework to examine the
frequency at which 'spaceship Earth' is bombarded by
extra-terrestrial debris. The Moon has a heavily impact-
marked surface, so why doesn't the Earth look similar?
The dinosaurs were very successful for around 300 million
years – will humans end in a similar way?

The human effect

Humans are also aware that continual uncontrolled
exploitation of the Earth's resources can lead to
accelerating pollution and degradation of our physical
environment. It can be shown that cultivation and
agriculture lead to higher rates of soil erosion. Fertilisers
applied to increase yields can wash into streams and
reservoirs, causing poisonous algal blooms and pollution
to water supplies. Recent calculations have highlighted
that humans have become the largest erosional force,
moving more rock than all the planet's rivers and glaciers.
Exploiting and burning coal, oil and gas ('fossil fuels')
means that the carbon dioxide in the atmosphere has risen
at a faster rate than at any time in geological history,
which is beginning to affect climate worldwide. However,
developing countries feel that they have a right to
advance in ways similar to the richer countries during
previous centuries. How can an acceptable balance be
achieved? Several conferences have been held to tackle
these matters, such as the Earth Summit in Rio de Janeiro
(1992) and Kyoto (1997). Phrases such as 'sustainable
development' and 'the polluter pays' have entered our
vocabulary. It remains to be seen how these principles can
be balanced against the need to feed an increasing world
population, with lifestyle expectations of housing,
transport, clean water and health care. Some of these
topics may seem distant from 'geology' but we shall
explain how they all have a geoscience basis.

Humans and Earth systems

Taking these perspectives into account the book introduces the reader to some of the basic principles of geological processes, as part of a model that stresses the interconnected nature of many processes in the natural world. Some scientists consider the Earth to be a continually self-regulating system, where, over geological time, natural processes that obey biological, physical and chemical rules constantly react to maintain the Earth conditions within reasonable limits suitable for life. This is done through positive and negative feedback loops within Earth cycles. We then need to consider whether these systems can cope with the extra stresses put on environments by one species of organism *Homo sapiens*, humans. Earth history is in contrast to neighbouring planets, where, if life ever existed, it seems to have been fleeting. Humans cannot surely want our planet, through their own actions, to become as uninhabitable as, say, Venus?

We believe that this Earth system approach to geoscience will provide a broad framework for understanding over the next few years, where all the disciplines can contribute their special methods and expertise to a better conception of how the Earth works. In the same way that many subdisciplines of medicine collaborate to advance knowledge of how the human body works, studying the geophysiology of the Earth should help us to reduce the amount of stress in the systems and so keep the planet healthy and habitable for generations to come.

CHAPTER 1

Planet Earth: an introduction

Introduction

The study of the Earth's origin, plus that of the solar system and the universe, draws upon the disciplines of astronomy, cosmology and astrophysics, but a brief summary sets the study of the Earth in a wider context. This is crucial to the understanding of some of the current 'big ideas' of Earth science, including the greenhouse effect and global warming. This chapter also introduces some of the 'Earth cycles', such as the water, carbon and rock cycles and how these are inter-connected with the processes of plate tectonics. The chapter concludes by considering how although most geological processes are slow and take place over millions of years, periodically there are catastrophic impacts by other planetary bodies. As a whole, this introduction aims to provide a framework for the detail of the Earth-focused chapters that follow.

1.1 Origin and evolution of the universe

1.1.1 THE EARLY UNIVERSE

It seems incredible that we can work out what happened when the universe began, billions of years ago, by looking to the furthest parts of the present universe. Most scientists believe that the universe first came into existence 15 billion (i.e. 15 thousand million, or 15×10^9) years ago in a 'Big Bang'. This was when time and space began. Soon after the event, the universe consisted of a dense, hot 'soup' of particles, moving away from each other at great speed. These elementary particles, called protons and neutrons, are the components, or building blocks, of atomic nuclei. At the beginning of the universe there was a great deal of energy and little matter, and the particles were ionised, i.e. they were charged particles within a hot gas state called a plasma. As the particles moved away from each other they cooled, so that within minutes of the Big Bang some of the particles could bind together into stable nuclei, such as the nucleus of hydrogen, with one proton; or helium, which has two protons and two neutrons. A universal ratio of twelve hydrogen nuclei for each helium nucleus was established. However, it took a further 10 000 years of cooling before the first atoms were formed, by capture of electrons. By that time, the universe was transparent to light. The hydrogen and helium formed clumps from which, after 10^7 years, stars and **galaxies** (groups of stars) were formed.

But will the universe go on expanding for ever? If the rate of expansion were to change, what might happen in the future? For example, some scientists believe that expansion will eventually cease due to gravitational forces and be followed by contraction of the universe into a 'Big Crunch'. This might then trigger a 'Big Bounce', where another Big Bang starts another cycle of expansion. However, if gravitational forces are weak, expansion may continue for ever; this is the 'Open Universe Theory'. Some possible futures are represented in Figure 1.1.

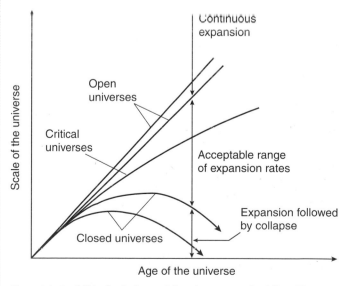

Figure 1.1 *Possibilities for the future of the universe: expansion followed by contraction (closed universes) and that of fast expansion (open universes). A position between these of continued expansion allows continuing growth*

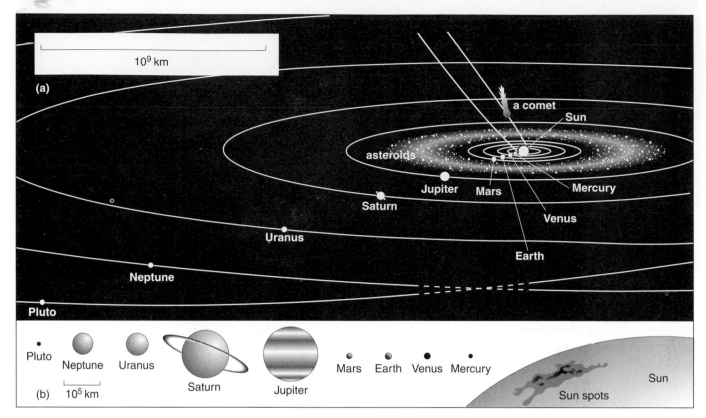

Figure 1.2 *Basic layout of the solar system: (a) distances to scale; (b) sizes of planets to scale*

During our lifetimes, there will be many further advances in knowledge of the early universe, as more advanced telescopes and other instruments are developed to be sent out of the solar system (Figure 1.2), to probe deeper into space and closer to the 'echoes' of the Big Bang.

Although these are fascinating topics, our interest is in those events that are particularly relevant to the origin and formation of the Earth.

1.1.2 FORMATION OF STARS AND PLANETS

Within the universe, star systems are being created continuously and are dying continuously, but this doesn't mean that there is an even pattern of stars and galaxies across the universe. The universe has a 'lumpy' appearance with regions of dense populations of stars, like the Milky Way in which our solar system exists, separated by vast expanses of empty space.

The first stars were huge balls of hydrogen and helium, but within them, nuclear fusion processes caused heavier nuclei to be formed. The process that produces the Sun's energy is the conversion of hydrogen ions into helium ions by nuclear fusion (called hydrogen 'burning'). This process also produces neutron particles. Gradually the core of a star such as the Sun is being depleted in hydrogen as helium is formed (Figure 1.3). Typically a

star like the Sun is composed of 75 per cent by mass of hydrogen (92 per cent of the **number** of nuclei) and 25 per cent by mass of helium (7.8 per cent by number), leaving only 2 per cent by mass for all heavier elements. The solar system was formed about 4.6×10^9 years ago, so these processes have meant that the Sun has been shining for 4.6×10^9 years, and is expected to continue to shine for about the same length of time in the future.

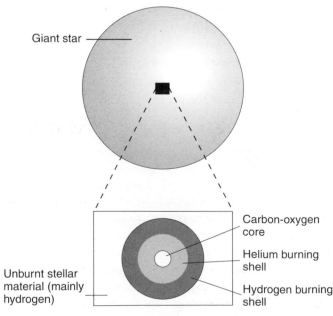

Figure 1.3 *An evolving star with burning shells*

Through the life of the star, its size and luminosity increase, enabling scientists to predict its past and future. As a star gets older it eventually runs out of fuel and collapses. This inward collapse may raise the temperature sufficiently for a new set of nuclear reactions to occur and the cycle to begin again. Through fusion, beryllium and carbon nuclei are formed. This process (and ones that form oxygen) is thought to occur in huge stars that glow orange, giving them their name **red giants**. When carbon fuses it produces neon and magnesium, giving out further neutrons so that more nuclear reactions can occur.

Occasionally, the end of a star's life is marked by a spectacular **supernova** explosion where all the particles are flung out to mix with the interstellar gas and dust and eventually form new stars. These explosions have been observed, at the rate of about one every 400 years; one was photographed in 1987 by an astronomer in Chile. It is only in this way that the heavier elements can be made, so we know that before our planet could form there must have been stars created and destroyed, since the Earth contains these heavier elements. Ultimately, in a star such as the Sun, the material may be converted to carbon, nitrogen, oxygen and heavier nuclei as it cools to a cold, dense sphere, perhaps only the size of the Earth, and takes no further part in stellar evolution.

It is by these processes, of star formation and reformation, and of nuclear fusion deep within stars that all the elements have been created – so we, and everything around us, have been created from star dust.

To summarise, the Earth is in many ways a very ordinary planet, orbiting an ordinary star called the Sun. There are millions of other similar stars in the galaxy called the Milky Way, and there are millions of galaxies in the universe beyond. All the evidence, from Earth based observation and space probes such as the Hubble telescope, shows that there are likely to be thousands of planets like ours, orbiting the stars, and some of these may even have evolutionary histories similar to our own.

1.2 Earth: a unique planet in the solar system

There are features of our planet that make it unique in the solar system. Only the Earth has surface conditions that allow liquid water to exist in large volumes, and water has been crucial to the development of life here, as well as to the development of many topographic features. On the surface of Mars, seen in photographs from Voyager missions, there are dried up river valleys. Recent examination of the surface rocks by the Sojourner craft

confirmed that water was on the surface in the past, but if it exists on the planet now, it can only be frozen at the polar ice caps or beneath the surface. On the outer planets, temperatures are too low for liquid water but some ice may be present.

The surface of planets such as Mercury have a cratered appearance which is the result of intense bombardment by meteorites and other debris. The Earth and the Moon were also subjected to this bombardment, particularly during the first 1000 million years of their existence, but processes on Earth, of plate tectonics and surface weathering, have obliterated all traces of this early phase. Since the evolution of life, vegetation and animals have actively joined the processes that are constantly reshaping the surface features of Earth, whereas our planetary neighbours (including the Moon) retain their lifeless appearance.

The atmosphere of the Earth is unique in the solar system. The composition of the Earth's atmosphere is quite different from that of the other planets, partly because the strength of gravity at the surface of each planet is different. Venus and Mars have carbon dioxide in their atmospheres, resulting from a runaway greenhouse effect. Venus has crushing gravity but Martian gravity is so small that it retains little atmosphere. Earth's atmosphere, however, appears to have stayed reasonably constant for millions of years (but not for the whole of geological time) with oxygen at about 21 per cent and the average temperature at the surface of around 288 K (15 °C), able to support plant and animal life. This is extraordinary, because the gases of the Earth's atmosphere are maintained in a state that is distinctly out of equilibrium, including oxygen which is very reactive. Scientists are actively examining the interactions between the atmosphere and oceans, in particular the bacteria, algal blooms, cloud formation and weathering, to discover the processes involved in the feedback loops or cycles that have kept surface conditions stable and suited to life. In this way, we may be able to tell if human intervention, for example by fossil fuel-burning increasing the carbon dioxide levels, might push the atmospheric system into an unstable state and permanently destroy the current balance.

1.3 The Earth and plate tectonics

It is time to focus on Earth and the processes taking place here. The structure of the Earth and plate tectonics are both explained in greater detail elsewhere in the book, but an overview will provide a framework for chapters to come.

1.3.1 THE FORMATION AND STRUCTURE OF THE EARTH

The Earth was formed from the accretion (sticking together) of dust particles and this was a process that did not involve heat. However, as the Earth grew in size, the pressures deep inside increased, causing the internal temperature to rise. Some melting allowed heavy elements, mainly iron, to sink to the centre of the Earth to form a metallic **core**. Occasionally we find iron-rich meteorites that have fallen from space and some of these may be the remnants of the cores of planets that disintegrated long ago. The detail of the structure of the Earth, and the ways that scientists have investigated the deep structure are explained in Chapter 2, so a short summary only is given here.

The Earth's core is surrounded by the **mantle** which is solid, and formed of less dense material than the core. The upper mantle has a composition similar to that of the rock **peridotite**, containing iron (Fe) and magnesium (Mg)-rich silicate minerals such as **olivine** $(Mg\ Fe)_2SiO_4$. Deeper in the mantle, the minerals take up different, higher pressure forms (see Chapter 3). The mantle is the largest proportion of the Earth, being 80 per cent by volume and 70 per cent by mass, but the processes active within it are still largely unknown. The minerals of the mantle do not contain a high proportion of the radioactive elements that decay to

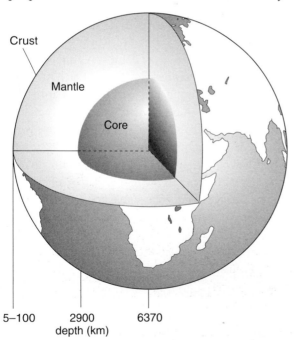

Crust

Mantle

Core

5–100   2900   6370
depth (km)

Figure 1.4 *Cross section showing the Earth's internal structure with depth to base of crust, mantle and core*

release heat, but because the volume of the mantle is so great, it provides much of the thermal energy that helps to drive the processes of plate tectonics.

The outer shell of the solid Earth is called the **lithosphere** (rocky sphere), composed of the **crust** and the topmost part of the mantle, called the **lithospheric mantle**. The crust varies in thickness from a minimum of 5 km or less under the oceans, to around 100 km or more beneath the highest mountains. The core, mantle and crust are shown in Figure 1.4, but remember that, at this scale, the lithosphere should be less than the thickness of the lines of the diagram. On and around the Earth is the **biosphere**, of living things, the **hydrosphere**, of oceans, rivers, etc., and the **atmosphere** of mainly nitrogen and oxygen. Traditionally, we study the 'spheres' of rocks (geology) separately from living organisms (biology), and the weather and oceans (meteorology, climatology and oceanography). However these divisions are artificial because the interactions between the spheres are strong, though very complex.

1.3.2 PLATE TECTONICS

The global theory of plate tectonics that shapes much of our geological understanding today was established during the 1960s. It provides ways of explaining the patterns of many of the surface features of the Earth, such as volcanoes, fold-mountain belts, and the largest mountain ranges on Earth, called **ocean ridges** (Figure 1.5). The outer part of the Earth, the lithosphere, consists of a number of interlocking plates which are in motion relative to each other. The **asthenosphere** (weak sphere) shown in Figure 1.6 allows movement of the overlying lithospheric plates relative to the solid mantle beneath. Some of the plates are composed only of oceanic crust, such as the Pacific plate, but most contain both oceanic and continental material.

The active edges of the plates are marked by earthquake zones and the depths of earthquake are characteristic of the type of boundary represented (Figure 1.5). At **ocean ridges**, the lithosphere is thin and here the plates are moving apart (diverging). Under these tensional forces, a **rift valley** can form, bounded on each side by steep normal faults. The high heat-flow can cause partial melting of the mantle to produce magma, which is contained in shallow **magma chambers**, only a few kilometres beneath the ocean ridge. The magma rises frequently through fractures to form pillow lavas at the surface, on the sea floor; this volcanism is one form of the process that is called **extrusion**.

These processes produce new plate material as the plates are pulled apart, resulting in extension of the oceanic lithosphere. These boundaries are known as **constructive plate margins** and are accompanied by shallow-focus earthquakes (around 5 km depth) at the spreading site.

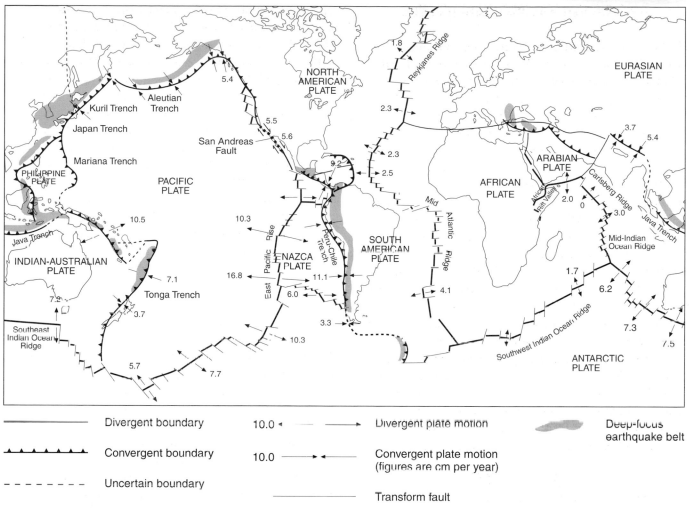

Figure 1.5 *Major plates of the Earth's surface and their boundaries*

————	Divergent boundary	10.0 ◄—— ——► Divergent plate motion	Deep-focus earthquake belt
▲▲▲▲▲	Convergent boundary	10.0 ——► ◄—— Convergent plate motion (figures are cm per year)	
– – – – – –	Uncertain boundary	———— Transform fault	

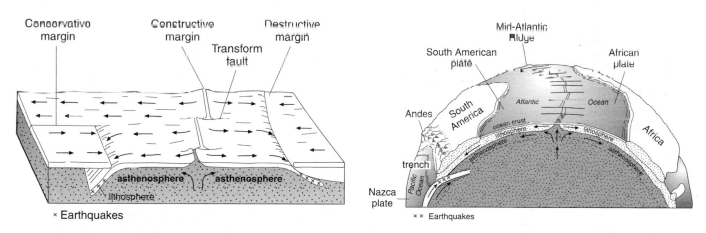

Figure 1.6 *The processes of plate tectonics in oceanic areas*

Figure 1.7 *Relationship between the African, American and Nazca plates*

Over a geological timescale of millions of years, about 40 mm of new ocean crust may be added to each side of the ridge per year, said to be about the same rate at which your fingernails grow. However, rates are very variable and can be up to 70 mm per ridge flank per year. On short timescales though, the growth is intermittent, with some parts of the ridge in active growth while others are quiet. As a consequence, fractures form at right angles to the ridge, to accommodate this differential growth. These are called **transform faults**, and are also the sites of shallow-focus earthquakes.

If new rock is being added at ocean ridges, some must also 'disappear' somewhere else (since there is no evidence that the Earth is getting bigger). This happens at **destructive plate margins**, where plate material is 'consumed' by being returned to the mantle. The ocean ridges are topographically high, buoyed up by the hot magma chamber beneath. The slab of new lithosphere slides downhill away from the ridge, becoming colder, thicker and denser as it moves away from the hot spreading centre. The growing plate is in contact with other plates at its edges. If the contact is with continental material, the oceanic plate starts to descend back into the mantle, sinking beneath the less dense continental lithosphere called **subduction**. It is aided by a pulling effect from the sinking slab which many scientists believe is the main driving force of plate tectonics. An **ocean trench** usually marks the junction between the descending plate and the over-riding plate. As the oceanic plate descends beneath the continent, it tends to stick to the continental plate, but occasionally slips to create earthquakes. These are shallow beneath the trench, increasing to deep (600–700 km) beneath the continent. This inclined region of earthquakes is called the **Benioff zone**, after the geophysicist who first described this pattern.

Part of the descending oceanic lithosphere begins to melt forming a magma that may rise to the surface in volcanoes, such as the Andes shown in Figure 1.7.

If two continents are brought together by subduction at a destructive plate margin, a **continent–continent** collision occurs and subduction stops. Usually, neither plate is subducted but both crumple, buckle and fold (see Chapter 8). Major fold mountain chains, such as the Himalaya and the Alps, mark areas where two continental plates have collided.

Transform faults are boundaries where parts of plates slide past each other horizontally and crust is neither created nor destroyed. Where major plate edges are involved, these are called **conservative** margins, such as the boundary between the Pacific and American plates near the coast of California. The well-publicised San Andreas Fault is a transform fault that is part of this conservative plate margin, and very prone to earthquakes.

The mechanisms that drive plate tectonics are not fully understood, though convection currents in the mantle must be involved. However, we do not know whether the convection is in many small, shallow cells or in several deep, thick ones. Mantle convection is discussed in Chapter 2.

The results of spreading ridges and consuming subduction zone activity form the complex 3-D jigsaw of the lithospheric plates shown in Figure 1.5. The sizes and shapes of the plates have changed through time, and the outlines and topography of countries have evolved as they move across the Earth on these lithospheric plates.

This evolution can be deduced from the environments and climatic conditions in which rocks were laid down. Later in this book you will read that Britain once lay south of the Equator, then was in the tropics, and more recently experienced desert conditions similar to those of the Sahara today. Plate tectonics can explain how it was possible at one stage of Earth history for Scotland to be part of a different continent, separated from the rest of Britain, and attached to what is now North America.

The thin outer skin of the Earth on which we live, and the processes that affect it, are the subjects of the following chapters; for example, both constructive and destructive plate margins are sites of igneous processes described in Chapter 4. It is important to remember that in relation to the volume of the whole Earth, we know in detail only that very small part represented by the surface and a few tens of kilometres beneath.

1.4 Other Earth cycles

The Earth is a dynamic planet, with many interacting systems. Individual scientists tend to study specialised topics, which are small parts of what we now think of as a large 'whole Earth engine'. Important components are elements such as carbon, nitrogen and sulphur, that move in cycles through the atmosphere; rivers and oceans, and the rocks themselves; carbon is particularly important in life cycles and the formation of carbonate (limestone) rocks. The water cycle is considered first, before studying another key integrating geological idea, the rock cycle.

1.4.1 THE HYDROLOGICAL (WATER) CYCLE AND ITS EFFECTS

Astronauts viewing Earth from space have commented on the appearance of this 'blue' planet, that might be more appropriately called Water than Earth. The oceans cover two-thirds of the planet's surface and the ocean currents, caused by differences in water density, temperature and salinity, are the driving forces of the Earth's climatic and seasonal weather systems. They in turn are powerful factors in the processes of weathering and erosion of the land surface, and the deposition of the resulting sediments (see Chapter 5). Water (as vapour) is the main gas produced in volcanic eruptions; water and ash form the towering clouds visible in most photos of eruptions (see Figure 4.1). Ancient volcanoes were also the source of Earth's water but now most water, even in volcanic eruptions, is recycled, little new water being added to the cycle. The whole hydrological cycle is driven by the Sun's energy and Earth's gravity.

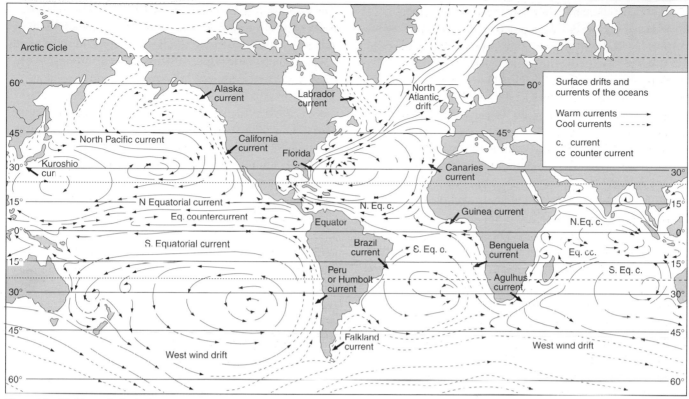

Figure 1.8a *World oceanic circulation patterns*

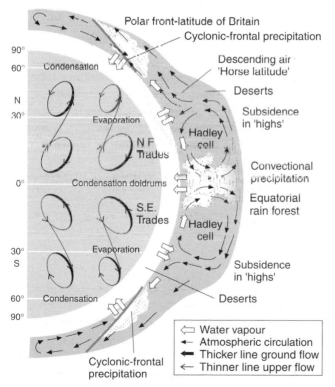

Global circulation (vertical). Thicker lines indicate ground flow. Thinner lines indicate upper flow. Warm, humid air rises at the equator, creating a low-pressure belt (doldrums) and dropping rain. The warm air travels to 30° of latitude, where it descends. This descent warms the air and decreases its relative humidity, creating a dry belt where the major deserts of the world lie (horse latitudes). A branch of the descending air travels as ground flow to 50° of latitude. There it meets and overrides the cold polar air *(polar front)*, dropping rain and snow. It returns to 30° of latitude as upper air flow.

Figure 1.8b *World air circulation patterns, and precipitation*

The major ocean currents are shown in Figure 1.8a and the atmospheric circulation in Figure 1.8b. Both are three-dimensional systems that change on all scales, minute by minute, seasonally, and also over much longer cycles that are associated with the Earth's rotation. Deep in the oceans, cold dense water flows from the poles towards the Equator. This water comes to the surface (upwells) in certain areas; the upwelling water is nutrient-rich and so provides extremely rich fishing areas. Surface ocean currents (Figure 1.8a) tend to flow away from the Equator towards the poles. These are 'warmer' currents moving into colder areas, like the North Atlantic Drift that keeps Britain warmer than most other countries at the same latitude. As the currents move away from the Equator they do not move directly north (or south), because they are deflected by the spinning Earth (the **Coriolis effect**). Consequently, in the major ocean basins in the northern hemisphere a clockwise circulation is established, while in the southern hemisphere the currents rotate anticlockwise. You may also know that periodic abnormal surface warming of the Pacific Ocean can cause the 'El Niño' effect, where currents flow in the reverse direction, causing catastrophic changes in weather over several continents and failure of the fisheries of Southern America (when the upwelling cold water stops).

Deep-water vertical circulation takes place on much slower timescales, in the order of thousands of years, and all ocean circulation is slower than the air currents above, which may change very rapidly.

Heating of the Earth's surface is strongest at the Equator, where the Sun is vertically overhead, or close to vertical for most of the year. This heating causes the air to expand and rise (giving low pressure) and to move away from the Equator, being deflected in the same way as the water currents (Figure 1.8a). In the tropics, this rising air causes daily rain, which, combined with the high average temperatures, means that biological activity and chemical weathering (see Chapter 5) are at their maximum. As air currents move towards the poles they become cooler and denser than the surrounding air and so begin to sink. The sinking air causes high pressure areas at about 30° North (N) and South (S), and low humidity means there tend to be deserts at these 'Horse latitudes'. In deserts, there is little chemical or biological weathering (as there is little water) but physical weathering may be moderate, because of high temperature ranges, from freezing at night to as high as 40 °C during the day.

At the poles, air is cold and descends (causing high pressure) then moves outwards to lower latitudes. Where these air currents meet the warmer currents from the equatorial regions there are the polar fronts, where the interactions between the air masses often produce rain. Although the polar front is not in a fixed position, in the northern hemisphere it is often close to 50°N, the latitude of Britain, and this explains the frequent fronts and depressions that are a feature of British weather. In these latitudes, both physical weathering (e.g. due to temperature changes), chemical weathering (involving water) and biological weathering are all moderately high.

Climatic patterns of the past can leave evidence in the rocks and so can help us work out the latitude of the time.

For example, at any time in Earth's history when climate was as it is at present we can expect deserts at about 30°N and 30°S. During extreme conditions, for example of an Ice Age, the climate patterns would not correspond to those of current latitudes, but would be compressed and shifted towards the Equator. However, there is evidence that even when the last Ice Age was at its maximum, there was still a narrow band of tropical climate close to the Equator.

Changes in the patterns of oceans and continents, caused by plate tectonics, can cause huge alterations in the circulation patterns of the oceans and atmosphere which can result in climatic change. For example, 50 million years (Ma) ago, Australia broke away from Antarctica, enabling the strong circum-Antarctic Ocean and wind circulations to be established. This changed world climate and an ice-cap on Antarctica developed. Ice ages lock up water on land and the sea level falls, exposing more of the continental shelf. Warming climates cause sea level to rise. Rising sea level can also result if volcanic activity increases at constructive spreading ridges, as the greater volume of the under-sea mountains reduces the volume of the flanking ocean basins (think what happens when you get into a bath). All the processes of sea level change can be 'recorded' in rock sequences, leaving evidence for us to find.

The ocean and the atmosphere interact very closely. It is the process of evaporation of sea water, and its subsequent condensation as rain, that produces all the fresh water on which human life depends, although it represents only 3 per cent of all the water on the planet. Warm air can absorb water evaporated from the surface

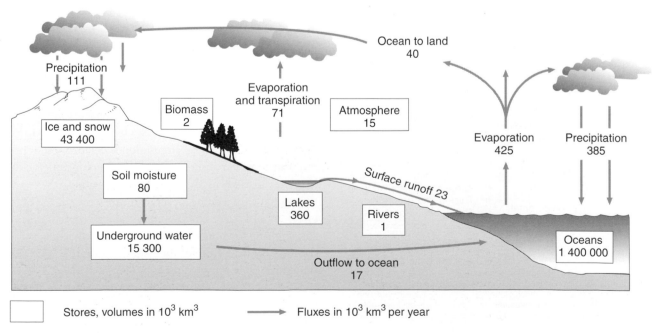

Figure 1.9 *The hydrological (water) cycle, showing the stores (reservoirs) of water, and the flows between them*

layers of the salty ocean. The air cannot hold as much water as it moves into cooler, higher latitudes, or altitudes, and this water falls as rain (or snow). It is the currents of air rising over the Himalayas that cause the monsoon rains of India, feeding the major rivers of India, Pakistan, Bangladesh and China. At a more local level, the west of Britain tends to be wetter than the east, because of the prevailing 'wet' westerly winds that deposit much of their rain on the hills of the higher west of Britain. The resultant rivers are important transport and deposition media in geological processes.

The hydrological cycle shown in Figure 1.9 has enormous geological impact. The amounts of rain affect river flows and also plant growth, which, in turn, feed back into cloud cover and climatic conditions. Tropical forests help to create clouds and rain; destroying the forests can have devastating effects on rain patterns and the hydrological cycle and can have similar dramatic effects on the carbon cycle. This is one example of the close interaction between the water and carbon cycles.

1.4.2 THE CARBON CYCLE

Carbon is a vital component of life on Earth. All living organisms contain carbon. Animals breathe out carbon dioxide into the atmosphere; plants draw down carbon dioxide from the atmosphere and then give out oxygen. Eventually some plant material may be buried and transformed into peat or coal. Buried organisms can also be transformed into oil or gas (see Chapter 9). Carbon in

fossil fuels is the most sought-after element in the world.

Carbon dioxide is regularly added to the atmosphere by volcanoes and is constantly exchanged with the surface of the ocean. There, it is taken up by photosynthesising phytoplankton (tiny marine plant life that cause ocean 'blooms'); upwelling cold ocean currents promote the growth of these simple plants. Microscopic and higher marine organisms live on the phytoplankton and these may transfer carbon to the mid-depths of the ocean when they die. For carbon to be preserved on the ocean floor, organic material must either be buried quickly, or be deposited where the bottom contains little oxygen. Today most organic carbon is probably being deposited as plant material in tropical deltas, such as the Niger delta in Africa.

Carbon is also found in the oceans as hydrogen carbonate ions (HCO_3^-), from the weathering of rocks by rainwater containing dissolved CO_2. This is taken up by various organisms to form their shells of calcium carbonate. When bottom-dwelling or planktonic animals die, their remains fall to the sea floor and may accumulate. Carbonate shell material falling from warmer surface water towards the floor of the deep oceans gradually dissolves, because carbonate is more soluble in cold deep water than warm shallow water. The depth at which this happens is around 4 km, but varies because of differences in temperature and water chemistry, and is known as the **carbonate compensation depth**. As a consequence, limestone, often made of carbonate shell material, is characteristic of shallow water environments; limestone

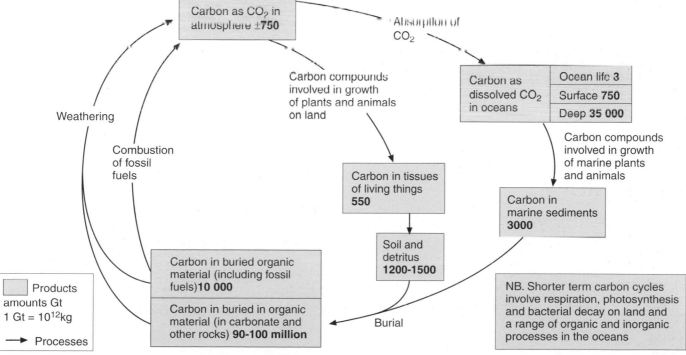

Figure 1.10 *The carbon cycle, showing the stores of carbon and the fluxes between them*

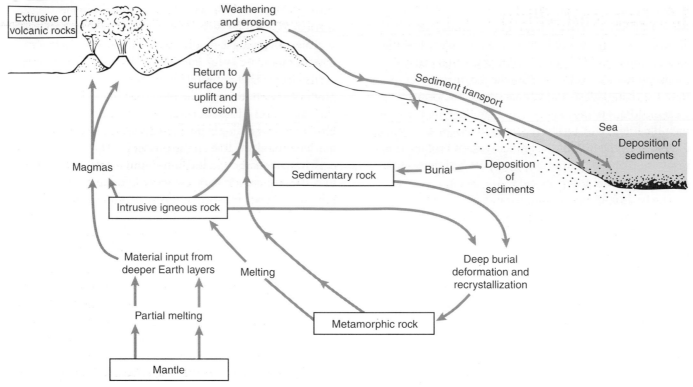

Figure 1.11 *The rock cycle*

cannot form below the carbonate compensation depth at the bottom of deep oceans.

The fluxes (movement) of carbon through the cycle and the sizes of carbon stores (places it stays) are shown in Figure 1.10. By far the greatest store of carbon is in buried carbonate rock (limestone). Carbon dioxide in the atmosphere is a 'greenhouse gas', that is it absorbs outgoing radiation, thus heating the Earth. Too much CO_2 in the atmosphere, through burning fuels such as coal, oil and gas, may result in global warming, causing sea levels to rise. Geologists now understand that the carbon cycle is also a vital control on the rates of rock weathering, the deposition of carbonate sediments, the production of oxygen and the variations in global atmospheric temperatures.

1.4.3 THE ROCK CYCLE

The water and carbon cycles both influence the rock cycle, shown in Figure 1.11 and Appendix 1.

It is convenient to begin with the formation of **igneous** rocks, as they would have been the first rocks to be formed on Earth. They are crystallised from **magma** (molten rock), for example in the volcanoes of constructive and destructive plate margins, explained in detail in Chapter 4. However, as soon as they are exposed at the surface of the Earth, rocks are broken down by a

range of processes, usually involving the carbon and water cycles, into fragments, particles or dissolved ions.

These materials are transported by air, water, ice or gravity and are eventually deposited, in deserts, deltas, seas and other sedimentary environments. Once laid down, sediment can be buried by later sediments and eventually transformed into **sedimentary** rock. The sedimentary part of the rock cycle is explained in detail in Chapter 5.

Deeper burial increases the pressure and temperature experienced by rocks. Eventually they will be changed (metamorphosed) through recrystallisation into **metamorphic** rocks. For example mudstones can be changed into slates. Metamorphism can also take place by contact with igneous intrusions, when the heat causes mudstone to be changed to a hard, splintery rock called **hornfels**. Metamorphic processes are discussed in Chapter 7.

If the temperature exceeds 750–800 °C some rocks will begin to melt, and these melts on cooling will become igneous rocks; thus we began with igneous rocks and one turn of the rock cycle has produced igneous rocks again. It is important to realise that these processes have been continuously acting since the first rocks were created so some rock components have been through several cycles. For example, a granite can be broken down to a clay sediment and sand, which will form sedimentary rocks. These may be metamorphosed into slate and quartzite, which when melted and mixed become the components of a new granite.

1.5 Occasional collisions

Many of the processes so far considered take place continuously and fairly steadily over millions of years. Some of them are cyclical but some are one-way; for example, once the Earth's core was formed, that change could not be reversed. Similarly, after plant life evolved, oxygen built up in the atmosphere and will not decrease while life exists. However, occasionally, catastrophic events occur that in geological timescales are instantaneous and that cause huge changes to life and geological processes. The Earth experienced a period of frequent bombardment by meteorites in its early history, over 3000 Ma ago, before life evolved. Since that time, most of the debris in the solar system has been incorporated into planets by gravitational attraction, though small planetary fragments (planetismals) constantly rain to Earth as meteorites. Sometimes there have been impacts with larger objects, of the order of 10–15 km in diameter or bigger. Usually these have their source in the asteroid belt (see Figure 1.2) but some may have been comets from the edges of the solar system.

Satellite photography has enabled us to see large structures on the Earth that may not be easily recognised at ground level. Circular structures are visible in the old rocks of the Canadian shield, and an oval structure at Sudbury, Ontario, has been interpreted as an impact structure (see Chapter 10) The most publicised impact crater is that formed at Chixulub, on the coast of the Yucatan peninsula of Central America about 65 Ma ago. The impacting object is believed to have been about 10–15 km in diameter. The structure can only be detected by geophysical means as the crater, about 200–300 km in diameter, has been infilled by more recent sediment, so is not visible at the surface. Thick breccias resulting from the debris thrown out by the impact have been mapped through Texas to Montana. This impact has been intensively studied because its timing appears to coincide with the boundary between two geological periods, the Cretaceous and the Tertiary known as the K-T boundary. At that boundary around 75 per cent of all species living on Earth disappeared (became extinct) including the dinosaurs and marine animals such as the ammonites. Controversy has centred on whether the impact was the cause of the extinctions or not; most geologists now agree that it was a major factor, though some palaeontologists argue that the dinosaurs and some other species were already in terminal decline. Many scientists believe that the impact caused fires that swept around the globe, of which the remains are preserved in a layer of soot that is found at this geological boundary worldwide. The fires and the impact would have released particles into the air that might have blocked out the light of the Sun, reducing photosynthesis so severely that the plants died. This was especially the case because the rocks beneath the impact site contained sulphates. The impact released billions of tonnes of sulphur oxides into the air which formed droplets that blocked out the sunlight and also caused acid rain. As a result herbivores would also have died, but scavengers might have survived for longer. What is puzzling is not that so many species died out but that some, like the crocodiles, appear to have been unaffected by the event. This example shows that impacts of objects of the order of 10–15 km diameter, only a small fraction of the size of the Earth, can have devastating effects on life and geological processes.

Cratering is now thought to be a significant geological process, affecting planetary and biological evolution. It has been calculated that craters less than 20 km across involving objects of less than 1 km diameter, have only local effects, but that the Earth can expect to receive larger impacts that may have more catastrophic effects every 50 million years on average. We hope the next one won't be too soon.

1.6 Summary

1 The Earth formed 4.6×10^9 years ago, with the other planets of the solar system. The universe, however, is 15×10^9 years old and several cycles of galaxy formation preceded the formation of our own galaxy.
2 The Earth has a core, mantle and crust (Chapter 2). The outer Earth is formed of a series of interlocking plates that move relative to each other by the processes of plate tectonics. Constructive and destructive plate boundaries are major sites of igneous processes (Chapter 4).
3 Continent–continent collisions are major sites of metamorphism (Chapter 7) and tectonic activity (Chapter 8).
4 Many geological processes acting on the Earth are both cyclical and interacting: examples are the water, carbon and rock cycles.
5 Occasionally, geological processes and life on Earth are disrupted by impacts from asteroids

1.7 Questions

1 There is some carbon in the Sun, but it must be called 'second-hand'. Why is this?
2 Explain how abstraction of water from rivers for human use does not permanently remove this water from the water cycle.
3 Assume from Figure 1.10 that of the 1×10^9 tonnes of carbon being deposited each year, half is as fossil fuel. At that rate, how long would it have taken to deposit all the carbon in the current fossil fuel store?
4 Describe the main features of plate tectonics. How would you recognise an ancient plate boundary?
5 On a copy of the rock cycle (Figure 1.11) highlight in green those processes linked to the carbon cycle (Figure 1.10) and, in blue, those processes linked to the hydrological cycle (Figure 1.9). Repeat for a copy of the hydrological cycle (rock cycle links in red and carbon cycle links in green) and for a copy of the carbon cycle. This will emphasise how closely these key cycles are linked together.
6 In what ways can plate tectonic processes be described as a cycle? Try drawing a plate tectonic cycle.

CHAPTER 2

Earth's structure: probing using geophysics

Introduction

For most of us, the Earth seems very stable, changing little in our lifetime. Even so, we are frequently reminded of the dynamic nature of our planet when confronted with news reports of the devastating effects of a large earthquake. At least 40 moderate earthquakes cause damage somewhere in the world each year and, with over 1000 earthquakes recorded daily, even Britain is not immune from the occasional tremor. So what are earthquakes? Why do they occur? Can they be prevented? How they contribute to our knowledge of the Earth's internal structure is one of the keys to our understanding of the way the Earth works.

2.1 Case Study: Shaking all over

2.1.1 KOBE, JAPAN – 17 JANUARY 1995... 5000 DEAD

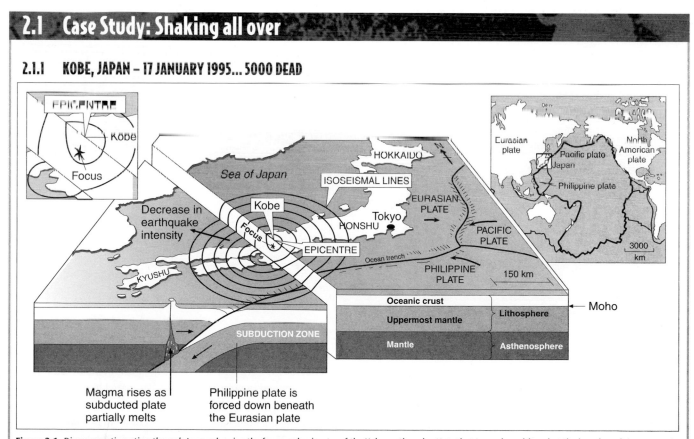

Figure 2.1 *Diagrammatic section through Japan showing the focus and epicentre of the Kobe earthquake. Note that Japan is positioned at the junction of three tectonic plates but that the fault which caused the earthquake is some distance from the main collision zone*

On the 16 January 1995, fishermen from Kobe, Japan's sixth largest city and the world's sixth largest port, reported some rather unusual phenomena. In the Strait of Akashi, a region to the south of the port, small fish were seen floating on water which had become turbid and brown in colour. Between 4.30 am and 5.30 am the following morning, many people witnessed strange flashes of red and blue light in the sky. At 5.46 am an earthquake, with a magnitude of 7.2 on the Richter scale, struck the northern part of Awaji Island, 32 km south of Kobe. This was the **epicentre**, the point on the Earth's surface directly above where the earthquake occurred (**focus**), where the destructive effects were greatest. (Figure 2.1)

The effect of this 'direct hit' on a city of 1.5 million people was devastating. Within 20 seconds, what was thought to be one of the most earthquake-proof cities in Japan was laid to waste. Traditionally built wooden-framed houses, many with heavy tile roofs, cracked and then collapsed, triggering numerous fires from fractured gas pipes. A surprising number of high-rise buildings, built in the mid-1970s, collapsed at the fifth floor as a result of a weaker superstructure above that level. Many roads and railway bridges were severely damaged because of fractures in critical support structures as the ground shook. The buildings and highways that collapsed were usually the older ones which had not been built to the stringent modern building regulations

that enabled newer structures to survive (Figure 2.2).

In areas near the coast, where reclaimed land was soft and waterlogged, the ground became liquefied as shaking reduced friction between grains (**liquefaction**). Structures sank and settled at odd angles as the sediment flowed from beneath or moved downslope as a landslide or mudflow. A section of the elevated Hanshin Expressway, built on alluvial (river) sediments, sheared at the base of 15 of its reinforced concrete pillars and tipped over at an angle of 45 degrees. The damage was worse in this area because unconsolidated sediment magnifies the earthquake waves, increasing the intensity of ground motion; this effect was also very damaging in the 1985 Mexico City and 1989 San Francisco earthquakes.

A comparison of satellite microwave-radar images, before and after the Kobe earthquake, shows that the earthquake was caused by a sudden movement along a fault running on the north side of Awaji Island. This resulted in horizontal slip of up to three metres in some places with a vertical displacement in ground levels of over a metre. This can be seen where fences and irrigation ditches have been pushed out of alignment and fault escarpments (small cliff faces) mark the vertical effects of the movement. The damage in the photograph (Figure 2.4) clearly shows the effects of the movement on the 'Bullet Train' tracks.

Figure 2.2 *Destruction and damage caused by the Kobe earthquake*

When the fault moved early that morning, a series of shock waves spread out from the earthquake focus, 14 km below the epicentre. The pulse shook the ground a maximum of 175 mm in a horizontal direction and 100 mm in a vertical direction, the greatest movement ever recorded in Japan. The areas most damaged showed that it was the strong horizontal pulse that

caused most of the destruction. After the initial earthquake, 716 **aftershocks** were recorded in the area within the next 24 hours as Japan, and the rest of the Earth, resonated like a bell for up to a month afterwards.

In all, the Kobe earthquake killed more than 5 000 people, injured 25 000 and caused an estimated $200 billion in damage.

2.1.2 HARMER HILL, SHREWSBURY UK – 8 MARCH 1996... ONE HAMSTER SLIGHTLY SHAKEN!

This Shropshire earthquake (one of many in the area in recent years) was hardly earth-shattering when compared to Kobe. It struck just before midnight and was measured at just 3.2 on the Richter scale. Even so, shock waves were felt up to 50 km away (Figure 2.3). The village of Harmer Hill, 10 km north of Shrewsbury, was the epicentre of the two-minute tremor which was caused by the rupture of a fault some 18 km below the village. Residents woke to what sounded like an explosion and although buildings were rocked and alarms set off, there were no reports of damage or injuries – apart from a few startled pets. On average, Britain can expect three 'quakes of this size out of the 400 or so British earthquakes recorded every year. Many of these are centred on the ancient rocks and faults of the Welsh borderlands.

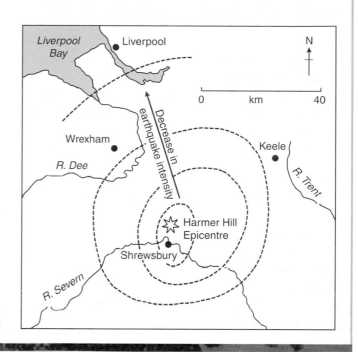

Figure 2.3 *A map showing the decrease in the effects of the earthquake with distance from its epicentre*

2.2 Clues from Earth and beyond

Why does the Earth 'ring' like a bell for up to a month after a large earthquake such as at Kobe? How can an earthquake, recorded within minutes on the other side of the world, fail to be detected in some areas closer to the event?

It is the answers to these questions which help provide the evidence for the structure and composition of the Earth's interior. But the significance of this evidence only becomes clear after a review of clues from past discoveries about the Earth (and beyond).

2.2.1 VITAL STATISTICS

The ancient Greeks considered the Earth to be spherical in shape but it is not a true sphere because it is slightly flattened at its poles. While the diameter at the Equator is 12 756 km, the polar diameter is only 12 714 km. This shape, the combined result of gravitational and centripetal forces, is termed an **oblate spheroid** and was accurately predicted by Sir Isaac Newton when confirming his law of gravitation in 1687.

Newton's law of gravitation describes the force of attraction F_g between two masses M (the Earth) and m (any mass on the Earth's surface) separated by a distance r (the radius of the Earth) and can be represented in the equation:

$$F_g = \frac{GMm}{r^2}$$

where G is the universal gravitational constant $G = 6.67 \times 10^{-11}$ Nm²kg⁻².

From this equation, the mass of the Earth has been calculated as 5.98×10^{24} kg (i.e. 598 with 22 noughts) which gives a **mean relative density** (the mass of a body compared with the mass of an equal volume of water) for the Earth of 5.5. There are no units because the quantity is a ratio of densities. Rocks from the surface of the Earth will normally give a relative density (RD) of between 2.5 and 3.0. You can investigate this yourself by taking common rocks, such as granite and basalt, and weighing a specimen in grammes, on a spring balance in air and then weighing it again suspended in water. The relative density can be calculated as follows:

$$RD = \frac{\text{mass of rock in air}}{\text{mass of rock in air} - \text{apparent mass of rock in water}}$$

Characteristic values are, for granite (typical of rock from the continents) 2.65, and for basalt (typical of rock from the ocean floor) 3.00.

You will have concluded from this that, if the density of surface rock is much lower than the mean density of the Earth, the densities of rocks deep inside the Earth must be greater than the mean density to compensate.

Even rocks from the bottom of the deepest boreholes (around 12 km) are only slightly denser than surface rocks. On rare occasions, however, we do find rocks at the surface that have been brought from much greater depth. An example is where volcanoes erupt lava containing unaltered fragments of country rock or the underlying mantle (called **xenoliths**, see Figure C.1) which have been broken off during the rise of molten rock to the surface. Xenoliths may come from as deep as 60 km and are a direct indication of the composition of rock at that depth. These rocks have a higher relative density of around 3.3.

But this only tells us about rocks from a depth of about 60 km. How can we find what the Earth is like at greater depths?

2.2.2 OUT OF THIS WORLD

Surprisingly, one of the clues about the very deep Earth comes not from the Earth but from outer space. The area of the solar system between Mars and Jupiter is strewn with asteroids, particles of which occasionally fall to Earth as meteorites. There are two main types: stony meteorites (consisting mainly of silicate minerals with 10 per cent nickel-iron) and iron meteorites (composed of 90 per cent iron and 10 per cent nickel). Both have high densities, unlike surface rocks, with iron meteorites being particularly dense (RD about 7.5). As these are considered to be typical of the material making up the rocky planets of the solar system, it is reasonable to conclude that they are more likely to represent the overall composition of rock from the centre of a planetary body rather than from its surface. Could this be the material of which the inner parts of the Earth are composed? It is the destructive power of earthquakes that will provide us with more clues.

2.3 Seismic waves

2.3.1 SHAKE, RATTLE AND ROLL

Japan sits at the junction between three plates: the Pacific, Eurasian and Philippine (Figure 2.1). During plate

Figure 2.4 *Massive damage misalignment of the 'Bullet train' tracks which buckled rather than broke during elastic rebound because they are less rigid than other structures, Kobe earthquake, January 1995, Japan*

Wall

Railway

Fault

Stress applied

Deformation (strain)

Elastic rebound

movement, the rocks at the boundaries are being either slowly squeezed together (**compression**), or pulled apart (**tension**) or moved past one another (**shear**). As a result, the rocks deform or store the energy until they suddenly break, forming a **fault**. Earthquakes are the vibrations of the ground caused by these sudden movements as the stored energy is released. You can demonstrate this by bending a stick, causing the middle to be under tension. More force (**stress**) on the stick will cause it to change its shape (**strain**) until it finally snaps, releasing all the stored energy at once. Major faults store energy as strain (a slight bending or stretching) in the rocks. The energy is released when the friction between rocks on either side is overcome and the strain is released by fracture or fault movement, usually in a series of jolts over a period of time. This process is sometimes referred to as 'elastic rebound' as the rocks on either side of the fault stretch like elastic and then spring back to their original undeformed shape (although to a different position) after they have 'snapped' (Figure 2.4).

It is clear from the Kobe earthquake that a huge amount of strain energy was released and transmitted through the ground. During an earthquake, the elastic strain energy stored in the rock is released in various ways. Some is used to do the work of moving fault blocks (up, down or sideways), some is converted into heat or sound and some into kinetic energy.

Some of the energy generated by movement along a fault is transmitted as shock waves which radiate from the focus. Although surface waves are mainly responsible for the destructive effects of an earthquake, it is the **body waves**, capable of travelling through the Earth, which are of most use in our search for knowledge of the Earth's deep interior.

Body waves are of two types: **P-waves** (primary or pressure waves) and **S-waves** (secondary or shear waves). P-waves are also called **longitudinal** waves and, like sound waves, the ground particles vibrate in the direction the waves travel. The effect on a rock is a series of compressions and **dilatations** where the rock is alternately compressed and stretched as the wave passes. S-waves are **transverse** waves in which the vibrations occur at right angles to the direction of the wave. These can be seen in Figure 2.5.

The amount by which a rock can resist a change in volume as the forces of the P-wave act on it is a measure of its **incompressibility** (or bulk modulus). Figure 2.5 shows the rectangular sections of rock as the P-wave passes through (all angles remain at 90 degrees although the volume is changed). A rock is more able to resist such deformation than, for example, a sponge, since a sponge is

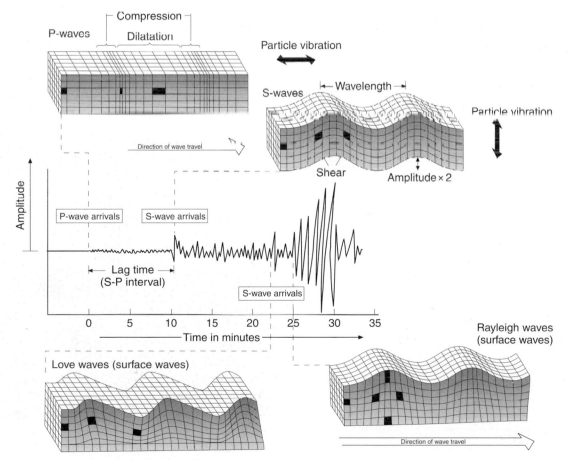

Figure 2.5 *A seismogram recorded at some distance from the Kobe epicentre and the forms of ground motion associated with earthquake waves passing through rock*

Figure 2.6 *Types of earthquake waves and their properties*

Earthquake wave	Other names	Mode of propagation	Properties
Surface waves	Love, L-waves Rayleigh waves	Lateral and elliptical movement of the surface	Large amplitude, long wavelength, responsible for rolling 'ground motion' that causes most destruction
Primary waves (body waves)	P-waves, push, pressure, compression/ dilatation, longitudinal waves	Compressions and dilatations of particles in direction of wave travel	Faster of the body waves; velocity depends upon density and incompressibility; travel through solids but more slowly through liquids
Secondary waves (body waves)	S-waves, shear transverse waves,	Movement of particles by shear at right angles to wave travel direction	Slower of the body waves; travel through solids only; not transmitted by liquids

easily compressed. Therefore, a rock is said to be more *in*compressible. In the case of S-waves, the rectangular section of rock is distorted and the degree to which a rock is able to resist this change in its shape without changing its volume is a measure of its **rigidity** (its shear modulus).

The velocity of body waves is related to both these moduli and the density of the rock as summarised by the formulae below:

$$\text{P-wave velocity} = \sqrt{\frac{K + \dfrac{4\mu}{3}}{\rho}}$$

$$\text{S-wave velocity} = \sqrt{\frac{\mu}{\rho}}$$

ρ = density;
K = bulk modulus (a measure of incompressibility or resistance to change in volume without change in shape);
μ = shear modulus (a measure of rigidity or resistance to change in shape without change in volume)

When rocks are subjected to higher confining pressures, i.e they are buried deeper, both density and elastic moduli increase. The formulae show that the velocity of P-waves will *increase* as incompressibility increases but *decrease* as density increases. As incompressibility increases faster than density, we find that the deeper the rock, the greater the P-wave velocity.

P-waves travel about 1.7 times faster than S-waves (in granite approximately 5.9 kms^{-1} for P-waves; 3.2 kms^{-1} for S-waves) and so are the first to be recorded at a seismic observatory some distance from the earthquake epicentre. P-waves are transmitted by solid and liquid rock, water and even gas (sound waves are P-waves). Indeed, early P-wave arrivals through the atmosphere are thought to be audible to some animals whose reactions are the first indication of an approaching earthquake.

S-wave velocity depends upon the rigidity of the rock as well as its density. The more rigid the rock, the greater the S-wave velocity. Unlike solids, which are held in shape by elastic forces, fluids (liquids and gases) have no rigidity and do not resist shear, but deform without a return to their original shape. Thus all fluids are incapable of transmitting shear waves. In practice, since rigidity increases faster than density with depth, like P-waves, S-waves also travel faster in deeper rocks. However, as S-waves are shear waves, they are not transmitted through liquids or liquid rock.

Surface waves travel along the Earth's surface and have long wavelengths (Figure 2.6). They are mainly responsible for the destructive force of an earthquake. Surface waves are of two types. **Love waves** which shake the ground from side to side with no vertical displacement and **Rayleigh waves**, in which the elliptical movement of the ground caused the rolling motion so evident in the Kobe earthquake (Figure 2.5). Both are particularly damaging to surface structures but the effects soon die out as the intensity decreases with depth as well as distance from the epicentre.

2.3.2 RECORDING THE EVENT

Seismometers are the instruments used to detect earth movements transmitted by seismic waves and **seismographs** record them as **seismograms**. They are designed to respond to, and amplify, the fairly low frequencies and minute ground motions caused by distant earthquakes. A seismic observatory will usually consist of three seismometers set out at right angles to each other to measure the vertical and the two horizontal components of the ground motion. In this way a three-dimensional picture of earth movements can be gained. The advantage of micro-miniaturisation is that modern instruments consisting of three-component seismometers, each element capable of measuring in one direction, can now

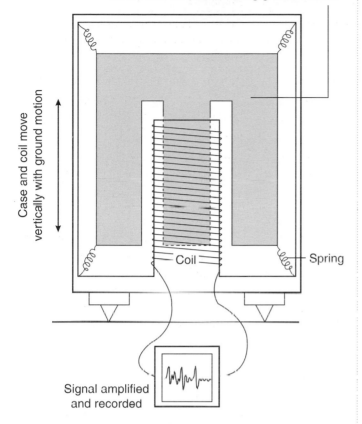

Heavy magnetic mass remains relatively still because of its inertia during ground motion

Case and coil move vertically with ground motion

Coil — Spring

Signal amplified and recorded

Figure 2.7 *Principle of a modern seismometer set up to record vertical ground motions*

be situated deep in boreholes, far from unwanted background noise and vibrations on the surface.

A seismometer essentially consists of a dampened mass which does not keep up with the movement of the ground because of its inertia, while the rest of the instrument, and the ground beneath move during an earthquake (Figure 2.7). Most modern seismometers use a weighted magnet on springs surrounding an electric coil. The relative movement between the magnet (which moves relatively little) and the coil (which moves with the ground and the body of the instrument) produces an electrical signal which, when suitably amplified, is recorded on magnetic tape or paper to produce a seismogram. This is the signature of the earthquake, a record of the amplitude and wavelength of the waves in a series of oscillations, as seen in Figure 2.5. By measuring the size and shape of seismic wave traces and the time intervals between them from several seismometers, the magnitude of the earthquake, location of the epicentre, depth of focus and sometimes even the orientation of the fault which caused the earthquake, can be determined.

2.3.3 LOCATING THE EPICENTRE

When seismograms from many seismic stations at different distances from an earthquake are compared, a graph can be drawn of the times of arrival of the first P- and S-waves to reach the stations (Figure 2.8). From this information, the distance of the epicentre for any earthquake can be calculated by working out the **lag-time** between the P- and S-wave arrivals (the S–P interval) and reading off the distance directly. In order to plot accurately the position of the epicentre, seismograms from at least three distant stations are needed and their calculated distances are plotted on a globe as a series of circles which overlap at the epicentre.

As this information was not always easy or quick to obtain, a more modern approach was devised using arrays of seismometers linked together with a common **base-time**. These can instantly pinpoint an earthquake (or an underground nuclear explosion for which the system was mainly devised) by comparing the lag-times across the array.

Such an array is found at Eskdalemuir, Scotland, which is part of the Worldwide Standardised Seismograph Network which links observatories around the world. It consists of two lines of vertical component seismometers set out in a geometric pattern. As the wave crosses the array, the first seismometer to record the wave indicates the direction from which the wave was travelling. The speed at which the wave crosses the array gives the distance to the epicentre.

2.3.4 DID THE WHOLE EARTH FEEL IT?

The effect of an earthquake depends very much upon how far you are from the epicentre. The Kobe earthquake, although recorded in Britain, had no felt effects, while the smaller Shrewsbury earthquake later that year was clearly felt, although only locally.

Early attempts to quantify the size or **intensity** of an earthquake were based upon how badly the ground shook and the damage caused to buildings and other structures. Consequently its value depended upon factors such as the nature of underlying geology and the way that buildings were constructed. One earthquake could generate a range of intensity values. Now the size, or **magnitude**, uses the **Richter scale**, devised by **Charles Richter** in 1935 and, although there are newer and better ways of measuring earthquake magnitude, it is still the most commonly cited. The scale measures the maximum amplitude of the ground motion which was recorded at a distance of 100 kilometres from the earthquake epicentre. It is effectively an indication of the seismic energy released. A rise of one

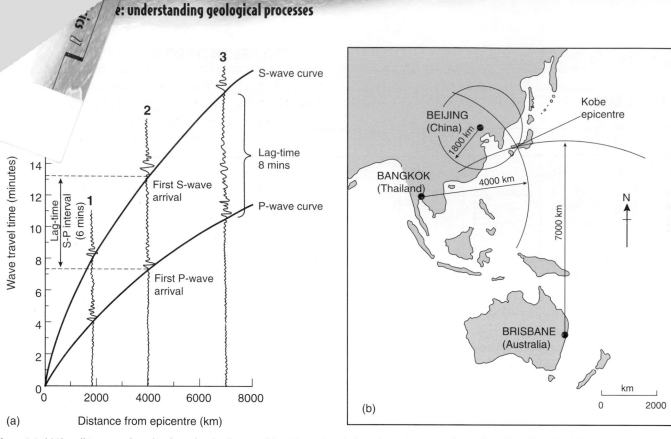

Figure 2.8 *(a) Time-distance graph used to determine the distance of the Kobe earthquake from three seismic recording stations: (1) Beijing (China), (2) Bangkok (Thailand) and (3) Brisbane (Australia); (b) Plotting the epicentre*

Place	(S-P interval)	Lag-Time	Distance to epicentre
(1) Beijing	8–4 mins	4 mins	~1800 km
(2) Bangkok	13.7–7.4 mins	6.3 mins	~4000 km
(3) Brisbane	18.7–10.7 mins	8 mins	7000 km

on the logarithmic scale represents a 10-fold increase in shaking and a 30-fold increase in the earthquake's energy. Reports of the devastation in Kobe differed with factors such as the distance from the epicentre, the ground conditions and construction standards illustrating that the intensity can vary locally (Figure 2.9), but the magnitude of the Kobe earthquake is always quoted as 7.2 (Richter).

The Kobe earthquake at 7.2 is 10 times greater than a 6.2 earthquake, 100 times greater than a 5.2 quake and a staggering 10 000 times greater than the Shrewsbury earthquake. In terms of energy released, the Kobe earthquake is equivalent to approximately 300 000 tonnes of TNT compared to 370 kilograms of TNT in Shrewsbury (a moderate quarry blast).

Figure 2.9 *The Richter scale and earthquake effects*

Richter magnitude	Earthquake effects
<3.4	Recorded by seismometers
3.5–4.2	Felt by people indoors
4.3–4.8	Loose objects rock, including cars
4.9–5.4	Sleepers awakened, bells ring
5.5–6.1	Damage due to overturning and falling of loose objects, plaster falls, walls crack
6.2–6.9	Masonry fissured, chimneys fall, some houses collapse, pipes break
7.0–7.3	Ground cracks badly, buildings destroyed, landslides on steep slopes
7.4–7.9	Few buildings remain standing, bridges destroyed, all services broken
>8.0	Objects thrown into the air, ground rises and falls in waves, almost total destruction

2.4 Earthquakes as probes

2.4.1 A JOURNEY TO THE CENTRE OF THE EARTH

Direct evidence for the structure of the deep Earth is scarce. The world's deepest mines, in South Africa, only go down to about 3 km and even deep boreholes rarely reach below 10 km. Samples from these depths simply reveal similar types of rocks to those exposed at the surface with which we are already familiar. However, in 1906, **R. D. Oldham**, a geologist working in India, suggested that seismic waves generated by distant earthquakes (or explosions) could be used as remote sensors to probe the depths of the Earth and reveal its structure and composition. Starting from the idea of a uniform, homogeneous Earth, the velocity change with depth, due to increased pressure, can be predicted. Then the travel paths and the travel times of waves from earthquakes to seismograms can also be predicted. What is then found is that waves arrive increasingly earlier than predicted, the further they have come. This implies that the waves are 'speeding up' during their journey, so the rocks of the deep Earth must be different from those at and near the surface.

When a wave moves through rocks of different compositions and elastic properties, it is seen to change direction or refract at any boundaries between layers. This results from the wave either speeding up or slowing down, depending upon the nature of the rock properties. Some of the incident energy of the wave may also be reflected at these boundaries, which are known as **seismic discontinuities**. In addition to these sudden changes at discontinuities, steady changes in the physical properties of the rock with depth cause seismic waves to be continuously refracted. Since the Earth is spherical, the earthquake waves will eventually be refracted back to the surface. Thus, body waves passing through the Earth travel along curved paths (Figure 2.10a). The velocity increase is a response to the rocks becoming increasingly more incompressible and rigid with depth. This generally applies to the crust and the thick layer beneath the crust, known as the mantle.

However, between distances of approximately 11 000 km and 16 000 km from an earthquake (representing angles measured at the centre of the Earth of between 103° and 142° from the epicentre), direct body waves are not recorded at all, while only P-wave arrivals are recorded beyond 142°. The area where no waves are received is called a **shadow zone**. Furthermore, the travel-time graph (Figure 2.10b) shows that the P-waves beyond 142° arrive later than expected and so must have been slowed down deep in the Earth.

Figure 2.10 *(a) Diagrammatic section showing the structure of the Earth as identified by the paths of earthquake waves; (b) Travel-time curves for body wave arrivals recorded at different distances from the Kobe epicentre which reveal the structure of the Earth*

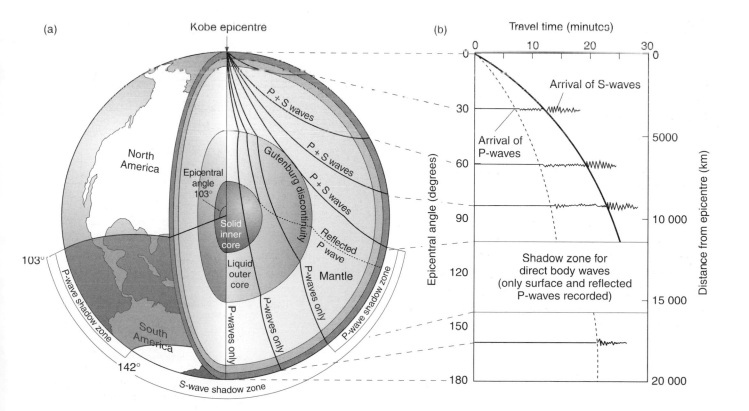

2.4.2 SHAKEN TO THE CORE

The absence of direct P- and S-waves in the shadow zone (only surface waves and weak reflected and diffracted body waves are recorded there) provides evidence that a major seismic **discontinuity** occurs at a depth of 2900 km. The boundary is called the **Gutenburg Discontinuity** after the German seismologist who first determined its depth in 1914. That S-waves do not reappear beyond 142° is evidence that the physical state of the rock changes from solid in the mantle to liquid in the **outer core** (liquids have zero rigidity and S-waves are not transmitted through them). The liquid outer core also has a major effect on the transmission of P-waves, slowing them down and causing the refraction seen in Figure 2.10a.

Figure 2.10a shows that some P-wave arrivals are recorded in the P-wave shadow zone. These waves have been reflected from a further discontinuity within the core. Analysis of other arrivals indicate an increase in elastic properties and evidence for a solid **inner core** at a depth of 5155 km, beneath the liquid outer core.

Laboratory simulations of seismic waves through a variety of materials suggest that the outer core is composed largely of an alloy of iron with nickel and some sulphur. The inner core is believed to be mostly iron and nickel, similar to the composition of metallic meteorites, but under pressures 3.6 million times greater than at the surface. It is this tremendous pressure that causes the liquid core to transform to the solid state at a depth of 5155 km.

The metallic core is estimated to have a relative density of between 10–16. The evidence for the size and density of the core explains why the mean relative density of the Earth (5.5) is so much higher than for most rocks found at the Earth's surface (2.6–3.0). The metallic core also helps to account for the presence of another important physical feature of the Earth: its magnetic field.

2.4.3 STRONG AND WEAK ROCKS

The mantle is the name given to the Earth shells between the thin crustal skin and the core. These shells are identified by weak discontinuities within the mantle, particularly at depths of 450 km and 670 km below the surface, the latter being the top of the lower mantle. Figure 2.11 shows that the mantle must be solid since S-waves pass through it. The discontinuities are thought to be the result of changes (phase changes) in the physical state of minerals, like olivine (Chapter 3), under high temperatures and pressures. At these pressures the atomic structure of such minerals is thought to collapse to form denser minerals. Laboratory measurements of seismic

wave velocities in test rocks suggests that the mantle is predominantly made of a rock called peridotite. This rock, similar in composition to stony meteorites, is rich in olivine and samples are sometimes brought to the surface as xenoliths (Figure C2.1) or, in larger volumes, as part of ophiolite emplacements (Chapter 4).

Figure 2.11 shows that within the upper mantle, at a depth of between 100 km to 300 km, seismic velocities decrease, then increase again deeper into the mantle. This **low velocity zone** (**LVZ**) is evidence for a transitional boundary between two important *mechanical* layers within the Earth: the lithosphere and **asthenosphere**. The decrease in seismic wave velocities indicates that the asthenosphere ('weak' sphere) has lower mechanical strength than the overlying lithosphere ('rock' sphere). As the temperature of the Earth at these depths lies close to the melting temperature for peridotite, it is estimated that about one to five per cent of the asthenosphere is molten. However, the remaining 95 per cent or more of solid rock allows S-waves to be transmitted. The asthenosphere behaves very much like a highly viscous fluid under long-term stress, which provides a mechanism for the tectonic movement of the overlying, more rigid lithospheric plates.

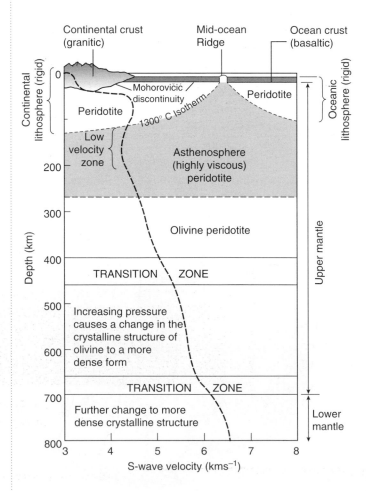

Figure 2.11 *Section through crust and mantle showing discontinuities, seismic wave velocities and composition*

By convention, the boundary between the asthenosphere and lithosphere is placed at the 1300 °C **isotherm** (a boundary joining places of equal temperature) although there is no sharp plane between the rigid and weak layers. The lithosphere is up to 300 km thick under the continents but thins to only a few kilometres at ocean ridges. It includes two layers identified by differences in their chemical composition rather than strength: the thin outer layer called the crust and the uppermost part of the upper mantle, called the lithospheric mantle.

2.4.4 SKIN DEEP

In 1909, a Yugoslavian seismologist, **Andrija Mohorovičić**, discovered that *two* very distinct types of P- and S-waves were recorded at stations close to an earthquake. He concluded that these waves had travelled by separate paths: one direct to the recording station and the other after having been refracted at a shallow seismic discontinuity, which he later found to be at different depths beneath the continents and oceans. This discontinuity, the **Mohorovičić Discontinuity** (**Moho** for short) marks the change in composition between the thin, outer skin of crustal rocks and the underlying upper mantle (Figures 2.12 and 2.13).

The crust is further divided into two major types based on composition. The **continental crust** is made predominantly of rock with intermediate- to silica-rich composition (Chapters 3 and 4), and is 35 km–40 km thick, but deeper under recently formed mountain chains. The denser **oceanic crust** is more **mafic** (magnesium and iron rich, silica-poor) with a thickness of between 5 km and 7 km. These two types of crust are formed by entirely

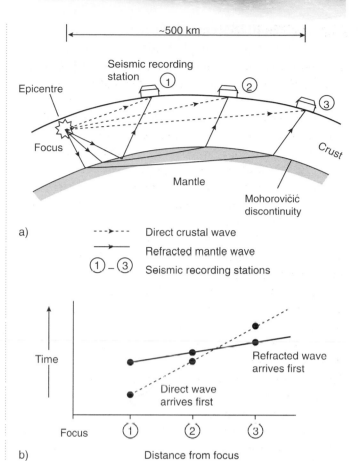

a)

- - - → - - - Direct crustal wave

———→ Refracted mantle wave

①–③ Seismic recording stations

b)

Figure 2.12(a) *Diagram showing direct and refracted waves in the crust/mantle;*
Figure 2.12(b) *Graph to show travel times with distance from the epicentre. Close to the focus it is the direct wave which arrives first, but as this distance increases, eventually it is the refracted wave which is first to reach the recording station, indicating that it must have travelled faster in the upper mantle*

different processes, explained in Chapter 4. The thickness of the crust compared to the Earth's diameter is similar to

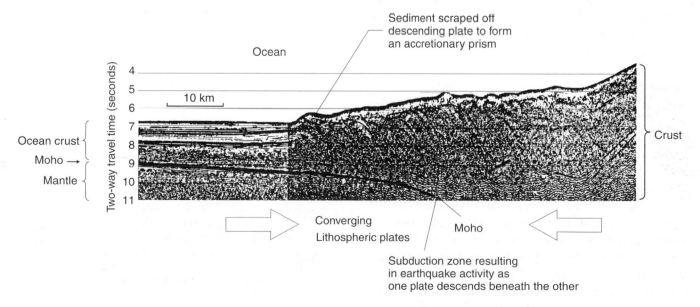

Figure 2.13 *A seismic reflection profile through two converging lithospheric plates at a destructive plate boundary. (The two-way travel represents the time it takes shock waves from a seismic survey to travel from the surface, down to a reflective boundary and back.)*

a postage stamp stuck on an Earth the size of a football! The variation in the depth of the Moho is seen to mirror the shape of the Earth's surface with the Moho at depths of 100 km or more under young or active mountains like the Andes, 35 km beneath the lowland areas of the continents and only 5 km beneath the ocean plains.

2.5 A question of balance

2.5.1 GRAVITATIONAL ATTRACTION

Mountains are small in relation to the size of the whole Earth. In the eighteenth century, they were thought of as simply extra masses 'stuck' on to and supported by the surface of the Earth. Detailed measurements of variations in the force of gravity over the Earth challenged this idea and gave rise to our present understanding of a more dynamic and buoyant Earth.

Newton proposed that any two objects in the universe attract each other by a force which depends upon the product of their masses and the distance between them; smaller masses are attracted towards larger ones. Newton's test mass (an apple) is attracted to the Earth and falls towards the Earth due to the Earth's gravitational force of attraction, or **gravity**, represented by the symbol g. The force can be expressed in the general equation known as Newton's First Law of Motion:

force = mass $\times$ acceleration, or $F = ma$,

where, in the case of the falling apple, m is the mass of the apple and a is the acceleration due to gravity (g) which is about 9.8 ms^{-2}.

However, gravity does not have the same value everywhere on the Earth. It depends upon the radius of the Earth, which is affected by the height of the land surface (altitude) and also the latitude (since the Earth is an oblate spheroid). As the radius of the Earth varies from the poles to the Equator, the force of gravity is greater at the poles (where the surface of the Earth is nearer to the centre of the Earth). Similarly, the higher you climb up a mountain from sea level the less will be the force of gravity, because you are further from the centre of the Earth. The effects of altitude and latitude can be removed by calculation (the Bouguer correction) revealing that the gravitational attraction is also affected by local differences in rock mass. As the density of the local rock varies, so does its mass (density = mass/volume) and the force of attraction between the Earth and an object will be higher (positive) or lower (negative) when compared with an average for all rocks.

Figure 2.14 *Maintaining equilibrium by isostatic readjustment in a mountain range undergoing active erosion and deposition*

2.5.2 THE ROOT OF THE PROBLEM

Local variations in the Earth's gravity field, known as **gravity anomalies**, were first noted in the Andes by **Bouguer** in 1749 and a century later by **Pratt** and **Airey** in the Himalaya. The Himalayan observations of the local deflections of a surveying pendulum from the vertical indicated that the rocks beneath the Himalaya were not as dense as expected. Thus there must be a root of lower density material (less mass) under the mountains when compared with the surrounding plain of India. This is to compensate for the mass of the mountains sticking up above the surrounding surface, much like the bulk of an iceberg is found beneath the surface of the water. It has been shown by seismic surveying that roots of less dense material are typical of all large mountain chains, some of which go down 14 times the height of the mountain. Mountain 'roots' are now known to be the result of crustal shortening, where the lower density continental material has been compressed and thickened by the plate tectonic processes of collision (Figure 2.14a). The result is that the thickened continent extends down into the denser rock of the underlying mantle. This suggests that the mountain (and indeed all crust whether continental or oceanic) is 'floating' on the denser underlying mantle which flows or 'creeps' away underneath, along the weak layer of the asthenosphere, until the mass is balanced.

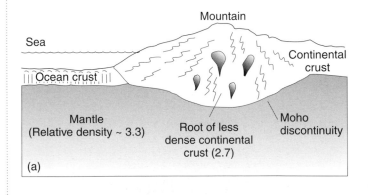

(a)

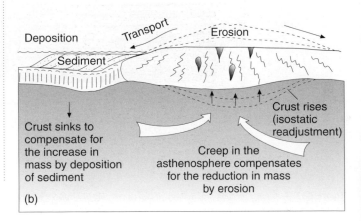

(b)

In 1889, **Dutton** proposed the term **isostasy** for this phenomenon which demonstrates that the surface of the Earth is in dynamic balance. When the top of a mountain is eroded, the reduction in surface mass is counteracted by the mountain root rising to a higher level, allowing the asthenosphere to flow in underneath to compensate. This is the process of **isostatic readjustment** (or isostatic **rebound**). It is what happened to your mattress when you got out of bed this morning, only the mattress 'readjusted' at a much faster rate. Figure 2.14 shows this process in action and the subsequent sinking of the crust under the area where the eroded sediment is deposited. Isostatic readjustment also explains why the roots of old mountains, formed many kilometres below the Earth's surface, eventually come to be exposed at the surface.

Isostasy can also account for more recent effects of the last Ice Age in Britain. When ice occupied much of Northern Europe, including Scotland, the mass of the ice, estimated to have been over 1800 m thick in the highlands of Scotland, caused the land to sink as the weak asthenosphere flowed from beneath. When the extra mass was removed during final melting, around 10 000 years ago, the land began to rise again as the denser mantle flowed back (Figure 2.15). Evidence of this can be seen in the 'raised beaches' seen along many parts of the Scottish coast (Figure 2.16).

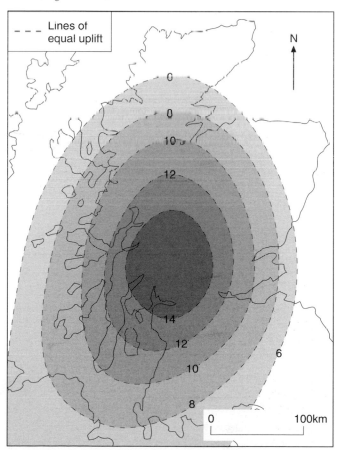

Figure 2.15 *Generalised isobane map (in metres) of post-glacial uplift in Scotland*

Figure 2.16 *Raised beaches north of Drumadoon Point, Arran.*

2.6 Hot Rock

2.6.1 THE TEMPERATURE RISES

What processes keep the Earth moving in a dynamic way? The main source of energy at the surface of the Earth is directly from the Sun but this is nearly all reflected back into space. The Sun's radiant energy drives the cycles that redistribute sediments in the surface processes part of the rock cycle (Chapter 5). However, it is the Earth's internal heat which is responsible primarily for maintaining the 'active' Earth beneath the surface. Thermal energy (heat) comes from the decay of radioactive minerals, such as uranium, thorium and potassium, in subsurface rocks, together with a little heat left over from the primeval Earth.

Rocks at the Earth's surface are mostly cold and brittle, but volcanoes, hot springs and the high temperatures of deep mines are evidence of the high temperatures involved in the interior. The increase in temperature with depth can be directly measured in the deepest boreholes; at 3 km deep the temperature is about 70 °C whilst at 10 km it rises to 300 °C in areas of average heat flow. This shows that an average increase in temperature with depth (the **geothermal gradient** or **geotherm**) is about 25–30 °C km^{-1}. Heat flow in regions such as constructive plate margins (ocean ridges) is far higher, and in ocean trenches heat flow is low. Temperatures rise at a slower rate to the asthenosphere (between 100–200 km depth) where the Earth is close to the melting point of mantle peridotite, which partially melts (Figure 2.17). The process of partial melting is explained in Chapter 4 and involves the melting of the lowest temperature minerals first, before the bulk of the rock.

Below the asthenosphere, the rise in the geotherm is less rapid. As pressure increases with depth, the geotherm falls below the melting point of peridotite and partial melting ceases. Seismic waves show the Earth to be solid until the mantle-core boundary is reached where the temperature (about 3700 °C) is above the melting temperature of iron at the prevailing pressure, hence the outer core is molten. It has been calculated that the temperature at the centre of the Earth's core reaches 4300 °C but because of the intense pressures the inner core is solid.

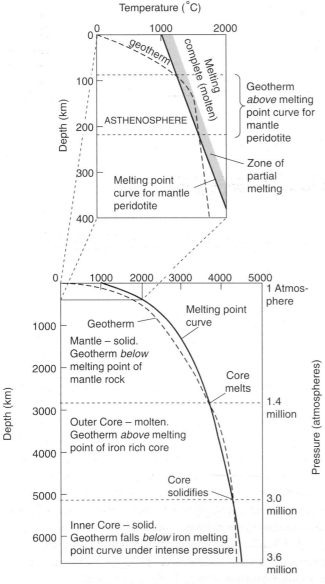

Figure 2.17 *Diagram to show probable change in the temperature of the Earth with depth. Where the geotherm lies close to or above the melting point of rock, as in the case of the asthenosphere and the outer core, the Earth is partly or completely molten. When below the melting point curve, as in the crust, mantle and inner core, the Earth is solid*

2.6.2 HEATED DEBATE

Annually, the Earth loses about three times the amount of energy which we humans consume in a year. This energy escapes from the Earth's surface and is radiated into space. As well as radiation, the Earth transfers heat by conduction. But rock is a particularly poor thermal conductor so the heat flow to the surface can't be the result of conduction alone (it has been estimated that for heat to be transferred from the centre of the Earth to the surface, by conduction alone, would take 10^{12} years).

To account for the heat flow recorded at the surface, some kind of deep convection system must be involved which implies that the 'solid' mantle is actually behaving as a fluid. Geophysicists have little doubt that this is happening throughout the mantle at about the speed that fingernails grow, and evidence from plate tectonic movement supports this argument. By this process, hot rock rises to replace cooler rock which sinks, warms up, and rises again, transferring the Earth internal heat to the surface (Figure 2.18).

But how the mantle convects is still a matter of 'hot' debate. Some researchers believe the upper and lower mantle form two separate convecting systems, with the upper mantle acting as a blanket to insulate the deep interior (Figure 2.19). Others suggest that heat is transferred from the molten core directly to the surface in mantle plumes. A third option is that both processes may operate. In this theory, the mantle convects in two layers but the layers 'leak' heat. The cold subducted lithosphere is sometimes transferred to the lower mantle while superheated 'plumes' from the core-mantle boundary reach the surface in pulses resulting in volcanic activity, such as is found in the Hawaiian islands or formerly in the Deccan Traps of India, 66 million years ago.

2.6.3 THE TEMPERATURE FALLS

Over geological time the Earth has cooled down. The current rate of crustal activity is relatively small compared to that of the newly formed Earth when radioactive heat production was greater. The current balance of radioactive heating and surface heat loss is not known exactly and through time it depends upon factors such as plate tectonic activity and the size and insulating properties of plates. Over geological timescales, heat energy is lost and the internal processes, which cause earthquakes, volcanoes and plate tectonic movement, will continue to slow down until, at a time far in the future, our dynamic world will cease being active. By then, the Earth will have crystallised completely to become a solid ball of rock and metal – a truly dead planet.

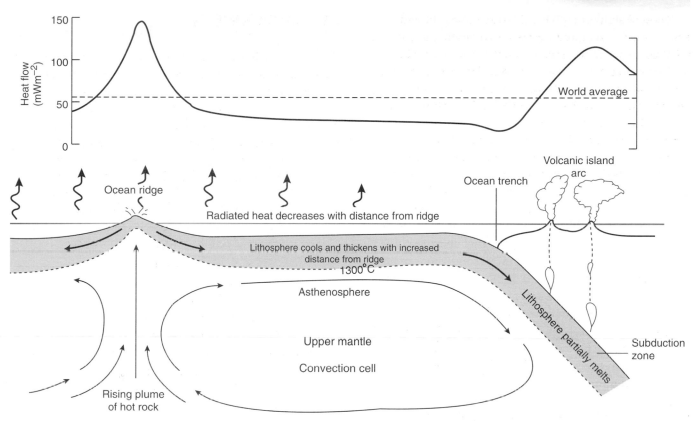

Figure 2.18 *Diagram showing heat flow/loss from the lithosphere and associated convection currents in the asthenosphere*

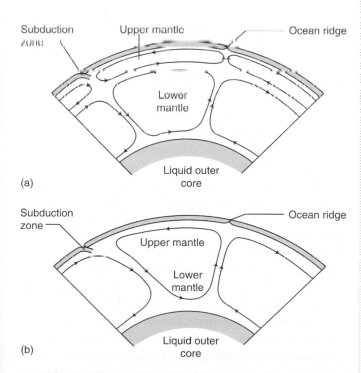

(a)

(b)

Figure 2.19 *Conflicting models of mantle convection: (a) Separate convection cells in upper and lower mantle; (b) Entire mantle convection*

2.7 Magnetic evidence of the Earth's structure

2.7.1 ELECTROMAGNETISM

One of the most convincing lines of evidence for the Earth's metallic core comes from the fact that the Earth produces a magnetic field which changes with time. Although physical attraction and repulsion of magnetic rocks was known to have been studied by the Greeks around 600 BC, it was **Sir William Gilbert**, the court physician to Queen Elizabeth I, who was credited with first describing the Earth's magnetic field. He knew that the north pole (strictly the 'north-seeking' pole) of a suspended bar magnet, free to turn horizontally, will line up pointing towards magnetic north. In addition, when pivoted to allow for vertical movement, a bar magnet will record the dip (or **inclination**) of the Earth's magnetic field which varies with latitude (Figure 2.20).

Gilbert suggested that this field resembled that of a huge bar magnet at the centre of the Earth, partly offset from the rotational axis of the Earth. However, although the field evidence does resemble that of a bar magnet, there are problems with this explanation that means there cannot be a bar magnet at the centre of the Earth. A simple experiment shows that when a bar magnet is heated above a certain temperature (the **Curie point**) all magnetism is lost. Therefore, a permanent bar magnet could not exist at the centre of the Earth because the prevailing temperature is far above the Curie point of any known magnetic material. In addition, the angle between magnetic north and true north (the **declination**) slowly changes with time (decreasing in Britain by about 0.5° every 3 years currently) which indicates that the north magnetic pole is moving. This could not be the case if it were due to a fixed bar magnet inside the Earth.

Currently, the Earth's magnetic field is explained by a 'dynamo theory', which considers the Earth's core to be acting as a self-sustaining electromagnet. In order to produce an electrical current, a metal conductor can be rotated to cut a magnetic field. If the current produced in this way is sent through a coil of wire, a magnetic field is also produced which in turn can be used to create an electric current and so on. This is the principle of the **self-exciting dynamo** because, once started, it will continue, provided energy is put into the system to rotate the conductor continuously.

The Earth's nickel-iron core is a good conductor and the combined effect of the Earth's rotation and convection currents in the liquid outer core are thought to create columns of liquid iron which spiral roughly parallel to the Earth's rotational axis. As these cut across the magnetic field, electrical currents are produced which in turn produce and reinforce the magnetic field. In this way, the mechanical energy of the Earth's rotation is converted to electrical energy which generates a magnetic field. Therefore, it is possible that the Earth behaves like a self-exciting dynamo, generating its own magnetic field.

2.8 Earthquakes: the human response

2.8.1 PREDICTING THE UNPREDICTABLE

Japanese scientists have explained the curious flashes of red and blue light seen in the skies immediately before the Kobe earthquake as light emitted from silica crystals (quartz) as they began to fracture. Whether this phenomenon (called fractoluminescence) could ever be used to help warn of an impending earthquake is not yet clear, but it is one of a number of similar phenomena which are being studied in the search for a reliable method of predicting earthquakes (Figure 2.21).

Attempts at earthquake prediction are as numerous as the methods of forecasting the weather, often with an even lower degree of success. For a weather forecast to be of any use it needs to accurately predict *where* and *when* it

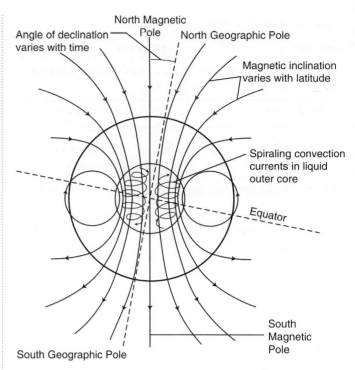

Figure 2.20 *Earth's magnetic field (Note the term 'magnetic north' is misleading – as it attracts the north pole of a compass it is equivalent to the 'south' pole of a bar magnet within the Earth)*

might rain and the *scale* of any possible downpour. If the forecaster gets it wrong you may, at worst, be inconvenienced. Accurately forecasting an earthquake also involves predicting the place, time and magnitude of the event but the consequences of failure are potentially much greater.

In 1969, Russian scientists reported that the P-wave velocity from minor earthquakes (<2 magnitude) could be used to predict a major earthquake. After studying the velocity of P-waves as they travelled through a fault zone, they identified anomalies which were apparent just before the fault broke. Figure 2.22 shows that P-wave velocities from minor tremors first fell, then rose immediately before each major episode and that the duration of the anomaly was directly related to the magnitude of the earthquake that followed (Figure 2.23).

It is known from laboratory experiments that, when under stress, water-saturated rocks sometimes *increase* in volume just before they fracture. This is thought to be the result of the opening of microcracks which results in an overall increase in rock porosity (the ratio of spaces to solid rock). Water will migrate slowly into these new cracks and so the overall water pressure within the rock is reduced. This has the effect of temporarily reducing P-wave velocities from minor earthquakes until more water from surrounding rocks is able to move into the area to restore the original pore-water pressure. The length of time this takes is an indication of the magnitude of the impending earthquake which occurs shortly after

Figure 2.21 *Physical indicators used to predict earthquakes*

Indicator	Explanation
Subterranean electromagnetic waves	Recorded signals precede some 'quakes.
Earthquake lights	Fracture of silica may light the sky before an event.
Electrical resistivity	Electrical resistance of rocks changes before rocks fracture.
Changes in groundwater levels	Water levels in wells fall as rock dilates.
Groundwater pressure changes	Pressure changes as rock dilates.
Tilts and bulges	Expansion of surface with rock dilatation.
Gravity changes	Changes in local gravity measurements as surface tilts/bulges.
Microseismic activity	Release of strain as microcracks open.
Minor foreshocks	Minor releases of strain prior to a major earthquake.
Seismic velocity changes	Anomalies in the velocity of P- and S-waves.
Changes in creep and strain rates	Measured on creepmeters and strain gauges.
Changes in the Earth's magnetic field	Minor variations noted during seismic activity.
Radon gas emissions	Gas liberated from rock under stress.
Seismic gap analysis	Historical records indicate fault zones which are 'locked'.
Animal behavioural changes	Animals more sensitive to 'changes' than humans.

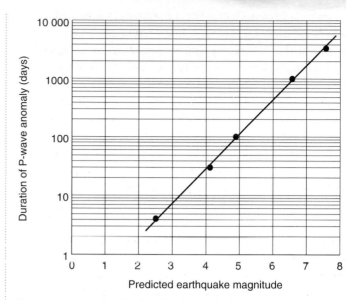

Figure 2.23 *Graph of predicted earthquake magnitudes based on the duration of recorded P-wave anomalies*

pore-water pressure is restored. From the limited evidence available, a tentative graph can be drawn to predict such earthquake magnitudes.

The 'dilatation-fluid diffusion' model (Figure 2.24) also appears to explain some of the other physical phenomena which have been recorded prior to a major earthquake (some of which are shown in Figure 2.21). The build-up of elastic strain since the last earthquake event occurs during Stage I. Changes in ground level are an obvious result of the expansion stage (Stage II), as are groundwater changes which are often indicated by the lowering of water in wells. The recorded increase in the inert gas, radon, in deep wells is thought to relate to its release from rock as the microcracks open. P-wave velocities fall and the number of minor earthquakes drops as the rock expands. During Stage III, ground uplift and tilt is seen to level off, along with radon gas levels, as new cracks cease to open.

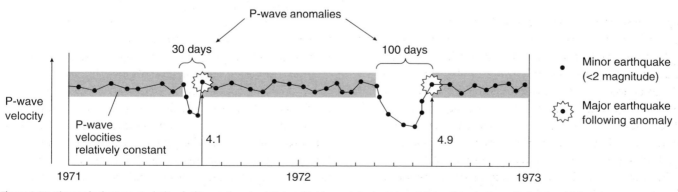

Figure 2.22 *Changes in the P-wave velocity of minor earthquakes (<2 magnitude) recorded prior to two major earthquakes (magnitude 4.1 and 4.9)*

The influx of water raises groundwater levels and the increased pore pressure transmits P-waves with higher velocity. The number of minor earthquakes (**foreshocks**) also increases until the rock finally ruptures and the built-up stress is released. The physical indicators then fall to previous levels during Stage V, which is marked by a decrease in the number of aftershocks. The electrical resistivity of rock is also seen to fall prior to an earthquake as water-saturated rock conducts electricity more easily.

Earthquakes are now regarded as cyclic rather than random events. Sections of major fault zones which have not ruptured for some time are more likely to have built-up stress which could be released in a major earthquake. These **seismic gaps** are sections of fault zones where the faults are 'locked' and are most likely to break disastrously at some future time. They can be identified using historical records. A recent study by the British Geological Survey (BGS) shows that earthquakes associated with ancient faults in the Straits of Dover occurred in 1382, 1580 and 1776. If a major event takes place roughly every 200 years, London and the south east could be due for another at any time now.

To collect data for these predictions, a vast amount of equipment is needed including seismic arrays, tilt and creepmeters, borehole strain gauges and laser-measuring devices. This equipment is used to measure the build-up of strain across a fault zone. Unfortunately, not all earthquakes follow the same pattern of earlier activity and so earthquake prediction is, as yet, inadequate. Indeed, many scientists are now sceptical that earthquake prediction is possible at all and suggest that earthquakes are 'critical' phenomena, events that occur in some systems which balance precariously on the edge of massive change. This makes prediction as reliable as trying to guess which snowflake will finally trigger an avalanche. They conclude that money spent on earthquake prediction is wasted and would be better used in trying to limit the effects of the resulting damage.

Finally, and less 'scientific' in that it is more difficult to quantify, is the abnormal animal behaviour that has often been reported prior to an earthquake. Chinese scientists were reportedly able to help predict the 1969 Tianjin earthquake by this method. It is thought that animals are very sensitive to minor changes in the physical properties of rock that is under stress and about to break. These may include minute changes in temperature, sound, smell or even in the magnetic field which, for example, causes snakes and rats to abandon their holes. However, this phenomenon is not easily measured and forecasters have concentrated their efforts on attempting to monitor the changes shown in Figure 2.21.

2.8.2 CONTROLLING THE UNCONTROLLABLE

In 1962, fluid waste was injected into a 3 km deep well near Denver, Colorado. Over the following four years, hundreds of small earthquakes were recorded in an area where no significant activity had been recorded previously. This was the first indication that human activity could trigger earthquakes. Further experiments in 1970 seemed to confirm the idea that, by injecting water into a deep well or filling a large lake behind a dam, rates of seismic activity could be increased. Pumping from deep rocks reduces minor earthquakes.

Theoretically, by using fluid injection to induce small earthquakes, a fault zone could become 'destrained', reducing the threat of a damaging earthquake. However, some scientists believe that the effects could not be controlled and the result might be an earthquake that could be even worse. The cost, unpredictability of the results, politics and the insurance industry are all factors that need to be taken into consideration before earthquake control becomes a reality, although these methods may become more practical in the future.

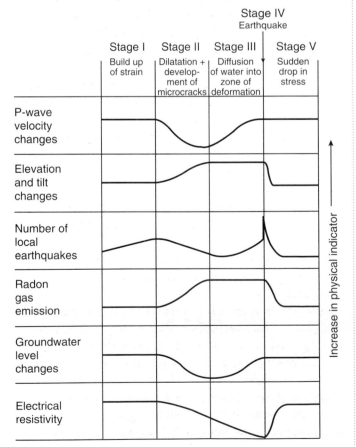

Figure 2.24 *Changes in some physical indicators recorded prior to a major earthquake*

2.8.3 PREPARING FOR THE 'BIG ONE'!

What concerned the Japanese after the Kobe earthquake was the extent of the damage in a country that prided itself on its readiness and its belief that it had made itself 'quakeproof'. When the ground shook on 17 January, 1995, it wasn't just the buildings that collapsed but Japanese confidence in their government's ability to predict and protect them from such a disaster.

The main hazards to life and property in the event of an earthquake depend on the magnitude of the event, the geology of the area, proximity to major population centres and even the time of day; had the Kobe earthquake struck during the morning or evening rush hours it is probable that many more people would have been killed on the roads and railways.

Earthquakes rarely harm people; they are killed by collapsing buildings and bridges and other structures, falling masonry, glass and also the resulting fires. It is now thought that the best method of preparing to deal with earthquakes is an effective **hazard reduction** programme rather than attempting to control the earthquake. This idea is based on the philosophy that earthquakes are an inevitable fact of life (or plate tectonics) and as they cannot be controlled, their effects should be minimised in heavily populated areas.

First, the population needs to be educated on how to react in the event of a major earthquake. Earthquake drill is as much a way of life in Japan, and California, as fire drills are in Britain. Personal protection plans are important to prevent unnecessary injury; these outline what to do before, during and after an earthquake. For example, the danger from falling objects is greatly increased for people leaving (or entering) a building during an earthquake. Many people were allowed to return to the crumbling ruins of their homes during the Kobe earthquake, thereby putting themselves at further risk.

The most effective way of minimising the possible destruction is to map areas of high hazard risk or, if it is impossible to avoid these areas, to design buildings which will withstand the effects of an earthquake of a given value. This value might be Richter 5.0 in Britain, but could be Richter 7.0 near the San Andreas Fault in California.

A building will sway back and forth in a given period of time at a frequency that depends upon its height and type of construction. For a 20-storey building, this time is about two seconds and the reciprocal of the period (i.e. 1/period) defines the natural frequency of its vibration (1 cycle per 2 seconds or 0.5 hertz). Where the natural frequency of a building is similar to the frequency of ground motion, the building will amplify the vibrations during an earthquake. This is called resonance. As most earthquakes vibrate with a natural frequency in the range 0.5 hertz to 5 hertz, buildings taller than 20 storeys (<0.5 hertz) are less likely to resonate than lower ones and, provided they are well designed, should survive better. The ability to flex during the earthquake is also important and in this respect wooden-framed structures have longer periods of vibration than stiffer materials such as brick or stone in buildings of the same height.

The buildings that collapsed in Kobe were often the traditional older houses built before stringent new building codes were introduced in the 1970s. The roofs of such houses are of heavy blue and brown tiles, supported only by a thin wooden frame with few internal partitions. In addition, small commercial buildings that had large shop windows and lacked interior walls showed similar structural weaknesses and collapsed during the earthquake. Most modern buildings, particularly where strengthened with triangular bracing (it is more difficult to shear a triangular structure than a rectangular one), were more effective in withstanding the severe lateral shearing of the seismic waves. Buildings can also be designed to flex laterally without collapsing vertically.

In both Japan and the USA, another approach is to incorporate stiff rubber bearings into the foundations of a building, so isolating the structure from lateral ground motion. Some are also equipped with oil-filled isolators to dampen any vertical movement. The state-of-the-art is the design of 'smart' buildings that incorporate counterweights in the roof, moved by computer-controlled hydraulic rams. These weights help to absorb and dampen the vibrations of the earthquake by moving with the ground motion, much like keeping your balance when standing on a moving train.

The failure of transportation structures such as bridges in the Kobe event was again the result of shear failure at the base of critical supports. In addition, inadequate restraint between the joints of elevated sections of some bridges caused them to fall from their supports as the ground moved. Modern bridge designs use steel cable restraints to prevent both vertical and horizontal movement during an earthquake, while support columns are prevented from shearing by horizontal steel reinforcements.

The port of Kobe is built on two artificial islands of reclaimed land. Liquefaction of waterlogged sediments during shaking can result in settlement, with buildings leaning or toppling over as the ground loses strength and is unable to support the load. From basic geological mapping of earthquake-prone areas (e.g. extent and thickness of superficial sediments) together with other seismological information (e.g. likely magnitude and intensity of an earthquake based on historical events), a **seismic zoning map** (a type of **hazard map**) can be drawn to indicate the potential response of the ground during an earthquake. Despite the uncertainty associated with these maps, they can be used to calculate the probability of seismic damage (**seismic risk maps**) which form the basis of building design codes for future construction in the area.

2.9 Summary

1 Evidence for the structure of the Earth can be obtained by indirect means, such as the analysis of earthquake (seismic) events; evidence for the core of the Earth also comes from meteorites.

2 Earthquake waves are of two main types: body waves that pass through the Earth and surface waves. P-waves (compressional) and S-waves (shear) are body waves. Body waves are most useful for study of the Earth's interior, though surface waves often cause most damage.

3 The Earth has an outer crust of oceanic (mafic) and continental (silica-rich) material. The lithosphere comprises the crust and lithospheric mantle.

4 The crust is separated from the mantle by the Mohorovičić discontinuity (the Moho).

5 The asthenosphere is the upper part of the mantle where one to five per cent of the rock (peridotite) is molten and allows movement of the plates above. The rest of the mantle is solid, mainly peridotite, but is also composed of a rock with higher density mineral forms.

6 Earthquake shadow zones show that, at 2900 km depth, the Gutenburg Discontinuity separates the mantle from the liquid outer core. The outer core is thought to be composed of iron-nickel-sulphur.

7 At a depth of 5155 km, pressure is such that the inner core is an iron-nickel solid.

8 The Earth has a geocentric magnetic field, thought to be the result of convection in the outer core.

9 Earthquake prediction has had few successes; hazard reduction has concentrated on avoiding areas of high risk and improving building codes.

2.10 Questions

1 Explain why at least:
   (i)   three seismometers are required to record earthquake waves at a single seismic recording station.
   (ii) three seismic stations are required to locate an earthquake epicentre on the basis of seismic wave lag-time.

2 With reference to Figure 2.8, estimate the approximate distance of the seismograph in Figure 2.5 from the epicentre.

3 Why is it inaccurate to suggest that seismic waves are not recorded in the P- and S-wave shadow zone of an earthquake?

4 Explain why earthquakes are features of the lithosphere rather than the asthenosphere.

5 Explain why in Figure 2.10a, the P-wave which travels directly through the centre of the Earth will arrive at approximately the same time as the P-wave reaching the surface at 142 degrees from the epicentre, despite having travelled further through the Earth.

6 Suggest why earthquakes are often associated with volcanic eruptions.

7 Attempt to account for the volcanic activity in Hawaii (which is not situated on a plate boundary) in terms of mantle convection.

8 Calculate the variation in the thickness of the crust across Figure 2.13. (Assume the velocity of seismic waves in the crust to be 6.0 kms^{-1} and remember the time given in the diagram is the two-way time.)

9 Using Figure 2.17, calculate the average geothermal gradient above and below the asthenosphere to a depth of 400 km.

10 Why are meteorites considered to be of similar composition to the rocks of the Earth's interior?

11 Explain why local sea levels on the coast of northern Europe are falling relative to the land, despite the global rise in sea level over the past 10 000 years.

12 Why was the intensity of the Kobe earthquake greatest in the areas of reclaimed land around the harbour?

13 Account for the following phenomena which have been reported prior to major earthquakes.
   (i)   small fish seen floating on the sea which had become turbid and brown in colour.
   (ii)   changes in the flow of water from some natural springs.
   (iii) minor decreases in gravimeter readings.

14 Explain why:
   (i)   a 10-storey concrete building with a natural frequency of vibration of 1 cycle per second (1 hertz) is more likely to collapse than a 20-storey concrete building of similar design and construction.
   (ii) an earthquake may be felt at the top of a 20-storey building but undetected (except by instruments) on the ground floor.

CHAPTER 3
Minerals: the building blocks of rocks

Introduction

Minerals are inorganic chemical substances, each with a definite composition and internal structure. In most minerals, the atoms are arranged in regular crystal units. The most important rock-forming minerals are silicates; that is they contain silicon and oxygen atoms in the crystal structure (**lattice**). This chapter explains how a mineral's composition and structure determine its physical properties, and hence its potential usefulness. Minerals can be identified through the properties of **hardness**, **cleavage**, **colour**, **streak**, **shape**, crystallography and chemistry. Many minerals form natural groups that have 'umbrella' names, such as the olivine group, or the pyroxene group. By studying the temperature and conditions of crystal formation from a silicate melt, **N. L. Bowen** saw that these groups were part of two sequences of minerals that are commonly found: these became known as Bowen's reaction series.

3.1 Case Study: the diamond

Diamond is a unique mineral. What other mineral could be used to adorn Britain's Imperial State Crown (Figure 3.1a) and also to drill through the hardest rocks (Figure 3.1b)? How is this mineral formed and why does it have such diverse properties?

Figure 3.1 (a) The Culinan 2 diamond in the Imperial State Crown (b) A borehole drill for obtaining rock cores; close up of diamonds in tip

Diamond is the hardest natural substance yet discovered. Its name is very appropriate, being derived from the Greek adamas, meaning 'unconquerable'! It is made of a single element, carbon in its crystalline form. Diamond is a mineral of contrast, combining both the ordinary and the extraordinary, uniqueness and diversity, strength and beauty, all within a crystal made of just one element, carbon. It is not, however, the only form of elemental carbon on Earth; there is also graphite, the grey material that pencil 'lead' is made of, or coal, which is also largely made of carbon. In the biosphere carbon is common, but is usually combined with other elements, such as oxygen or hydrogen.

The origin of diamonds has been the subject of myth and debate for centuries. Until the late nineteenth century, most diamonds had been found at, or very close to, the Earth's surface. This, allied to their rarity led to many theories relating to diamonds originating in space and coming to Earth via meteorites. However, this is not now as fantastic as it might seem, as microdiamonds were formed by the impact of an asteroid at the Ries crater in Germany (see Chapter 13).

In 1870, Kimberley, South Africa was the site of an important and historic discovery. Diamonds were found associated with an unusual kind of rock and the town gave its name to the new rock type: **kimberlite**. This occurred as a 'carrot-shaped' body, and diamonds have been mined from it down to a depth of 940 m, leaving the huge and famous Kimberley 'Big Hole'.

Recently, it has been possible to manufacture industrial diamonds by simulating the conditions of diamond formation. This leads geologists to believe that pressures of 100 000 × atmospheric pressure and temperatures of 2000 °C are needed; equivalent to depths in the Earth of about 300 km.

One reason why diamonds are so rare is that such conditions of high temperature and pressure occur deep beneath the Earth's surface, so that rocks and minerals formed there are not commonly found at the surface. The primary source of all diamonds is kimberlite, but they are recovered (mined) from two quite different sources. About 50 per cent are mined directly from kimberlite, whilst the remaining 50 per cent are extracted from placer (or alluvial) deposits which result from the weathering and erosion of diamond-bearing kimberlite. The rock is further broken down during transportation by rivers, and the diamonds are deposited with gravels and sands when the water currents slow down.

The diamond crystal structure is compact, resulting in a fairly high relative density of 3.52, so this property is used in the separation of diamond from waste material (gangue), which usually has a lower density. Diamonds also resist physical and chemical attack; in placer deposits they are found associated with other minerals resistant to weathering and erosion.

The internal structure of diamond consists of a three-dimensional framework of carbon atoms with each carbon being linked to four others by strong bonds. The atoms form a tetrahedral arrangement shown in Figure 3.2a that is similar to that of quartz (SiO_2) shown in Figure 3.5b. As the bonds are very strong, diamond is extremely hard; on Mohs' scale of relative hardness, diamond is rated 10 (the highest possible value). In contrast, the structure of graphite is a layered one with weak bonds, so the layers slide over each other making graphite a very soft mineral (hardness 1 or 2), used for pencils and lubricants (Figure 3.2b).

The hardness of diamond makes it the natural choice for cutting hard materials. For example, diamonds are used to grind spectacle lenses, shape billiard balls and drill through rocks when looking for oil. Eighty per cent of natural diamonds, and all the manufactured industrial diamonds, are used in modern industrial technology. The remaining 20 per cent of natural diamonds are used as gemstones, since they have properties giving the brilliant sparkle required for jewellery, as well as being durable. Diamonds can be classified according to their quality (using criteria such as colour and clarity). The best quality diamonds make up a high proportion of placer deposits, since imperfect crystals tend to break during transportation.

Diamond illustrates very well how chemical make-up, bonding and structure determine the chemical and physical properties of a mineral and these in turn control the industrial and other uses of this vital raw material. We will now examine how these close links work for other, more common minerals.

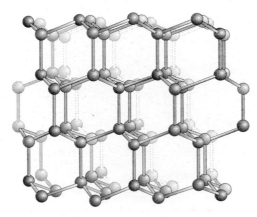

Figure 3.2a *Part of the diamond crystal structure*

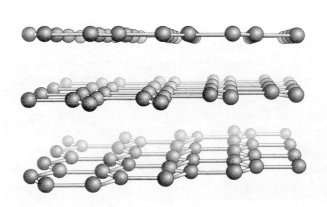

Figure 3.2b *The layered structure of graphite*

3.2 Minerals: chemical composition

Some naturally occurring minerals contain only one element, for example, gold (Au) or diamond (C); but most are compounds of elements, such as **galena**, which is lead (Pb) combined with sulphur (S). Minerals are inorganic materials with a definite chemical composition, a definite atomic structure and physical properties that vary between known limits.

Figure 3.3 *Common elements of the Earth's crust*

Element	Chemical symbol	Percentage by mass
Oxygen	O	46.60
Silicon	Si	27.72
Aluminium	Al	8.13
Iron	Fe	5.00
Calcium	Ca	3.63
Sodium	Na	2.83
Potassium	K	2.59
Magnesium	Mg	2.09
Titanium	Ti	0.44
All other elements		0.97
Total		100.00

The most commonly found minerals are compounds of the most common elements in the Earth's crust, shown in the Table in Figure 3.3. Consequently, if a mineral contains one of the less common elements, it will not be very abundant. Since carbon does not appear in this list, diamonds are not expected to be common, especially as carbon in rocks is usually in the form of graphite or organically derived carbon, e.g. coal. Rarity is one reason for the high value of diamond. Diamond and graphite are different minerals because although they have the same chemical composition and formula (C), their atomic structures (bonding) differ and so they have different physical properties. Such minerals are called **polymorphs** (many forms), revisited in Chapter 7.

Minerals formed of the common elements are likely to be frequently found. The Table in Figure 3.3 shows that oxygen and silicon form a high proportion of the Earth's crust and it is not surprising that the most common rock-forming minerals are **silicates**, compounds of silicon and oxygen, combined also with aluminium, iron, calcium, sodium, potassium and magnesium.

Less common minerals, usually non-silicates, can also be very important. If they contain an element or elements valuable for industrial use, such as copper, then they can be vital economic minerals. But as Chapter 10 explains, these minerals are not generally common or rock forming. There is also a wide range of other minerals which are neither major rock-forming nor economically important and we have no space to consider them further here.

3.3 Minerals: how are they constructed?

Every mineral has a regular arrangement of atoms forming its atomic structure. Some minerals are formed of atoms that have either gained an electron (becoming a negative ion) or lost an electron (positive ion). Since opposite charges attract strongly, these ions are attracted together to form **electrovalent** or **ionic bonds**. **Halite** (NaCl or rock salt) is formed in this way. It consists of sodium (Na^+) and chloride (Cl^-) ions, bonded together in a 'face-centred cubic' structure, in the ratio 1:1 as shown in Figure 3.4a. Overall, the charges balance out.

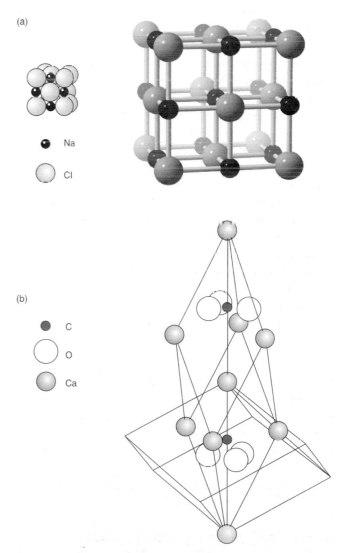

(a)

- Na
- Cl

(b)

- C
- O
- Ca

Figure 3.4 *The crystal structures of two common minerals: (a) Halite (face-centred cubic); (b) Calcite (rhombohedral)*

3.3.1 STRUCTURE OF SILICATES

The basic building block of the silicate minerals is the **silicon-oxygen tetrahedron** (Figure 3.5). In this structure, one silicon atom is surrounded by four oxygen atoms in a tetrahedral arrangement. All minerals are electrically neutral (zero charge). A silicon atom can share four of its electrons (called **covalent bonding**) with those of four oxygen atoms and each oxygen has an electron remaining 'unattached', shown in Figure 3.5b. These electrons are available to form bonds with other ions. In the case of the mineral quartz (SiO_2), the electron would bond with another Si ion.

Different proportions of silicon and oxygen combine with other common elements such as aluminium (Al^{3+}), iron (Fe^{2+}), magnesium (Mg^{2+}) and sodium (Na^+). In these ways, the four electrons of the silicon-oxygen tetrahedron that form a negative charge are balanced by bonding with positively charged ions (**cations**), such as iron (Fe^{2+}) and magnesium (Mg^{2+}).

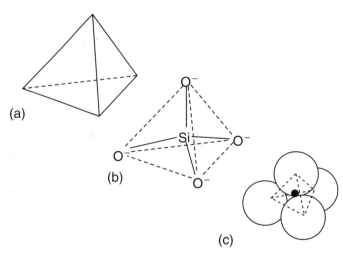

Figure 3.5 *Three representations of the Si-O structure: (a) Tetrahedron; (b) Tetrahedron with electrons available for pairing; (c) Tetrahedron showing relative sizes of ions*

The silicon-oxygen tetrahedron is unusual among negatively charged ions (**anions**), as it has the ability to polymerise, or link together to form chains in various ways, through 'oxygen sharing'. This results in tetrahedra forming large anionic units, producing several distinctive structural types of silicate: the single chains, double chains, two-dimensional sheets and three-dimensional framework structures shown in Figure 3.7. The charges on these anion units are usually balanced by a combination of simple cations, mainly K^+, Na^+, Ca^{2+}, Fe^{2+}, Mg^{2+} and Al^{3+}. These may substitute for (replace) each other, provided that the charge has the same value to maintain neutrality, and the ionic radius is similar (very big ions cannot fit into the space of small ones).

The atomic structure of silicates is linked closely to their **crystallisation temperature**, the temperature at which a mineral forms from the molten state as a magma cools. If a melt were to contain all the constituents of these silicate minerals, the first, highest temperature mineral to crystallise would be **olivine**, but when the temperature drops to a certain point, crystals of **pyroxene** start to form (see the left hand side of Figure 3.6).

At the same time, the calcium-rich mineral **plagioclase feldspar** begins to crystallise, shown on the right hand side of Figure 3.6. As these crystals form, the composition of the melt changes slightly and the next feldspar crystals to form contain slightly less calcium, but more sodium. This process is known as the **continuous reaction series** of plagioclase feldspars. The olivine-pyroxene iron-rich series is a **discontinuous series**, with the different mineral structures becoming increasingly complex as the temperature drops. These crystallisation sequences were first recognised by N.L.Bowen in the 1920s and have since been called **Bowen's Reaction Series**, shown in Figure 3.6.

Minerals that form at high temperatures are not stable at Earth's surface temperatures, especially in the presence of oxygenated water, as they are out of chemical equilibrium. So, the resistance to weathering of the silicate minerals (i.e. their chemical stability) is directly related to Bowen's series, with the minerals at the top of the series on Figure 3.6 being least stable and those at the bottom being most resistant to weathering.

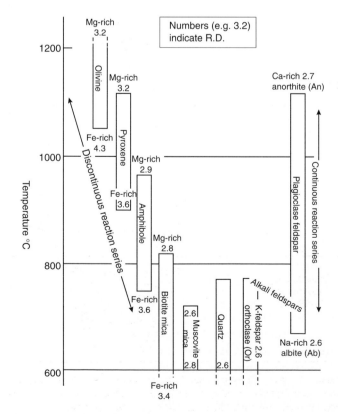

Figure 3.6 *Bowen's Reaction Series*

Mineral types with examples of formula	Structural type and silicate unit	Additional comments
Olivines: e.g. Mg_2SiO_4 Garnets: e.g. $Mg_3Al_2(SiO_4)_3$ (a)	Single tetrahedra $(Si_2O_4)^{4-}$  (a) Relative scale (b) Schematically	Dense compact structures. Crystals have equidimensional shapes but no cleavage.
Pyroxenes: e.g. $Mg_2Si_2O_6$ (b)	Single chains $(Si_2O_6)^{4-}$ 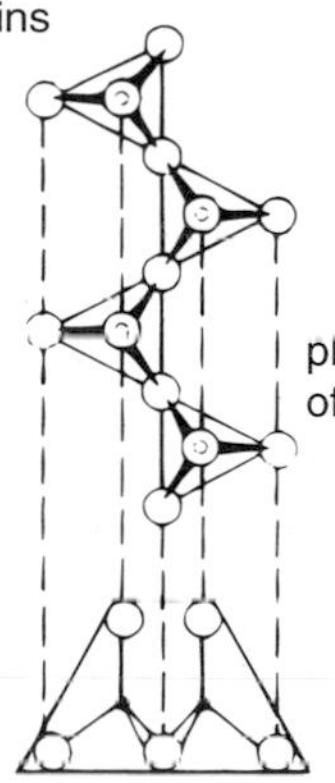 plan view of chain end-on view	Pyroxenes are generally equidimensional and dense, but they have two well-developed cleavages (nearly at 90°) because cation bonding is weaker between chains than along the chains. 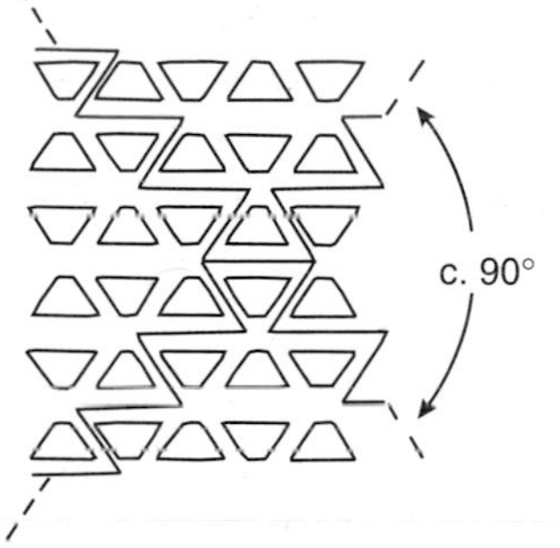 c. 90° Stacking of chains in crystal: cleavage develops where cation bonding between chains breaks down 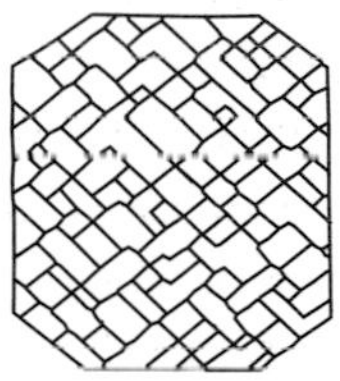 Typical cleavage pattern in pyroxene viewed end-on to chains
Amphiboles: e.g. $Ca_2Mg_5(Si_8O_{22})(OH)_2$ (c)	Double chains $(Si_4O_{11}(OH))^{7-}$ 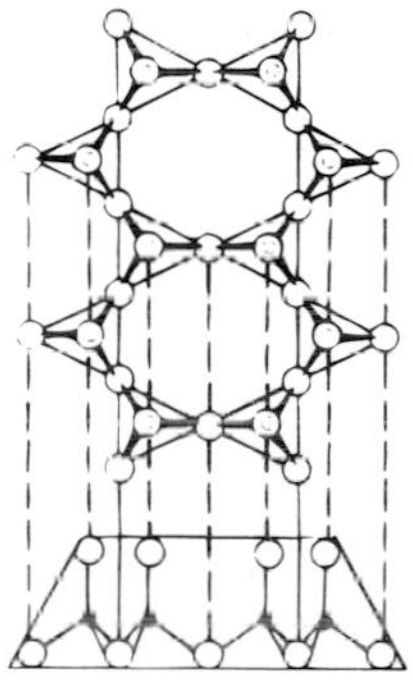 plan view of double chains end on view	Similarly shaped, but less compact and less dense than pyroxenes because there are holes in the double chains, which accommodate $(OH)^-$ groups. Cation bonding is generally weaker than in pyroxenes, though there is a similar internal arrangement of two cleavages at c. 60° c. 60° 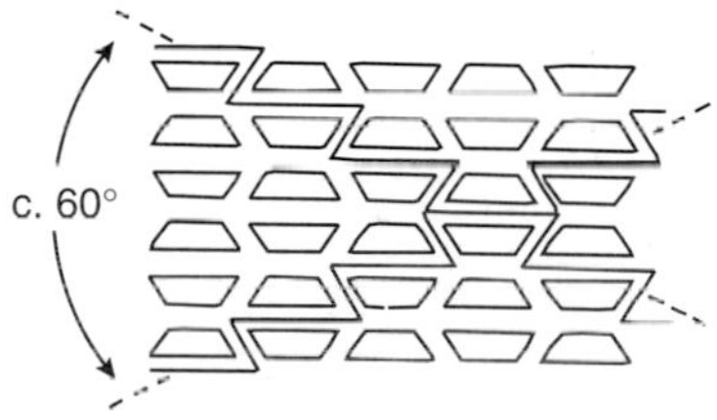 Development of cleavage in amphibole along weakly-linked chains 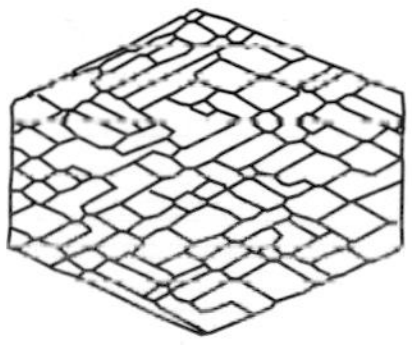 Typical cleavage pattern in amphibole viewed end-on to double chains
Micas: e.g. $KMg_3(AlSi_3O_{10})(OH)_2$ (also clay minerals) (d)	Sheet silicates $(Si_4O_{10})^{4-}$ 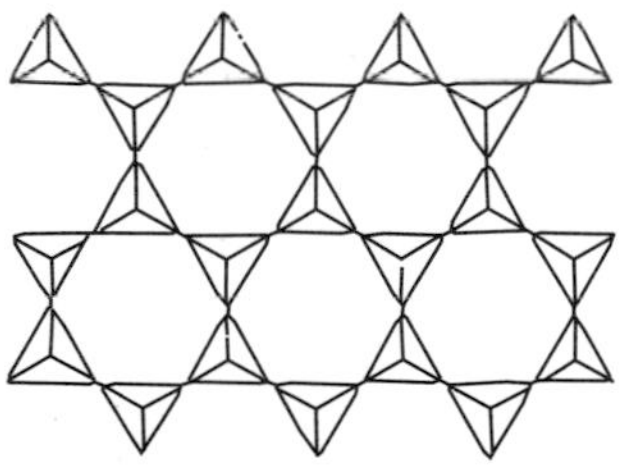 	Tabular minerals with open structures and low densities. The open spaces in the sheets accommodate $(OH)^-$ groups. The sheets are bonded by weak K–O bonds in mica. Although the sheets themselves are strong, there is a very well-defined cleavage between them.
Quartz: SiO_2 Feldspar: e.g. $NaAlSi_3O_8$ (e)	Framework silicates (SiO_2) 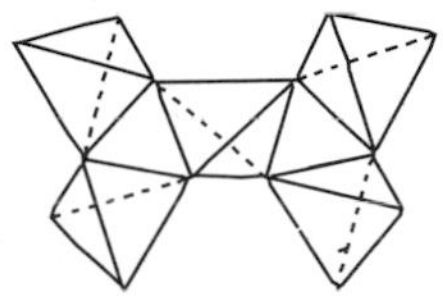 	Quartz has a rigid framework with strong Si–O bonds only. Feldspars have some weaker bonds (between alkali metal atoms and oxygen) and show two cleavages, nearly at 90°. Although their structures are more compact than micas, for example, neither mineral group contains heavy elements and so densities are low.

Figure 3.7 *Silicate mineral structures: (a) The structure of olivine (Mg, Fe)$_2$SiO$_4$, of isolated tetrahedra; (b) The structure of pyroxene (Ca, Mg, Fe)Si$_2$O$_6$, a chain silicate; (c) The structure of amphibole, a hydrated aluminium double chain silicate; (d) The structure of mica, a hydrated aluminium silicate sheet; (e) The structure of feldspars, framework silicates: plagioclase (CaAl$_2$Si$_2$O$_8$) albite NaAlSi$_3$O$_8$ or orthoclase KAlSi$_3$O$_8$*

3.3.2 VARIABLE CHEMICAL COMPOSITION: SOLID SOLUTION

Chemicals on the shelves in a chemistry laboratory usually have fixed formulae, but this is not the case with many rock-forming minerals. Instead, different ions can substitute for one another within the structure, providing they have similar sizes and/or charges. The formula of olivine is shown in Appendix 2 as $(Mg,Fe)_2SiO_4$ which means that it is a group of minerals that may have a composition varying from an end-member Mg_2SiO_4 (called forsterite) to an end-member Fe_2SiO_4 (fayalite), with any combination of Mg and Fe between. This is called a **solid solution series**. The first (higher temperature) olivine to crystallise, Mg_2SiO_4, is less dense than the later Fe-rich type. This is shown in Figure 3.6 and is true for minerals in the olivine, pyroxene and amphibole groups. The density of minerals is related to the mass of the ions, but also their ionic radii, and the way in which they are bonded.

Of the common rock-forming minerals, only quartz has a fixed formula of silicon and oxygen and so has fixed chemical and most physical properties (except colour). Other silicates are groups of minerals in which solid solution gives a range of chemical compositions and this results in a range of mineral properties, as summarised in Appendix 2.

The feldspars show solid solution between three end members: calcium-rich **anorthite**, sodium-rich **albite** and potassium-rich **orthoclase**. It is fairly easy to see how potassium (K^+) can substitute for sodium (Na^+) since they have the same charge and so can fit into the lattice in the same way. However the ions are rather different in size, the ionic radius of potassium is 1.33 and that of sodium is 0.97.

Calcium (Ca^{2+}), with two charges, substitutes for the sodium (Na^+) of albite because the ionic radius of calcium at 0.99 is very similar to that of sodium at 0.97. The charges are balanced by one of the silicon atoms (four charges) being replaced by an aluminium atom (three charges), giving the formula of anorthite $CaAl_2Si_2O_8$. All the feldspars in the albite to anorthite solid solution series belong to the plagioclase group.

Since the feldspars vary between three main end members, this variation is normally shown on a **triangular diagram** (Figure 3.8) where the shaded areas represent the naturally occuring feldspars at a typical igneous temperature. The diagram shows that in plagioclase feldspars there is complete ionic substitution between albite ($NaAlSi_3O_8$) and anorthite ($CaAl_2Si_2O_8$), with all possible Na^+/Ca^2 ratios. There is limited solubility between albite ($NaAlS_3O_8$) and orthoclase ($KAlS_{13}O_8$), the **alkali feldspars**, because of the difference in ionic radii of Na^+ and K^+. Solubility is extremely limited between

anorthite and orthoclase since K^+ and Ca^{2+} have different ionic radii as well as different charges.

The variation in chemistry that occurs in solid solution affects physical properties that depend upon the atomic masses of the atoms and on bond strengths, but does not affect others, such as crystal shape and cleavage which depend on the overall atomic structure.

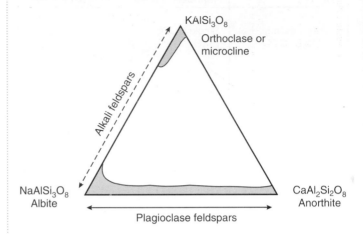

Figure 3.8 *Triangular diagram showing solid solution in the feldspars*

3.3.3 PHASE DIAGRAM OF SOLID SOLUTION IN PLAGIOCLASE

One method of examining how chemical variation develops in minerals is to use **phase diagrams**, which are graphs that show how the mineral varies according to temperature. To illustrate the concept of a phase diagram, we will use a familiar example of water (H_2O), which is transformed from one phase to another through the water cycle. At sea level and at the surface of the Earth below 0 °C, water freezes into ice; at 'normal' temperatures (0 °C–100 °C) water is liquid and above 100 °C, its boiling point, water becomes a vapour. Increasing or decreasing the pressure changes the temperature values at which the phase changes happen: for example, high in the Himalaya of Tibet, where air pressure is lower than at ground level, water boils at about 70 °C, so climbers complain that it is impossible to make a decent cup of tea. The values at which water turns to ice, or to vapour, can be plotted on a graph of temperature against pressure, shown as Figure 3.9.

The area in which each phase is stable (called the **stability field**) is edged by solid lines called **phase boundaries**. Figure 3.9 shows that at approximately atmospheric pressure, liquid water and water vapour are in physical equilibrium, lying on the phase boundary line. Decreasing pressure, while staying on the phase boundary (i.e. sliding down the line) means that liquid water and water vapour are in equilibrium at a temperature below 100 °C. If a temperature or pressure change causes conditions that move off the phase

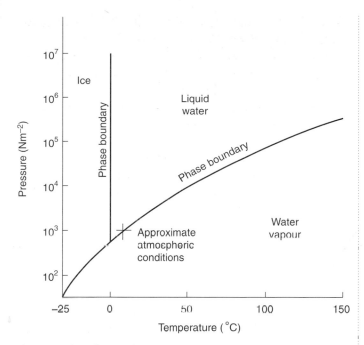

Figure 3.9 *Phase diagram of water*

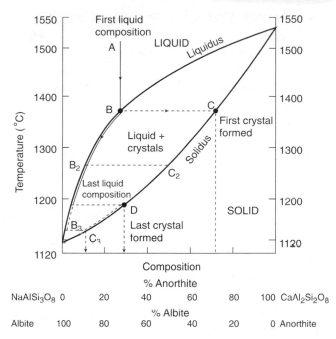

Figure 3.10 *Phase diagram for the reaction series anorthite (An) albite (Ab)*

boundary into either the liquid water field or the water vapour field, then water vapour will change to liquid water, or vice versa. At low pressures, ice *sublimes* into water vapour directly, without passing through a liquid phase.

A phase diagram which closely resembles Figure 3.9 is that showing the stability fields of the minerals kyanite/sillimanite/andalusite; they all have the formula Al_2SiO_5, so are polymorphs (Figure 7.7). The changes from one form to another depend crucially on the temperature and pressure at the time of formation during metamorphic processes, as discussed in Chapter 7.

Water, as a pure substance, has fixed freezing and boiling points; minerals do not all melt or crystallise at the same temperature. Minerals with different chemistries in a solid solution series have different crystallisation points, as Figure 3.7 showed. Magmas are generated at depth, representing pressures of 5000–10 000 times that at the surface of the Earth, and these pressures affect the temperatures of melting and crystallisation.

Figure 3.7 showed that the plagioclase feldspars formed over a range of temperatures, changing in composition during the crystallisation. Figure 3.10 shows the phase diagram for the continuous reaction series between 100 per cent Ca-plagioclase (anorthite) and 100 per cent Na-plagioclase (albite). The lower line that separates the field containing only solid crystals from the field containing crystals + liquid is called the **solidus**. In a similar way, the upper line that separates the field containing crystals + liquid from the field of liquid only is called the **liquidus**. These lines represent boundaries of chemical equilibrium.

If a liquid that consisted of 30 per cent anorthite and 70 per cent albite were to cool under equilibrium conditions from a temperature above the liquidus, it would cool following the vertical line AB on Figure 3.10 until it reached the liquidus at B. At that point, crystals would begin to form at a temperature of about 1375 °C. The composition of the first crystals to form can be found by drawing a horizontal line at that temperature to point C (on the solidus) and finding the composition at that point, i.e. 75 per cent anorthite, shown by the dashed vertical line. If the melt continued to crystallise very slowly and *the crystals reacted with the liquid*, the composition of the crystals would follow the solidus, to C_2. However, while the composition of the crystals was changing, the composition of the remaining melt would also alter following the liquidus, to B_2. At D the crystallisation would be complete as all further cooling is below the line of the solidus, and the solid would have a composition of the original melt, 30 per cent anorthite and 70 per cent albite. If, however, *crystals were removed from the melt* before they reacted, then the melt would follow the liquidus to B_3, where the last crystals would have the composition C_3: about 90 per cent albite and 10 per cent anorthite.

3.4 Identifying minerals

Around 4000 minerals have been identified, but only a few are commonly found. They can be identified in a number of different ways, but a common sequence is:

1 in a hand specimen using a hand lens, accompanied by
2 in a very thin slice of rock, (called a '**thin section**') using a petrological (rock) microscope; and lastly, if rare or unknown
3 by chemical analysis, using specialist apparatus.

Most common minerals can be identified in a hand specimen quite quickly using a few simple tests to determine the key properties; these are the **diagnostic properties** of the individual minerals. A Table summarising the properties can be found as Appendix 2.

The structure of an unknown mineral may be studied using X-ray crystallography, or electron microprobe analysis to determine its chemical composition. These techniques are the most precise and accurate, but also the most expensive and complex. The study and identification of minerals under the petrological microscope require special preparation of the sample and some experience to provide correct identification, but we will introduce this technique in section 3.5.

3.4.1 HARDNESS

The **hardness** of a mineral, the resistance of the mineral to scratching, is a particularly useful diagnostic property. The scale of hardness used for minerals was developed by **Mohs**, who listed 10 minerals in order of their relative hardness. He gave the hardest mineral, diamond, a value of ten, and the softest, talc, a value of one, with the rest in between (Figure 3.11). For the minerals of hardness one to nine, the relationship is roughly linear; but diamond (hardness ten) is considerably harder than corundum (hardness nine).

Mohs' scale is applied by attempting to scratch a mineral with another, or one of the 'standards' such as a

Figure 3.11 *Mohs' scale of hardness*

Hardest mineral	10	Diamond
	9	Corundum
	8	Topaz
		Steel file 7.5
	7	Quartz
	6	Feldspar
		Steel pin or penknife 5.5
	5	Apatite
	4	Fluorite
		Copper coin 3.5
	3	Calcite
		Finger nail 2.5
	2	Gypsum
Softest mineral	1	Talc

steel file. A harder mineral will scratch a softer one but cannot be scratched by the softer one. You need to try both ways to be sure. It is useful to know that the hardness of a finger nail is about 2.5, a copper coin 3.5, a steel pin 5.5 and a steel file 7.5, as shown in Figure 3.11.

Hardness depends on the atomic structure of the mineral, and more particularly on the density of packing within the structure, the charge of the ions and their ionic radius. Diamond (hardness of 10) and graphite (hardness of between one and two) illustrate this; diamond has a much more tightly packed structure than graphite, where the atoms are in layers that slide over one another, shown in Figure 3.2.

The silicate group of rock-forming minerals can also be used to illustrate how hardness varies with atomic structure, with micas having a hardness between two and three due to the loosely packed, extended sheets; and olivine having a hardness of 6.5, due to its very compact structure. Quartz has a hardness of seven due to its strong covalent structure (three-dimensional tetrahedral framework).

3.4.2 CLEAVAGE AND FRACTURE

Cleavage is the tendency of a mineral to break along distinct and well-defined planes of weakness. These planes are directly related to the internal atomic structure and represent weaknesses in the chemical bonds between chains and layers of atoms. Halite (NaCl, Figure 3.4) has three cleavage directions, perpendicular to each other, resulting in cubic cleavage (Figure 3.12c). Octahedral cleavage is shown by fluorite which has four cleavage directions across the corners of the crystal faces of a cube.

The relationship between atomic structure and cleavage is well illustrated by the silicates. Pyroxenes and amphiboles show how the configuration and size of the large anionic units (comprised of silicon-oxygen tetrahedra sharing oxygens) determine the angles of cleavage of these minerals. Weaknesses between the single silicate chains in pyroxenes result in two cleavage directions intersecting at about 90°. The wider double silicate chains of amphiboles result in a greater angle of cleavage intersection, at about 60°/120° (Figure 3.7).

Micas have one well-developed cleavage direction (called a **perfect basal cleavage** since it is parallel to the base of the mica crystal (Figure 3.12a)), so the mineral easily splits into thin flexible sheets (Figure C3.2). Here the bonds between the sheets are much weaker than the strong bonds within the sheets.

Minerals with 'weak' directions through the crystal structure exhibit cleavage, but all minerals can **fracture**, producing irregular breakage surfaces; fracture is most obvious in minerals which have a poor cleavage.

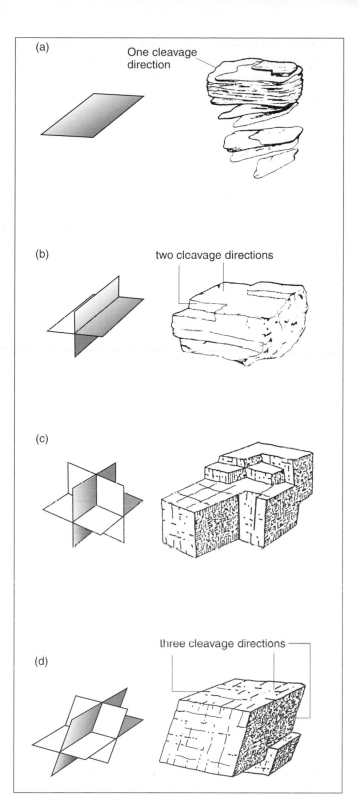

Figure 3.12 *Cleavage directions of common minerals: (a) Mica: one perfect basal cleavage; (b) Feldspar, pyroxene: two cleavages, almost perpendicular; (c) Halite, galena: three cleavages, perpendicular; (d) Calcite: three cleavages, not perpendicular (see also Figure 3.4b)*

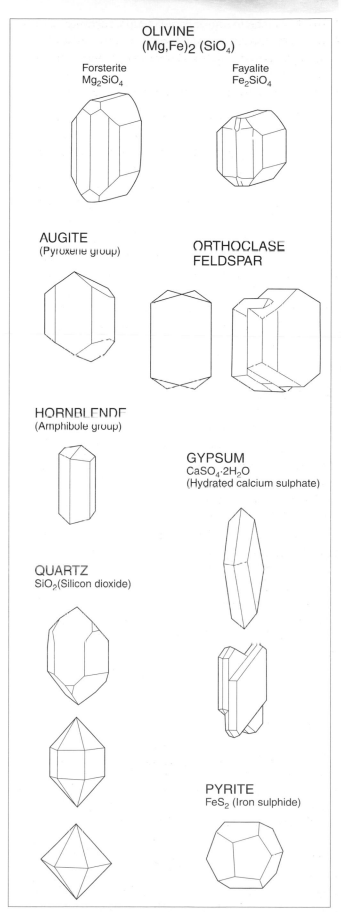

Figure 3.13 *Crystal forms of common minerals*

Minerals that have a strong and compact arrangement of atoms can show an unusual form of fracture called **conchoidal** (shell-like). This can also be used as a diagnostic property; quartz, for example, has no cleavage because of its tetrahedral atomic structure, but it does have a conchoidal fracture.

3.4.3   CRYSTAL FORM

Crystals allowed to grow freely, for example in a cavity inside a rock, will adopt a particular shape that depends upon the internal atomic structure. This shape is called the **form** of the mineral. The angle between any designated pair of crystal faces will always be the same, although crystals of different shapes may result, depending on how fast individual faces grow during crystallisation – some crystals may be short and fat while others are long and thin.

It is also important to remember that if a mineral has cleavage, then the cleavage is usually related to the crystal faces – but quartz, for example, has no cleavage yet it can form perfect crystals with faces.

If the chemical and physical conditions are appropriate, a wide variety of spectacular crystals can develop, shown in Figure 3.13. When crystals grow in rocks, they usually interfere with each other's growth so crystal faces cannot develop, but they still have an internal crystal structure determined by their chemical composition.

3.4.4   COLOUR AND STREAK

Although colour is often a mineral's most obvious feature, its use in identifying a mineral is limited. The colour of naturally pale-coloured minerals may be affected by impurities of just a few atoms of an element such as magnesium or chromium; or crystal defects in the structure; or sub-microscopic inclusions. The overall chemical formula, structure and properties are not changed. For example, quartz (SiO_2) can be found in a range of colours including colourless (rock crystal), white, pink (rose quartz), black (smoky quartz) and purple (amethyst) (Figure C3.3). The properties of hardness and cleavage (or lack of it) are not altered by any difference in colour. The gemstones sapphire (blue) and ruby (red) are merely different coloured varieties of the mineral corundum (Al_2O_3).

Colour can be a valuable diagnostic property for dark minerals and, for example, **pyrite** (FeS_2) is the only mineral with its particular brassy yellow (fool's gold) colour (Figure C3.4), and **malachite** ($CuCO_3.Cu(OH)_2$) is always a characteristic bright green.

Streak is the colour of the mineral when powdered and can be obtained by rubbing it across an unglazed porcelain tile, known as a **streak plate**. Sometimes the colour revealed by the streak is different from the colour in hand specimen. Pyrite, brassy yellow in hand specimen, has a streak that is greenish-black. Streak is most useful as a diagnostic property for opaque ore minerals, which often have a coloured streak; it is considerably less useful for white minerals which almost all have a white streak. Minerals harder than the streak plate will scratch it, and confusingly this can appear to leave a white streak. In these cases, powdered mineral can be obtained by crushing a small part of the specimen on to white paper.

3.4.5   RELATIVE DENSITY

The relative density (RD) of a mineral is the ratio between its mass and that of an equal volume of water (Chapter 2). RD depends on the atomic masses of the constituent elements and how closely their atoms are packed in the crystal structure. Diamond and graphite are both composed of carbon with an atomic mass of 12, but the packing of carbon atoms is different in the two minerals, resulting in an RD of 3.52 for diamond and 2.30 for graphite. Halite (NaCl) and galena (PbS) both have a cubic crystal structure, but they have very different relative densities, largely due to the differences in atomic masses of their cations. The sodium (Na) ion has an atomic mass of 23 and halite has an RD of 2.20, but the lead (Pb) ion with an atomic mass of 207 gives galena a much higher RD of 7.50.

There are a number of ways of determining the relative densities of minerals and rocks. In one common method, the specimen is weighed on a chemical balance, then its volume is found by measuring how much water it displaces from a graduated can. A second way involves weighing the specimen in air (attached by a thin thread to a spring balance), then reweighing the sample when fully immersed in a beaker of water. In water, the specimen is lighter by an amount equal to the mass of water displaced. The RD is calculated using the equation on p23.

Most common minerals have relative densities between 2.5 and 3.5, with the exception of minerals containing heavy metals such as barium (barite, barium sulphate $BaSO_4$, RD 4.5). Metallic-looking minerals tend to have relative densities in excess of 5.0. Pyrite has an RD of 5.0, and gold has an RD of up to 19.3.

Relative density is a useful diagnostic property for distinguishing dense barite from other pale coloured minerals and for identifying metal ores, but is otherwise of limited use.

3.4.6 OTHER PROPERTIES

There are a number of other properties which are useful in describing and identifying some minerals. **Lustre**, for example, is the appearance of a mineral's surface under reflected light, and is described by reference to well-known materials. **Metallic** lustre is the 'tin can' shiny appearance of galena and pyrite, whereas haematite sometimes shows a feeble metallic lustre termed submetallic. Quartz and halite have **glassy** or **vitreous** lustre, whereas sphalerite has a **resinous** lustre. Other lustres include **silky** (gypsum), **pearly** (talc) and the sparkling **adamantine** lustre of diamond and topaz. However, lustre has limited use as a diagnostic property.

Phosphorescence is a property notably exhibited by diamond, which emits light after being exposed to X-rays. This valuable physical property is used in the separation of diamond from gangue minerals during mineral separation. Fluorite emits light while exposed to ultraviolet (u.v.) radiation, a property known as **fluorescence**. **Magnetism** is a physical property displayed by magnetite and can be used in its identification. A large number of minerals can, however, be attracted by an electromagnet and this can be a useful technique in mineral separation.

All the properties discussed so far are physical properties, but a valuable diagnostic chemical property is the reaction of a clean mineral surface with dilute acid. Carbonate-bearing minerals react with acid and effervesce, releasing carbon dioxide gas. Some sulphide-bearing minerals (for example, galena) react to release hydrogen sulphide gas, obvious due to its powerful odour. Finally, the common mineral halite is soluble and the solution tastes salty. So, you can distinguish halite by licking it – a practice frowned on by health and safety regulations, in case what you lick isn't halite after all!

3.5 Minerals under the microscope

Minerals (and rocks) can be studied using a petrological microscope. This instrument has a rotating stage and has filters of polarising material fitted in the light beam below and above the object being examined. The lower, fixed filter means that the light passing through the slide is vibrating only in one direction (N–S) and is called **plane polarised light** (PPL). The same effect is produced by wearing polaroid sunglasses. The second filter can be put in the light path above the sample, or removed; using it examines a specimen in **cross-polarised light** (XPL). The second filter is oriented at right angles to the first, which means that only light vibrating E–W can pass into the objective lens and up to the eye.

To prepare a sample for examination, a thin slice of mineral or rock is stuck on to a glass slide and then ground down by diamond-impregnated wheels until the thin section is 30 microns thick (0.03 mm). At this thickness, most minerals are transparent or translucent and display a range of optical properties as they interact with the light beam. The appearance of minerals using plane polarised light (PPL), and light that has passed through both filters (XPL) can be used diagnostically in the same way as other methods described above. The advantage of the microscope is that crystals which are small and dark in hand specimen, such as pyroxene and amphibole, show distinctive properties, as do common pale minerals such as quartz and feldspar. Also, in hand specimen it can sometimes be difficult to distinguish between igneous and fragmental rocks when they are very fine-grained. The rock **texture** (the relationship between the crystals/grains) is usually clear in a thin section.

It is beyond the scope of this book to consider the use of the polarising microscope in detail but some of the physical properties discussed earlier are easily seen.

Thin sections are two-dimensional slices of three-dimensional crystals and thus the shape seen under the microscope can be extremely variable, but sometimes very distinctive. In sections cut perpendicular to the length of the crystal, pyroxenes (Figure C.3.5a) are usually eight-sided, with two sets of cleavage planes intersecting at about 90°, whereas amphiboles are six-sided with two sets of cleavage intersecting at about 60°/120°. Micas show clearly visible cleavage traces too (Figure C.3.5b).

A small number of minerals can be identified because they have the property of **pleochroism** (change of colour) as the stage of the microscope is rotated under PPL (Figure C.3.5b, colour section). The most common minerals to do this are brown mica (biotite), and also amphibole. However, it is difficult to identify most minerals under PPL alone.

Under crossed polars (XPL) minerals rich in Mg or Fe often show very bright colours. These are not the true colours, but **interference** effects, like an oil film on a puddle, and all the colours change like a kaleidoscope as the microscope stage is rotated. The intensity and range of colour shown are diagnostic.

Orthoclase and plagioclase feldspars can often be easily distinguished under the polarising microscope by their 'twinning'. This occurs where two or more portions of the same crystal are joined so that they share a common plane. Under crossed polars (XPL), feldspar twins appear as stripes with different shades of white, grey or black; they never show bright interference colours. As the stage is rotated, each stripe changes through white, grey, black. The simple twinning common in orthoclase crystals often appears as wide pale and dark segments. Plagioclase feldspar displays lamellar twinning which appears as a series of black and white stripes (Figure C3.6). Quartz under XPL shows shades of grey with no distinguishing features, as it has no cleavage, or twinning of crystals (Figure C3.6).

Some minerals develop concentric zones as they grow, seen as parallel bands within crystals under the microscope. These may represent changes in the composition of the fluid in which the crystal was growing during its formation.

3.6 Our crystalline world

Most of this chapter has concentrated on explaining the chemistry and structure of minerals that are the building blocks of rocks. However, it is important to realise that, for example, not just the diamonds in the Imperial Crown (Figure 3.1) are crystalline, but also the gold it contains. **Malleable** (bendable) metals such as gold, copper, lead and silver all have definite chemical compositions and crystal structures, so they are part of the crystalline world, too.

Water, ice and even clay have crystal structures – indeed, most of the solid inorganic world is crystalline.

One familiar material, window glass, does not have a crystalline structure. It is a liquid that has been cooled extremely rapidly, too quickly for regular crystal lattices to have formed. This process can also take place on a large scale in the natural environment when a molten rock (magma) cools rapidly to a volcanic glass, so individual crystals are not formed.

3.7 Summary

1 A mineral is an inorganic material that has a definite crystalline structure based on an ordered internal arrangement of constituent atoms and with a chemical composition that may be expressed in terms of a unique chemical formula.
2 Minerals are electrically neutral, so the charges on cations and anions must balance in the structure.
3 Most rock-forming minerals are silicates, that can be bonded as isolated tetrahedra (olivines), chains (pyroxenes), double chains (amphiboles), sheets (micas) or frameworks (quartz and feldspars).
4 Bowen's Reaction Series explains the changing crystallisation pathways of minerals in igneous rocks.
5 Elements may substitute for others in a structure, provided that the charges balance and the ionic radii are similar. Thus solid solution series of minerals exist, for example, in olivines and feldspars. This can be illustrated using a phase diagram.
6 Minerals may be identified in hand specimen by physical properties such as hardness, cleavage and crystal shape.
7 The optical properties of individual minerals can be distinguished using a petrological microscope and a thin section of a rock.

3.8 Questions

1 Using Appendix 2, identify the following minerals:
  Colour, white; cleavage three not perpendicular; hardness 3.0
  Colour pink; cleavage none; hardness 6.5
  Colour pink; cleavage two not at right angles; hardness 6.5
  Colour white; cleavage one; hardness 3.0
2 The minerals calcite and aragonite are polymorphs and so have the same chemical formulae but different crystal structures. Explain whether you would expect (a) their chemical properties (b) their physical properties to be similar or contrasting.
3 Explain how a broken piece of calcite (a cleavage rhomb) can be a different shape from the original crystal.
4 How could Bowen have worked out the mineral sequences in his Reactivity Series (Figure 3.7)?

CHAPTER 4

Igneous processes: crystallising rocks

Introduction

This chapter focuses on the processes that create the primary or first-formed rocks of the Earth's crust, the igneous rocks. It builds on the ideas introduced in previous chapters, of Earth cycles, especially plate tectonics, and the minerals that form igneous rocks.

The volcanism associated with different plate boundaries gives rise to rock types that differ in both texture and composition. Direct impact of volcanoes on humans may seem remote for some readers, but the potential climatic changes can have global effects.

4.1 Case Study: volcanoes compared

Figure 4.1a *Volcanism in Iceland, showing a 'fire fountain' eruption along a fissure*

Figure 4.1b *Montserrat 1997. Here a pyroclastic flow is travelling at speed down the Tarr River valley to the coast*

The two photographs in Figure 4.1 show different volcanic areas. Despite the similarity of these environments, there are also great contrasts. It is by trying to explain such differences that geologists have gained a deeper understanding of volcanic processes.

In Iceland, eruptions occur from individual volcanic centres but also along **fissures**, as shown in Figure 4.1a. Volcanoes of this type can build up very large structures called **shield volcanoes**, which typically have gently sloping sides built up by

successive lava flows. The material erupted is a low viscosity ('runny') lava that cools to form a dark, fine-grained igneous rock called **basalt**. Basalt lava eruptions are generally not very hazardous to humans, as they are gentle and effusive or 'oozing'. Even though spectacular 'fire fountains' can occur, as shown in Figure 4.1a, they can be viewed safely from a distance. The effects are mainly local. Volcanoes like this are found particularly where the ocean ridges of constructive plate margins are above sea level. This type of volcanism is often called **Hawaiian**, because it is typical of the volcanism there (although Hawaii is not on a constructive plate margin).

Chances Peak on the Caribbean island of Montserrat began to erupt in 1995. The island had been closely monitored and people were evacuated from danger zones, so there were few deaths. The material erupted was ash, dust and pumice, not lava, and by 1997 the island's capital, Plymouth, 10 km from the volcano's vent, had been evacuated and was covered with a thick layer of ash. The most dangerous aspect of the eruptions on Montserrat are the **pyroclastic** (fire-broken) flows of gas and particles that travel at great speed and can flow uphill and over water.

During an eruption, strong upward convection currents can be created in the atmosphere above the volcano, associated with rising ash and gas clouds. These conditions can trigger violent thunderstorms and heavy rain. The rainwater may combine with the loose ash to form mudflows called **lahars** which can also flow catastrophically down slopes and valleys and over ridges.

Explosive volcanoes, such as Chances Peak, tend to have a steep-sided, conical form typical of the classic volcano shape and they can be found around the margin of the Pacific Ocean and at other destructive plate margins. The material produced is different in composition from that of shield volcanoes and is mainly **andesite**, named because it is common in the Andes Mountains. This type of volcano can not only have catastrophic

effects on the surrounding region, but can also have a global effect through climatic changes.

The contrasting eruptive styles of volcanoes like Montserrat and those found in Iceland are a reflection of the different chemical composition (and hence mineralogy) and plate tectonic setting of the volcanoes. Figure 4.2 summarises some of the contrasting features of the volcanism in Figure 4.1 and the differences in igneous processes and their products which are the focus of this chapter.

Figure 4.2 *Summary Table of two types of volcanism*

Iceland	Montserrat
Fissure eruptions, shield volcanoes	Cone volcanoes Strato volcanoes
Lava flows common	Ash and pumice, scoria, some lava Volcanic mud flows (lahars) common
Composition of erupted material – usually basalt	Composition of erupted material – usually andesite
Human impact low(ish), local and little danger	Local human impact high; regional impact high and unpredictable
Global impact low(ish)	Global impact may be high through climatic effects
Constructive plate margin location	Destructive plate margin location

4.2 Introducing igneous rocks

There is a great variety of igneous rocks: they can have large crystals of different colours, or tiny crystals that all look the same. We need ways of examining and sorting them into different 'types', as one would when studying plants or animals, and then relating our observations to the ways and geological contexts in which the rocks were formed. Appendix 3 contains a Table of common igneous rocks with a summary of their mineral content and where they were formed. Some of these rock types will be familiar to you, such as granite, basalt, pumice and perhaps also gabbro, peridotite and dolerite. This chapter will explain the formation of these rocks, and a few others that may be new to you.

Overall, rock colour and crystal size are two important starting points. A dark coloured crystalline rock contains minerals rich in iron and magnesium that are characteristic of constructive plate margins. Conversely, a pale-coloured rock contains silica-rich minerals that are associated with a continental source. The chemistry of

igneous rocks, and the types of minerals which they contain, is related to temperature, viscosity and plate tectonic context.

Crystal size gives an indication of the rate of crystallisation: small crystals form quickly, for example in a **lava flow** at the Earth's surface, whereas large crystals need longer to form slowly beneath the surface. From these properties, of chemistry and crystallisation rate, most aspects of volcanoes and igneous rocks can eventually be explained; during the next subsections other factors such as dissolved gases, including water will be discussed.

Most of the minerals found in igneous rocks are silicates and the sequence of crystallisation of these is explained by Bowen's Reaction Series (Chapter 3).

4.2.1 CLASSIFYING IGNEOUS ROCKS: CRYSTAL SIZE AND COMPOSITION

Igneous rocks are formed by the crystallisation of a rock melt or magma. The crystallisation occurs during cooling, as the atoms become organised into crystals that grow from **nucleation centres**, which may be specks of impurities in the melt. Crystals continue to grow from the centres, according to the geometry of the mineral (explained in Chapter 3), in random orientations relative to each other. Eventually all the crystals will grow until they meet each other, forming an interlocking three dimensional structure when crystallisation is complete. This is an igneous rock texture (the relationship between the grains or crystals forming a rock).

Magmas that reach the surface of the Earth in volcanoes cool quickly, forming fine-grained **extrusive** volcanic rocks. If the rock is cooled extremely rapidly (called quenching) a **volcanic glass** results, where no ordered lattices (i.e. crystals) have had time to form. Crystallisation also takes place very slowly deep within the Earth's crust, to form coarse-grained **plutonic** rocks. These are **intrusive**, that is, they are forced into (intrude) existing rocks. Both of the volcanoes in the Case Study are visibly producing extrusive igneous rocks, but magma that does not reach the surface while the volcano is active may eventually crystallise deep within the crust below the volcano, to form plutonic rocks. Millions of years of erosion acting on the Earth's surface can remove several kilometres of overlying material so that, in due course, the plutonic igneous rocks may be exposed at the surface, even though they were not originally formed there. So the size of the crystals is an indication of where an igneous rock was formed, and is the basis of a classification.

The name given to a rock is only a 'shorthand' way of describing what a rock is made of and the conditions in which it formed. It is more important to be able to describe a sample accurately, and from the description draw conclusions about the rock's mode of formation, than it is to attach a name to it. For example the name, 'basalt', could be replaced by the following description:

- A fine-grained (<1 mm) crystalline rock, very dark in colour.
- Crystals are randomly oriented and a few small feldspar crystals may be visible with a hand lens or the naked eye.
- The small crystals indicate that the rock cooled rapidly at the surface of the Earth as a lava, i.e. it is an extrusive volcanic rock.
- Its dark colour indicates that it contains a relatively high proportion of dark minerals such as pyroxene, which are iron (Fe)- and magnesium (Mg)-rich minerals; this is called **mafic** composition.

Granite could be described as:

- Coarse-grained (crystals 2–5 mm or bigger), pale coloured crystalline rock composed of feldspar (about 60–65 per cent), quartz (about 25–30 per cent)

and mica (about 10–15 per cent). The pale colour indicates that there are few Fe- or Mg-rich minerals present.
- The random orientation of the minerals indicates an igneous origin and the medium-large crystal size implies slow cooling at depth (intrusive/plutonic); the mineralogy shows that this magma came from within the continental crust.

Such rock descriptions are made purely by observation with a hand lens or microscope (Figure C4.1) of the texture and minerals present, and lead into discussions of how the rock was formed. A more precise way of defining a rock is to analyse its chemical composition, and typical results are shown in Figure 4.3.

Figure 4.3 Chemical composition by mass (%) of fine-grained crystalline rocks. The coarse-grained form is in brackets

Rock name	Column 1 (peridotite)	Column 2 basalt (gabbro)	Column 3 andesite (diorite)	Column 4 rhyolite (granite)
Element given as oxide				
SiO_2	43	50	60	70
Al_2O_3	4	14	16	14.5
$Fe_2O_3 + FeO$	12	12	7.2	3.0
MgO	34	8.5	3.0	0.8
CaO	3.5	11	10	2.0
Na_2O	0.5	2.7	2.2	3.2
K_2O	0.25	0.3	1.0	5.0
Others	2.75	1.5		1.5

Note: Peridotite is the rock type that is thought to form the Earth's mantle but it has no fine-grained extrusive form.

The chemistry of igneous rocks is reflected in the minerals that they contain, shown in Figure 4.4. This can be regarded as a large three dimensional graph, with silica (SiO_2) content along the horizontal axis and percentage of minerals on the vertical axis. The third axis shown, which appears to be out of the plane of the paper, indicates crystal size, with coarser-grained (plutonic) rocks on the front face. It is important to realise that the fine-grained, extrusive forms, have an identical mineral content to their coarse-grained equivalent, the only difference being the crystal size which indicates how fast they formed.

By dropping a vertical line from the position of the various named igneous rock types on the top of the diagram, the minerals present in the rocks mentioned in Figure 4.4 can be worked out.

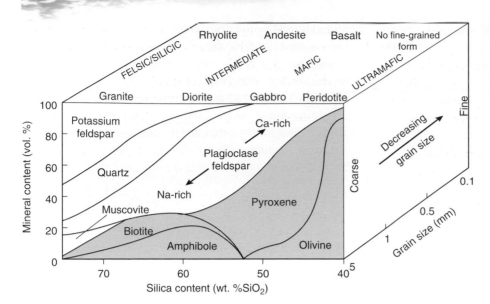

Figure 4.4 *Block diagram showing the approximate silica content, mineral content and grain size of some igneous rocks. Plutonic rock types are near the front of the top surface and volcanic rocks towards the back*

Figure 4.5 *Mineral content (%) of common igneous rock types*

Rock name	Column 1	Column 2	Column 3	Column 4
		basalt	andesite	granite
	(peridotite)	(gabbro)	(diorite)	(rhyolite)
Mineral name				
quartz	0	0	4	25
feldspar (plagioclase)	8	40	58	15
feldspar (alkali)	0	0	5	49
micas (all)	0	0	4	9
pyroxene	12	52	17	0
amphibole	0	0	12	2
olivine	80	8	0	0

[Note: It is usual to quote the chemical composition of a rock in terms of oxides of elements, even though within the rock they are combined in silicate minerals

From the trace of the line on the front face, gabbro, for example, contains about 40 per cent plagioclase feldspar, 52 per cent pyroxene and 8 per cent olivine. This mineral content is shown in the Table in Figure 4.5 with the mineralogy of several other igneous rock types.

Compare the data contained in the columns in Figures 4.3 and 4.5. What trends can you see as changes in the chemical composition of the rocks in successive columns? (Hint: look particularly at the oxides of Si, Fe and Mg). What are the trends in the minerals present?

From peridotite to granite there is a *decrease* in elements such as iron and magnesium, matched by a decrease in iron and magnesium-rich minerals such as olivine and pyroxene. There is an *increase* in silicon dioxide (SiO_2) across Figure 4.3 matched in Figure 4.5 by the appearance of the mineral quartz (SiO_2) in andesite/diorite and granite. In rocks such as peridotite and gabbro/basalt, all the SiO_2 is combined within the silicate structures of minerals such as olivine, pyroxene and feldspar; there is little or no 'free' SiO_2 (i.e. quartz) found in these rocks. As a rule of thumb, if a rock analysis contains less than 60 per cent SiO_2, there will be no quartz in the rock.

Igneous rocks which contain a high proportion of ferromagnesian minerals (shaded in Figure 4.4) tend to be dark in colour and are called mafic (also called basic). They usually have around 45–55 per cent SiO_2. Rocks with less than about 45 per cent SiO_2 are called **ultramafic** (or ultrabasic); however, the proportion of silica is not rigidly applied and the mineral content is more important. Rocks with a high proportion of minerals such as feldspar and quartz are classed as **silicic** or **felsic** (also called acidic) and usually have a high SiO_2 content, typically 60–70 per cent. Rocks that fall between felsic and mafic composition are called **intermediate**.

These differences in chemistry and mineralogy are crucial in determining the physical properties of a magma; those with high iron and magnesium content, such as basalt (column 2 of the Tables in Figures 4.3 and 4.5), have low viscosity. The low viscosity means that a lava flows freely and dissolved gases can escape relatively easily. The low-angled slope of a basalt shield volcano results. Magmas low in iron and magnesium have a higher silica content and are viscous, that is, very thick and 'sticky'. Gases become trapped in viscous magma, and these gases under pressure contribute to more 'explosive' behaviour. A steep-sided conical volcano is the result. The composition of magma from which a granite would crystallise beneath such a volcano is represented in column 4 of the Tables in Figures 4.3 and 4.5.

4.2.2 CRYSTALLISATION PATHWAYS

The temperature of melting/crystallisation is closely linked to the magma's chemical composition: magmas high in iron and magnesium begin to crystallise at around 1100 °C or higher. Magmas high in SiO_2 crystallise at lower temperatures, around 800 °C. This difference is shown in Figure 4.6, where the typical composition of basalt/gabbro (basaltic) and granitic magmas can be seen, at 1100 °C and 700 °C respectively.

The sequence of mineral crystallisation, Bowen's Reaction Series, (p44) is also part of Figure 4.6. It can explain some of the features of crystal settling in igneous rocks such as those seen in the mafic Palisades Sill shown in Figure 4.7. In this explanation, the olivine crystals formed first and settled out, changing the composition of the magma so that it then crystallised plagioclase feldspar. The less dense plagioclase feldspar stayed in suspension or floated towards the top of the magma chamber, eventually forming the upper part of the sill. The crystallisation sequence of minerals in the field could be explained by Bowen's laboratory experiments.

When this explanation was first put forward, some geologists thought that by starting with a magma of basaltic composition and continuously crystallising minerals (taking fractions) from the magma, the residual composition would approach that of a granite. This process is called **fractionation** or **fractional crystallisation**. The result is a number of different end products, and so the magma was chemically **differentiated**. Now it is generally thought that although a small amount of granitic magma *may* be generated by continuous fractionation of a basalt magma, as indicated by the bottom of the basalt 'teardrop' in Figure 4.6, most granite bodies found in continents are probably not formed by the differentiation of a basaltic magma (see later in this chapter).

4.2.3 PHASE DIAGRAMS

Phase diagrams of minerals were introduced in Chapter 3; they can also be constructed for rocks. This means subjecting rocks of different composition to varying conditions of temperature and pressure in laboratory experiments to find out what minerals form under different conditions.

If a rock powder is heated in the laboratory long enough to reach equilibrium at a specified temperature and pressure, and is then quenched rapidly, the different

Figure 4.6 *Crystallisation temperature ranges of common igneous minerals and rocks. The relative densities of the minerals are shown by the rectangular crystallisation boxes. The temperature ranges of igneous rocks are shown by the 'teardrop' shapes, where the width of the 'drop' indicates how much rock is formed. The components of the rock are the minerals stable at a given temperature, found by drawing a horizontal line*

Figure 4.7 *Cross section through the Palisades Sill, New York. The interpretation of the vertical section, the variation of minerals and their texture uses application of the ideas of fractional crystallisation of the discontinuous reaction series*

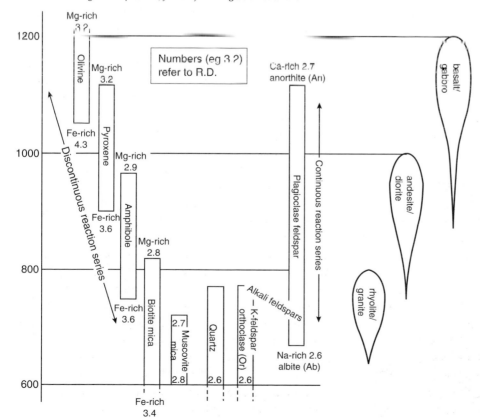
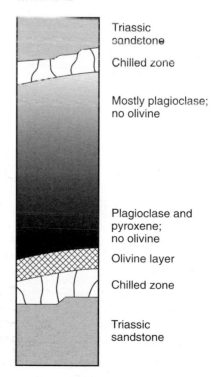

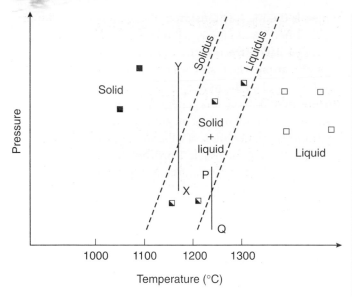

Figure 4.8 *Phase diagram for a mafic rock that melts over a range of pressures and temperature*

phases cannot react together while cooling. The results of many experiments are shown in Figure 4.8, where the solid squares represent solid material (crystals), the half shaded squares are a mixture of crystals and glass and the open squares are glass (quenched melt). The slope of the phase boundaries show that both for the liquidus and the solidus, increase in pressure also increases the temperature of melting. Figure 4.8 shows that by taking a point X in the field of crystals + melt, at a fixed temperature, and increasing the pressure by moving vertically up to Y, it is possible to cross to the solid field.

So a liquid + crystal mix is changed to a solid simply by increasing the pressure. This is the explanation of why the outer core of the Earth is liquid, but the inner core is solid: a phase change (crystallisation) has taken place.

Starting again from a point P in the field of crystals + melt, at a fixed temperature, and *decreasing* the pressure by moving vertically down to a point Q, it is possible to cross to the liquid field. This is part of the reason why magma chambers can be created within the asthenosphere, by thinning the crust above and so reducing the confining pressure. By continuing the line PQ downwards on Figure 4.8 it is clear that a high temperature magma can rise to be erupted in liquid form at the Earth's surface.

Another important factor that influences the style of eruption of magma is the dissolved gas content. The fire fountains described in the Case Study at the beginning of this chapter are the result of dissolved gases being released from the magma. Dissolved gases also have an effect on the position of the solidus and liquidus in phase diagrams, and the most important dissolved gas is water. Increasing the pressure increases the amount of water that can be dissolved in the magma. More water dissolved in the magma decreases the amount of polymerisation, with the result that the magma *can remain liquid longer, or will enable solid rock to melt at a lower temperature* than it would if no water was present. So, when water is dissolved in a magma, pressure has the *opposite* effect of that on a magma with no dissolved water (called **anhydrous**) as it *decreases* the melting temperature. This is shown in Figure 4.9. When a magma contains as much water as it is

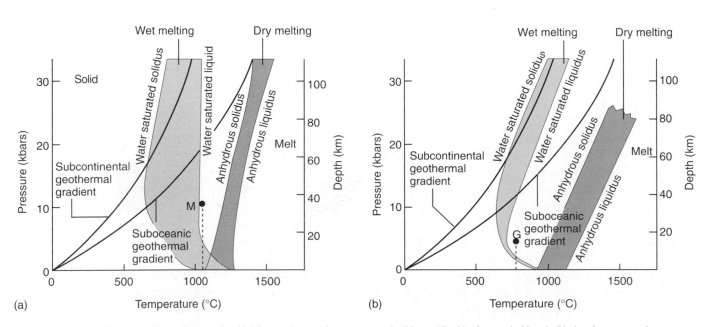

Figure 4.9 *(a) Plot of pressure against temperature showing the anhydrous and water-saturated solidus and liquidus for a typical basalt; (b) Plot of pressure against temperature showing the anhydrous and water-saturated solidus and liquidus for a typical granite*

possible for it to hold at a given pressure, it is called **water saturated** or **hydrous**.

What would happen to a water-saturated basaltic magma (M) rising to the surface from a depth equivalent to 35 km (10 kb pressure), at a temperature of about 1075 °C on Figure 4.9a? Dropping a vertical line on Figure 4.9a, the magma reaches the surface between the water-saturated solidus and the liquidus, so it will erupt as a partly crystalline liquid. A dry basaltic melt at the same pressure and at a temperature of 1200 °C, starting from between the anhydrous solidus and anhydrous liquidus, will rise to surface and erupt as a partly crystalline liquid.

Granitic magmas do not behave in the same way and the pattern of the temperature of solidus and liquidus with increase in pressure is shown in Figure 4.9b.

What happens to a granitic melt at 750 °C at a depth of about 17.5 km, i.e. the point G on Figure 4.9b? Can this melt erupt at the surface? Drawing a vertical line from G shows that it will start to crystallise as it crosses the water-saturated liquidus at about 7 km depth and is in the solidus field for water-saturated melts at a depth of about 3 km. So it will solidify at 3 km depth, and cannot erupt on the surface. By contrast, an anhydrous melt at a temperature of greater than 1100 °C can erupt as a liquid.

Minerals such as biotite mica and amphibole are **hydrous** minerals, with H_2O in their crystal lattices. These minerals are common in granitic rocks, not basalts. The reason is that granitic melts usually contain more dissolved water than basalts which have low water content. Hydrous granitic melts should crystallise before they reach the surface, which is why **rhyolite**, the eruptive rock of granitic composition, is rare and must have started as a nearly anhydrous magma. The release of only small amounts of water from these viscous magmas is responsible for the explosive nature of rhyolitic volcanoes. Anhydrous melts of basaltic composition usually have no difficulty reaching the surface in a liquid condition and so are extremely common as extrusive igneous rocks.

It is worth remembering that the rocks we have described are not discrete types, with sharp boundaries between rocks of different composition; there is a gradation from one type to another, with other named rocks in between. However, not all these kinds are common; some are far more frequently formed (and found) than others and these are the rocks that have been discussed.

In the next section, the chemistry and mineralogy of igneous rocks are related to the processes characteristic of different plate tectonic settings, and hence to where they are found forming today. This discussion helps to explain the different styles of volcanism in Iceland and Montserrat featured in the Case Study.

4.3 Plate tectonics and igneous processes

4.3.1 CONSTRUCTIVE PLATE MARGINS

Constructive plate margins (Figure 1.6) occur mostly in oceans, where they form ocean ridges. In rare cases the large mountain chain that forms the ridge has built up above sea level, to form a volcanic island – Iceland, for example. Here, the processes are more easily observed than beneath several kilometres of sea water. Ocean ridges are zones of tension, so fractures (faults) develop which are zones of weakness. These faults form a rift valley called the **axial rift**, shown in Iceland in Figure 4.10.

Figure 4.10 *Axial rift in Iceland, looking towards the south. The sheep on the left are on the European plate, whereas the right hand side of the picture is the American plate*

At a constructive plate margin the crust is thin, typically only around 5 km thick, and consequently the mantle is close to the Earth's surface.

Scientific investigations indicate that the uppermost part of the mantle is composed of peridotite, formed of the mineral olivine with a little pyroxene (Figures 4.5 and 4.6). The main igneous process involved below constructive plate margins is the **partial melting** of mantle peridotite, to form a basaltic magma held in a shallow **magma chamber**, less than 5 km beneath the surface. A high temperature magma of low viscosity is produced which is extruded from the centre of the axial rift in the ridge, which, when below sea level, forms fine-grained basalt **pillow lavas** on the sea bed.

Geologists have been able to film pillow lavas forming today at ocean ridges. A crack appears in the axial rift and a tongue of lava comes out, like red-hot toothpaste oozing from its tube. The outside rim quickly cools in the sea water and the lava forms a rounded shape that looks like

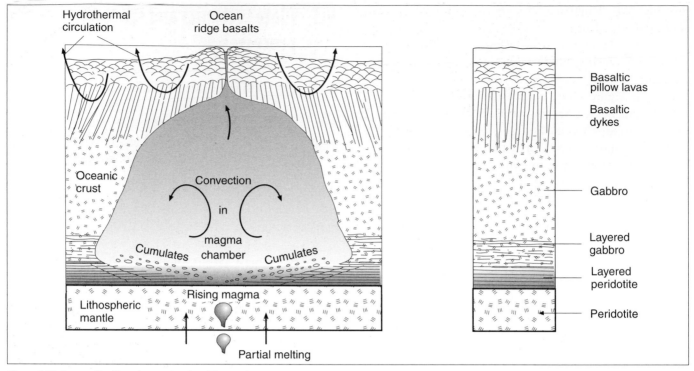

Figure 4.11 *Cross-section through a constructive plate margin*

a pillow, often with one longer dimension but sometimes almost as round as a football. Escaping gas bubbles and sea water being changed to steam by the hot lava make the surrounding sea water look like fizzing lemonade. The sea floor becomes covered with hummocky pillows, each sagging into the hollows of the pillows below.

Pillows vary in size but are typically up to two metres in length and one metre in diameter. They often have a **glassy** rim, because the lava is quenched by the cold sea water to form a volcanic glass. Further into the pillow, the basalt often contains gas bubbles, forming what's called a **vesicular** texture, because the solid rim does not allow gas to escape. The vesicles may later become filled with other minerals, such as calcite, when they are called **amygdales**. The confining pressure increases towards the middle of a pillow and the vesicles are far smaller, or absent.

Pillow lavas are so characteristic of submarine basalt volcanism that, when they are found in ancient rock sequences, they define the environment as one of underwater volcanic activity.

The temperature inside a cooling pillow basalt is about 1100 °C. By tracing across the horizontal line at 1100 °C on Figure 4.6, the minerals that will crystallise in the pillow can be seen to be olivine, pyroxene and plagioclase feldspar. There are also some minerals that cannot crystallise, such as quartz and mica, because Figure 4.6 shows that they do not begin to crystallise until about 800 °C. Quartz and mica do not occur in the majority of mafic rocks.

Looking at a cross section through a constructive plate margin (Figure 4.11), beneath the pillow lavas are basalt

dykes, where the lava has crystallised in vertical cracks. Each pulse of magma comes up through the cracks to be extruded on the sea floor.

At a depth of several kilometres, the basaltic magma at constructive plate margins cools very slowly, because of the insulating effect of the rock above. As the chemical composition of the magma remains constant, the same minerals are produced, but they are larger than the crystals in basalt because they have longer to grow in the slowly cooling magma. The rock is given a different name, **gabbro**, but as Figures 4.3 to 4.5 show, basalt and gabbro are chemically and mineralogically identical: the only difference is the crystal size. So beneath the basalt pillow lavas and dykes of the ocean ridge, coarse-grained gabbros are found, formed of large crystals of feldspar and pyroxene (Figure C3.6a). This can be seen in Figure 4.11 which shows a cross section through a constructive plate margin.

Magma is added to the magma chamber by **partial melting** of the underlying mantle. In this process, the component or mineral with the lowest melting point melts first, so the composition of the magma being added is not pure melted peridotite (mostly olivine), but the pyroxene/plagioclase feldspar composition of basalt/gabbro.

The magma chamber beneath an active part of the ridge will convect as hot material is added from beneath, constantly mixing the crystals as they grow, so the usual random texture typical of igneous rocks is formed. The first-formed crystals may fall to the bottom of the magma chamber, especially if convection slows down, to form layered gabbro and **cumulates**, shown in Figure 4.11,

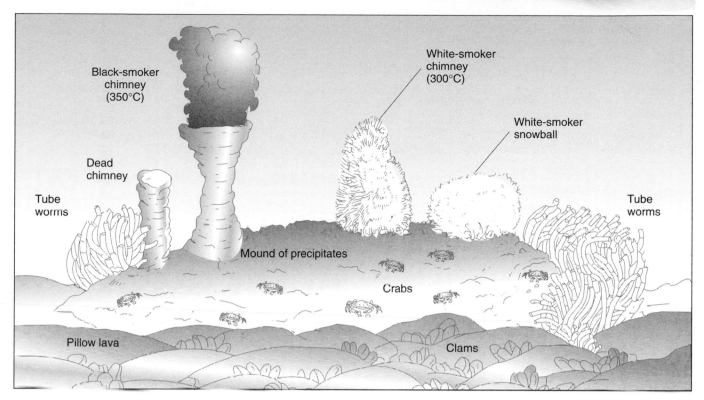

Figure 4.12 *A 'black smoker' in the Pacific. Sea water heated by the ridge circulates through the pillow lavas and dykes, dissolving minerals from them. The mineralised water deposits metal sulphides at the surface, that form chimneys above vents. The sulphur rich fluids provide food and energy for bacteria and other fauna*

which are layered accumulations of minerals such as olivine and magnetite.

These processes create the rocks of the new ocean floor, which is almost exclusively formed of pillow lavas at the surface. Underneath these are dykes, gabbro and cumulates, and beneath these is mantle peridotite.

On a geological timescale, the processes of eruption along a constructive plate margin appear to be continuous; however, on shorter timescales the process is intermittent, with some parts of a ridge being active while nearby sections are not. The intermittent nature of the process means that in a particular magma chamber, crystals may begin to form and reach a size of 3 mm–5 mm during a non-eruptive phase. If crystallisation was complete, a gabbro would be formed. However, if eruption took place *before* crystallisation was complete, the rest of the magma would cool rapidly and would be fine-grained. A rock with a **groundmass** (fine-grained rock material) surrounding some well-formed large crystals (**phenocrysts**) of feldspar and pyroxene will be formed. The two-stage cooling history gives a **porphyry** or **porphyritic** texture of larger crystals in a fine-grained groundmass (Figure C3.5a).

Sea water in fractures and joints in the pillows and dykes becomes heated by the magma below, and this sets up convection cells extending to a distance and depth of several kilometres around the ridge. The constant circulation of sea water causes chemical changes in the minerals of the surrounding rocks, known as **hydrothermal** alteration. It has been calculated that the whole volume of ocean water is circulated through the ocean crust every 10 million years.

One of the most exciting discoveries during the 1980s was by geologists exploring and filming ocean ridge processes from small submarines. They found vents spewing out large volumes of black 'smoke' and so they called the features **black smokers** (Figure 4.12). These are hot sulphide-rich liquids containing elements such as copper, iron and gold that have been **leached** (dissolved and removed) from the rocks below by circulating sea water. When the sulphide-rich liquids mix with the cold sea water, they precipitate metal-rich minerals around the vent, in the form of a 'chimney'. The chimneys may grow several metres a year; the tallest chimney found so far is 50 m high, off the coast of Oregon.

Thermocouples (a type of thermometer) which were extended from 'Alvin', a small submarine, measured the black smoker temperature as 350 °C. The scientists were then warned by the control ship that the melting point of the submersible's plastic windows was thought to be only 150 °C! However, they were in little immediate danger as the sea water 5 cm from the vent is 4 °C (or lower), so the temperature gradient close to the vents is extreme.

Previously, it had been thought that living organisms could not survive in the high temperatures and pressures in total darkness and in the hostile chemical environment of hydrothermal vents. However, bacteria thrive at these sites, using hydrogen sulphide as their energy source, not sunlight. Their body processes (metabolism) do not require oxygen: they are **anaerobic**, and can withstand higher temperatures than any other known organisms. When a new vent was forming, scientists watched a 'snow storm' of bacteria settling to colonise it. These bacteria form the beginning of a food chain that supports a bizarre fauna of previously unknown species, such as large, fast-growing anaerobic tube-worms (in the Pacific near the Galapagos Islands) and blind shrimps (in the Atlantic). They gain all their nutrients from the bacteria and the water, and live totally without light. In turn, these animals are food for giant clams, crabs and fish. Scientists are still unsure how the metabolisms of the animals cope with the toxic chemicals that normally kill shellfish. Consequently, at present they are not a potential food source for us because their intense sulphur content gives them an extremely 'rotten' smell and they would be toxic to humans.

Some scientists believe that it may have been at sites like black smokers that life on Earth began, with organisms like the vent bacteria. Since the evidence shows that plate tectonic processes have been a feature of the Earth since its earliest stages and that oceans have also been present, so the ecological niches of the constructive plate margin and associated black smokers have existed throughout geological history. They are closely interconnected systems that have been isolated from the fluctuating conditions at the Earth's surface.

When iron-rich minerals cool below the Curie point (p36), they become magnetised, in alignment with the orientation of the local magnetic field. So as the iron-rich minerals of the basalt being formed at an axial ridge cool in the prevailing Earth's magnetic field, the direction of the field at that time becomes 'frozen' into the rock. The basalts of the spreading ridge on Iceland have been dated using radioactive dating methods (Chapter 11). Moving away from the active ridge, the basalts are found to be progressively older, and they indicate periodic reversals of the Earth's magnetic field. A reversal in a magnetic field occurs when the magnetism changes so that the north pole becomes the south pole and *vice versa*, and this can take 15 000 years to complete. The reversals are recorded in the rocks which act as a 'magnetic tape recorder'. A similar pattern covers the ocean floor, as shown in Figure 4.13. This magnetic pattern and the increasing age of the ocean floor away from active ridges were vital evidence for establishing the theory of plate

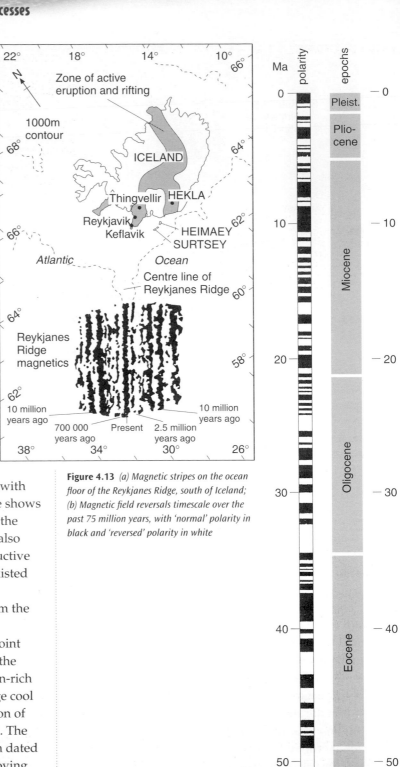

Figure 4.13 *(a) Magnetic stripes on the ocean floor of the Reykjanes Ridge, south of Iceland; (b) Magnetic field reversals timescale over the past 75 million years, with 'normal' polarity in black and 'reversed' polarity in white*

Figure 4.14 *Formation of island arcs at destructive plate margin*

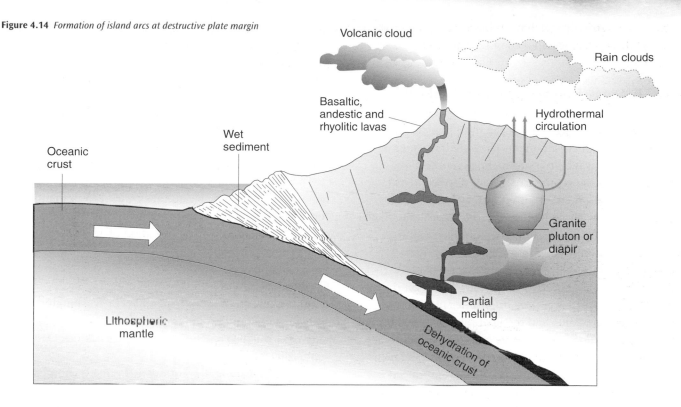

tectonics and calculating the rates at which ridges are spreading.

If ocean floor material is later thrust over another ocean plate by plate collision processes, it may become land, where it is known as an **ophiolite** complex. Examples of ophiolites can be found in Cyprus, Oman, bordering the Persian Gulf, the Shetland Isles and the Lizard Peninsula in Cornwall. They may contain rich mineral deposits, the remains of the cumulates beneath the ocean ridge and black smoker structures formed on the ocean floor. It was from the examination of the rocks of Cyprus – a sequence

of pillow lavas, dykes and gabbros – that the structure of the ocean floor began to be understood in the 1960s. This work also played a key role in the establishment and acceptance of plate tectonic theory.

Gabbros, the coarse-grained mafic rocks formed in the magma chambers of constructive plate margins, are found in several places in Britain, including Mull, the peninsula of Ardnamurchan and the Cuillin Hills in Scotland. Because they are coarse-grained, they must have been formed beneath the surface, with rocks including basalt lavas above them. As they are now exposed at the surface,

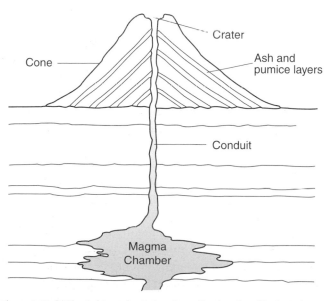

Figure 4.15 *(a) The structure of a strato-volcano like those found in the Andes mountains; (b) The alternating layers of pumice and ash of andesitic composition in the Andes mountains*

several kilometres of rock have been removed by erosion in the millions of years since their formation.

4.3.2 ISLAND ARCS AND DESTRUCTIVE PLATE MARGINS

Island arcs are located in the oceans and there is no continental crust beneath them. They are formed as a result of volcanism over a subducting oceanic plate.

When a slab of oceanic crust slides down into a subduction zone, it takes with it water, in gas bubble vesicles and between the pillows and dykes. Some of the wet sediment that has accumulated on the ocean floor is also carried downward with the slab. The water is important because it lowers the melting point of the rocks. There is a great deal of friction beneath the descending and overriding plate, creating intense seismic activity along the Benioff zone, and the liberation of heat. The descending slab is also heated by conduction, from the adjacent hot mantle. Together, the lowering of the melting point by the release of water, and the heat produced through friction and by conduction leads to melting and the formation of magmas that are erupted by the volcanoes along island arcs (Figure 4.14). As temperature and pressure increase with depth, the oceanic slab loses water (dehydrates) or begins to melt, releasing volatile material into the overlying mantle wedge. This results in more partial melting to feed the rising magma and is shown in Figure 4.14.

The magma can either be formed from the partial melting of some of the rocks of the oceanic plate *or* those of the overriding plate against which it is grinding. Both, of course, might also melt to some degree and the first melts that are produced do *not* have the same composition as that of the melting rock, but rather that of the lowest melting component.

The down-going oceanic plate moves, but the overlying plate stays in the same position with respect to the subduction zone beneath it, shown in Figure 4.14. Magma is produced continuously at the same site, relative to the overriding plate. The magma passes upwards through the *same* zone in the overlying plate, which is progressively heated. The material produced changes in composition as magma is either added to it by partial melting or removed from it by crystallisation. Consequently, the first magmas differ from those developed later on. The first lavas are basalts, similar in composition to those of the oceanic crust, but the later products are quite different, containing a higher proportion of SiO_2.

These later more siliceous rocks are characteristic of ranges of volcanoes found parallel to the type of ocean margin marked by a deep trench, and are known as andesites. Andesites have chemical compositions between those of basaltic and granitic rocks (Figures 4.3 to 4.5), so they are called intermediate. Many of their physical properties such as colour and density are also intermediate: for example, they are generally paler in colour than basalts and lower in density, indicating that they contain fewer iron- and magnesium-rich minerals and more felsic ones (feldspar and some quartz). If a magma of this composition cools beneath the surface, the coarse-grained equivalent of andesite is formed, **diorite**.

There is one vitally important difference between andesites and basalts. Basalts are created from mantle rocks and can return to the mantle through the ocean floor conveyor belt system. The formation of andesites is a one-way process; andesites are never returned to the mantle. So, when one of these volcanoes erupts, such as on the Caribbean island of Montserrat in the Case Study, or the famous eruption of Mount St Helens in Washington State in 1980, it not only provides a firework display of lavas and ashes but also creates an *irreversible addition to the continental crust*.

Broadly speaking, the continental crust is composed of a low-density igneous rock, between granite and basalt in composition, with a veneer of sediments. This is the intermediate rock andesite, and the continents themselves originated largely through the andesitic volcanism described above.

Island arcs are eroded, and may even disappear below sea level, but the material will *not* disappear into the mantle because its density is too low. When island arcs collide they become welded together to form a 'mini continent', or an arc is added to an existing continent. As more and more island arcs are accreted (welded) together, the size of the combined mass increases until it reaches continental dimensions.

In this way, at an island arc where initially nothing but oceanic crustal rocks are present, increasingly siliceous crust is generated, which becomes progressively more continental in character. This process seems to take place relatively quickly in geological terms because, in areas where island arcs are no more than 20 million years old, continental crust up to 30 km thick has been identified by seismic studies. A growing body of evidence suggests that much of the crust of continents like Africa and Asia was formed by processes at island arcs over the last 1000 million years. It is also possible that most of the oldest continental rocks were formed in this way, becoming increasingly more stable with time.

Eruptions of silica-rich magmas are frequently very explosive, as the trapped, dissolved gases try to escape, and are accompanied by large volumes of ash and pumice. The eruption of Mount St Helens in May 1980 was an explosion of this type. Because earlier material had solidified in the vent of the volcano, the rising pressure caused a dome to grow on the side of the mountain, which rose at a rate of two metres a day. The dome eventually ruptured, suddenly and catastrophically, in an eruption that resulted in a huge crater being formed on the side of the volcano; in the process the top 1000 metres of the mountain were pulverised. In explosive volcanic eruptions, larger fragments of debris fall to Earth quickly, and quite close to the main vent site. Smaller fragments can be carried by gas currents and wind for some distances, but they too will be deposited like sediment to form a volcanic deposit with sedimentary characteristics (called a **volcaniclastic** rock). Volcanoes in the Andes typically have layers of volcaniclastic particles that may look like bedded sediments, shown in Figure 4.15b. These layers build up the classical conical shape of a composite **strato-volcano**, found in the Andes, and Japan, shown schematically in Figure 4.15a. The smallest particles from the eruption, of dust size, may be carried high into the stratosphere, to be carried around the world by air currents.

Explosive volcanism is often accompanied by the formation of extremely hot clouds called **nuées ardentes** (glowing clouds), fluidised and turbulent mixtures of gas and ash particles that can travel at hurricane speeds (50 ms⁻¹). When Mt Pelée on the Caribbean island of Martinique exploded in 1902, a nuée ardente destroyed the town of St Pierre, killing all 30 000 inhabitants within minutes, all except for a convict in the town's gaol, where the thick walls and small window protected him from the hot gas cloud.

Pyroclastic 'fire broken' flows have a higher proportion of rock and pumice fragments than gas, so travel as mixed gas/rock density currents over the ground surface. They also travel at high speed (20–50 ms⁻¹), are extremely destructive, and contain gases which are poisonous. Pyroclastic flows have been common on Montserrat during 1997, and are one of the most dangerous aspects of the eruptions because of their great speed, and their ability to flow uphill and over water. The island's area has been extended by pyroclastic flow deposits forming deltas at the coast. The names and particle sizes of material deposited from the air, together called **tephra**, are summarised in Figure 4.16.

When siliceous magmas are erupted they [form] **pumice**, a glassy rock full of gas bubbles enab[ling it to] float on water. White-hot pumice particles and a[sh] weld together into rocks called **ignimbrites**, whic[h are] generally poorly sorted because of the violence and turbulence in the pyroclastic flow.

All of these materials were seen by a Roman writer called Pliny when he described the eruption of Vesuvius in 79 AD. He wrote of how the towering ash cloud had the form of a pine tree. Later he described the bombs which made people tie pillows over their heads, as well as the ash fall and the accompanying earthquakes. The sea in the harbour retreated, leaving boats high and dry. Pyroclastic ash and pumice deposits eventually buried the towns of Herculaneum and Pompeii and they were not rediscovered and excavated until the 1700s. Large explosive eruptions with tall columns and large volumes of tephra are called **Plinian**, after Pliny.

Vesuvius is close to the modern city of Naples which has grown considerably since the last major eruption of the volcano in 1945. Before that date, eruptions occurred with reasonable regularity, every 10 years or so. It is possible that a major eruption of Vesuvius could occur even while you are reading this book!

4.3.3 PRODUCTION OF GRANITES

Granites are found in huge volumes at destructive plate margins, especially in areas such as the Andes where the continental crust is very thick. But granites form only a few per cent of the dominantly andesitic continental crust. How then do they form? In the simplest case of an island arc, basaltic and andesitic magmas are produced by partial melting of mantle material. Granites are formed within continents by carrying this process a stage further; in a sense, they are refined andesites, resulting from either fractional crystallisation of andesitic magma or by partial melting of andesitic crust.

In the early stages of the process, the overriding plate is

Figure 4.16 *Pyroclastic materials (tephra) classified by size*

Name	Size	State during ejection	Shape or other features
volcanic bombs	>10 mm	molten or plastic	'spindle', often modified during passage through the air 'bread crust' bombs
blocks	>65 mm	solid	variable usually angular
lapilli	65–2 mm	solid or molten	round to angular, usually not vesicular
scoria, pumice	variable	solid or molten	usually vesicular
ash	<2 mm	solid or molten	very fine

relatively cold and brittle. Early formed andesite magmas gather together into blobs or **diapirs** (shown in Figure 4.14), which then rise up into the upper crust. Initially, the melts do not rise very far before they solidify, as we saw when studying the phase diagram. However, the process is continuous, and as more and more diapirs rise, so the base of the overriding plate becomes hotter and hotter. Eventually, partial melting of some of the early formed rocks takes place, to give more siliceous magmas, which will then form granite. These then rise to higher levels in the crust before solidifying to form coarse-grained plutonic rocks.

The viscosity of granite melts is much higher than basaltic magma. It is thought that a granite magma is more like a pasty mush than a free-flowing liquid; hence, when crystals form in it, they do not settle out but grow larger *in situ*, eventually interlocking with other crystals (Figure C3.5b). The density of granite is less than that of other common igneous rocks. A granitic magma of relative density 2.4–2.6 can be formed at the base of continental crust with relative density 2.9, and since the magma is less dense than the surrounding rocks, it will try to 'float' up to the surface. This density difference enables magma to rise great distances through the crust.

If a rising granite body enters a region of rocks of lower density, it will stop rising. Similarly, if it cools and solidifies, it will also grind to a halt. Until either of these two things happens, a granitic magma will rise in pulses through major cracks in the crust, or by pushing aside the surrounding rocks. On a small scale, a process called **stoping** occurs where blocks of existing rock, the **country rock**, fall into the magma, thus allowing it to rise. Gradually these blocks may be assimilated and eventually may disappear, but sometimes they are visible in exposures of granite, as shown in Figure C4.2. The outlines are often rounded, because the corners of blocks are melted by contact with the hot magma. They are known as xenoliths (foreign or strange rocks). **Autoliths** may also be formed: these are blobs of magma, of a slightly different composition, mixed with the main magma. Most often, the earlier magma is slightly more mafic and therefore slightly darker C4.3. But these autoliths, often containing crystals of the same minerals as the main intrusion, can sometimes be distinguished from xenoliths derived from sedimentary country rock if traces of original sedimentary bedding are still visible.

Occasionally, granitic magmas come so close to the surface of the Earth that a **conduit** (a channel followed by magma) is blasted through, and magma is extruded. In this case, a rare type of volcanic rock with the same

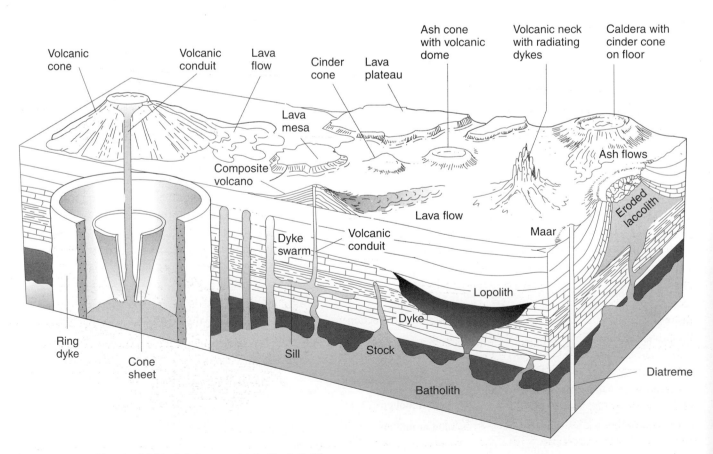

Figure 4.17 *Some of the volcanic/plutonic features associated with a batholith*

composition as a granite is formed, called **rhyolite**, which often has a glassy texture. The Glass Mountains in the USA are so named because they have been formed of glassy rhyolite. Sometimes small feldspar crystals may be visible in rhyolites, formed prior to final eruption, and the rock often shows **flow-banding**. The flow-banding is caused by different concentrations of minerals produced as the lava flowed downhill. **Obsidian** is a black volcanic glass formed when granitic lava cools very quickly (C4.4).

The Sierra Nevada and Rocky Mountains in the west of the USA are underlain by large bodies of granite (hundreds of km^3), called **batholiths**, some of which may be connected at depth. These are a result of crystallisation in the magma chambers of 'failed' volcanoes. Similar batholiths are forming today beneath volcanic ranges such as the Andes and the Coastal Range in the USA. Millions of years of erosion can later expose these plutonic rocks at the surface. The granites visible at the surface in SW England, the Lake District and Scotland are also the remains of batholiths. When these granites were formed, they were deep beneath mountains caused by subduction at destructive plate margins. Some of the features associated with a batholith can be seen in Figure 4.17.

During the final stages of crystallisation in a granite batholith, the magma will be water-rich and this hot fluid contains many dissolved ions, particularly metals, from both the magma and from leaching of the surrounding country rocks. The fluids percolate into the country rock and cool, depositing minerals in granitic veins which may contain extremely large crystals, called **pegmatites**. The processes involved are hydrothermal, like those of the constructive plate margin, but the plate tectonic setting and associated rocks are different. These processes will be discussed further in Chapter 10.

4.3.4 HOT SPOTS

There are other volcanoes that appear to be independent of plate margin processes. These are located over '**hot spots**', or **mantle plumes**, columns of rising magma which remain for periods of tens of millions of years beneath the same latitude and longitude, while the tectonic plates move over them. There is evidence that these plumes have their source deep in the mantle, near the boundary, with the core, far deeper than other volcanic sources so far considered. They pierce the plate above causing within-plate volcanism, whereas most volcanic activity is at plate boundaries. Over millions of years the magma source continues to be productive as the overlying tectonic plate moves over the hot spot. At the surface is an active volcano, with a train of older dormant and extinct volcanoes in a line away from it. Some of the best known volcanoes in the world, in Hawaii, are over a hot spot within the Pacific Plate (Figure 4.18). The volcanoes to the NW, in the Hawaii-Emperor chain, are older and show the movement of the Pacific Plate. Sixty-five million years ago the part of the plate that is now near the Kamchatka peninsula in Russia was over the hot spot, and the volcanoes of the Emperor chain were formed as the plate moved northward. These volcanoes are now extinct and have subsided, with no buoyant magma beneath them.

Forty million years ago the direction of plate movement changed to north westerly, as shown by the change in direction of the line of volcanoes. The volcanoes of the Hawaiian chain then began to form, continuing at the rate of one volcano every two million years.

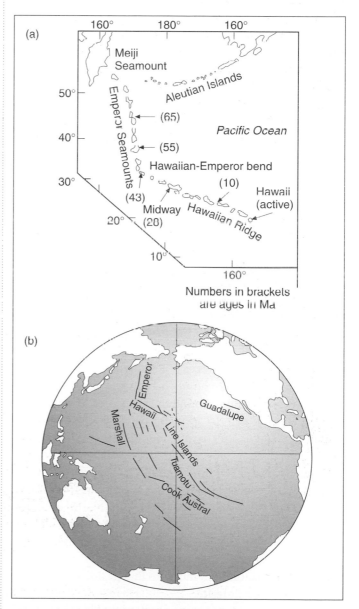

Figure 4.18 (a) The Hawaiian-Emperor chain, over a hot spot beneath the Pacific plate; (b) Other aligned volcanic chains in the Pacific

The composition of the erupted material in Hawaii is basalt, which explains the relief of the volcanic islands (broad shield with low angle slopes built of successive lava flows) and the relative safety with which tourists can watch the lava lakes in the summit craters of Kilauea and Mauna Loa of Hawaii.

Other hot spots occur beneath oceanic ridges and feed the ridge for hundreds of kilometres each side. The quantities of material involved in building Iceland over 65 million years indicates that a hot spot exists beneath the island, that in this case is coincident with a constructive plate margin.

4.4 Emplacement processes and structures

Igneous processes and products have been described by chemistry, mineralogy and plate tectonic setting. However, there is also *form* (how they appear, for example in outcrop) which is a reflection of their mode of emplacement. To some extent this has already been discussed in the form (shape) of volcanoes in different settings; so this section is generally, but not exclusively, concerned with smaller scale igneous features.

4.4.1 DYKES AND SILLS

Dykes occur where magma enters (is intruded into) cracks in existing rocks of any type, cutting across and through them, so they are called **discordant** igneous bodies (Figure 4.19 a, b). The dykes that form the top of the ocean crust have been created in this way (Figure 4.11), but you may be more familiar with dykes on land which can often be seen at the coast. Large numbers of dykes, called **swarms**, are found for example around the islands of Arran, Mull and Rhum in Scotland. Generally, dykes are small in scale, and up to a few metres across (Figure 4.19b) so that they are fine-grained, or tens of metres across when they may be medium-grained (1 mm–3 mm). They may extend for many tens of kilometres across the countryside (look at the 1:625 000 ('ten-mile') Geological Map (North) of the British Isles for examples). At the contacts with existing country rocks the margins are often baked, and the dyke may be finer-grained or even glassy there. Dykes can have variable composition but most are fine-grained basalt, or medium-grained **dolerite**.

Sills are **concordant** igneous bodies, that is they follow the bedding of adjacent rocks. They often appear roughly

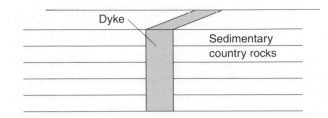

Figure 4.19(a) *Diagram of dyke emplacement*

Figure 4.19(b) *A basalt dyke cutting gabbro on the shore at Coverack, Lizard, Cornwall*

horizontal, with top and bottom surfaces roughly parallel, or gently dipping. A sill can be several hundred metres thick, such as the Palisades Sill in New York State, or more modest, such as the 10–50 metre thickness of the Great Whin Sill in Northern England. They are often thicker than dykes, so the central part of a sill may reach medium crystal size (1–3 mm) and be formed of dolerite. Crystal settling in very thick sills can follow the same processes as those outlined in the section on magma chambers beneath constructive plate margins, and may even result in density layering (see Figure 4.7). Cooling in

Figure 4.20 *Devil's Post Pile, California, showing basalt in columns*

sills can also result in a joint pattern producing hexagonal columns called **columnar jointing** (Figure 4.20). These joints develop at right angles to the cooling surfaces. Columns that are slightly bent or curved can be formed if the material moves while it is still plastic. The columnar joints of the Giant's Causeway in Antrim N. Ireland are famous, but there are columns in other places too, including the Scottish island of Staffa (Fingal's Cave) and the Lion's Haunch volcano in Edinburgh.

The Great Whin Sill outcrops in many areas of north east England (Figure 4.21a). Close study of the rocks in which it occurs shows that it occasionally steps down into different beds, so does not perfectly follow bedding. The Romans in Britain during the second century AD took advantage of the north-facing scarp of the Whin Sill to build Hadrian's Wall as a defence against invasion from the north. Where the River Tees crosses the Whin Sill at High Force, there is a spectacular waterfall caused by the relative hardness of the dolerite. Undercutting of the softer Carboniferous rocks below the sill caused the waterfall to retreat, producing a gorge downstream as shown in Figure 4.21b.

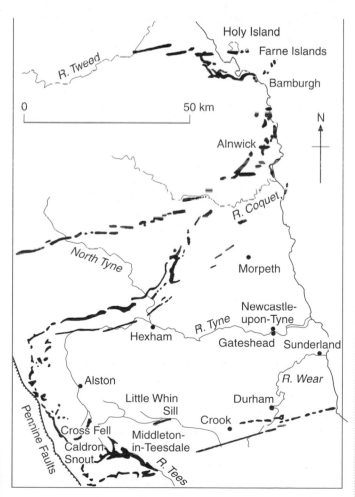

Figure 4.21(a) *The outcrop of the Whin Sill and associated ENE–WSW trending dykes*

Figure 4.21(b) *High Force waterfall where the River Tees crosses the Whin Sill. Layered rocks are visible above the plunge pool; these are Carboniferous limestones, passing up into sandstones. The top two 'layers' visible at the top of the waterfall are the dolerite of the Whin Sill*

4.4.2 OTHER FEATURES ASSOCIATED WITH VOLCANISM

Plutons were considered in the section on the formation of granites, but, on a smaller scale, other features associated with them are visible in the field. For example, in forcing their way up through the crust, offshoots of the magma may intrude surrounding rocks, forming dykes, which in this case are of granitic composition, but will be finer grained because of the rapid cooling, though not glassy. These dykes are formed of **microgranite**.

Conical and cylindrical sheets of material can also occur, called **cone sheets** and **ring dykes**, shown in Figure 4.17. If a sill has a lens shape, bulging towards the top, it is given the name **laccolith**. Large intrusions concordant with the bedding of country rock that bulge downwards in a saucer shape are termed **lopoliths**. Lopoliths are usually mafic in composition and coarse-grained (slow cooling), often with layering or differentiation within the intrusion.

4.4.3 CALDERA FORMATION

Sometimes when magma is ejected explosively from a volcano, emptying the magma chamber beneath, the roof collapses to form a **caldera**, a circular depression.

Figure 4.22 *Lac d'Issarles, Auvergne, Central France. A crater lake fills the vent of a volcano that last erupted 10 000 years ago. There are many such lakes in Auvergne*

A caldera-collapse during the eruption of Krakatoa in 1883 produced a tsunami (great wave) that flooded the coastal regions of Indonesia, killing 30 000 people. Calderas can be several kilometres across and extinct volcanoes often contain a crater lake. Many of these are visible in the Auvergne of France and Eifel of NW Germany (Figure 4.22) but perhaps the most photographed is Crater Lake in the Cascade Range of Oregon, USA, caused by an eruption of 50 km³ of magma, 8000 years ago. The crater has a diameter of 10 km with a small central cone produced by a subsequent eruption. Many calderas in the

western USA are much larger than this, pointing to huge eruptions in the past. The most recent volcanism in the Auvergne dates to only 5000 years before present and magma can be detected not far below the surface: can we say that these volcanoes are extinct, or are they merely dormant, like Mount Vesuvius in Italy?

4.4.4 LAVA FLOWS

Figure 4.23 *Pahoehoe textured lava*

The surface textures of basalt lava flows are often 'ropy' and called **pahoehoe** (the Polynesian word for rope) because the rock looks like a coiled rope, or called **aa** when it has a surface that is rough and cindery.

However, basaltic lava flows can also be extremely large, involving hundreds or thousands of cubic kilometres of lava; these are called **flood basalts**. In Britain, the basalts of the Antrim Plateau and the Scottish islands are associated with the opening of the Atlantic Ocean, and the formation of the constructive plate margin that is now the mid-Atlantic ridge. The huge flood basalts of the Deccan and Siberia have been linked to global mass extinctions and possible climate change (4.5.2).

4.5 Hazards and benefits of igneous processes

4.5.1 VOLCANIC HAZARDS AND BENEFITS

The plate tectonic setting of Britain means that we do not directly suffer the hazards associated with volcanic eruptions. The Case Study and previous sections also show that the style and geochemistry of basaltic

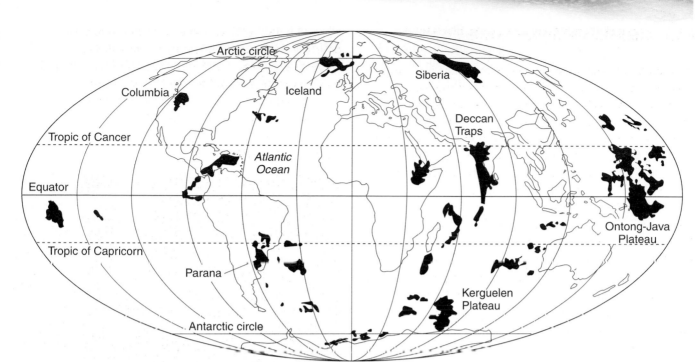

Figure 4.24 *a) Map of global distribution of large igneous provinces, showing the flood basalts of the Columbia River, Deccan and Siberia b) Ages and volumes of material erupted in flood basalts and their association with geological boundaries and mass extinctions*

Location	Volume × 10^6 km³	Age × 10^6 years	Close to Geological Boundry (date Ma)	Mass Extinctions at that Boundry?
Siberia	1.5	247 ± 2	Permian/ Triassic (245)	Yes
Karroo (S. Africa)	1.4	190 ± 5	No	
Parana (Brazil)	0.7	160–150	No	
Deccan (India)	0.5	66 ± 1	Cretaceous/ Tertiary (KT 65 Ma)	Yes, many species (thought to be due to asteroid)
Columbia (USA)	0.2	17 ± 0.2	No	

volcanism at constructive plate margins and over hotspots are not usually hazardous. Where they have threatened villages, towns or harbours, there have been attempts to divert lava streams by, for example, hosing them with sea water (Iceland). The situation at destructive plate margins is completely different, since volcanism there can have sudden, dramatic and devastating effects.

In order to be able to predict when individual volcanoes are likely to erupt, scientists study the mechanisms and processes involved. The development of plate tectonic theory now means that the type of volcanism can be predicted, and this can be regarded as progress. On the scale of individual volcanoes, however the eruption pattern is far less clear. When the US Geological Survey forecast that Mount St Helens would erupt in 1980, the area was evacuated and as a result there were few deaths. However, in 1992, during the fieldwork part of a conference on predicting volcanic eruptions in Columbia, several volcanologists were killed by the unheralded eruption of Galeras volcano. During 1997, there was close study of the nuée ardente activity and ash falls from Chances Peak on Montserrat, but none of the scientists could predict whether there would be a major eruption, or whether the activity would die away. Islanders who had been temporarily evacuated to the 'safe' north part of the island were very annoyed that they were not allowed to return home to tend their fields. When the volcano erupted pyroclastic flows on 24 June 1997, 29 people who had returned to feed their animals were killed.

Many volcanoes are being monitored by a range of methods, for example stations note changes in the gravity on the mountain (rising liquid magma would lead to lower gravity), tilt-meters measure deformation and other instruments measure airborne gases. Satellites monitor the heat being radiated by volcanoes and others can detect small rises or falls in the ground surface. All these can give advance warning of change. Whether such changes always precede an eruption can still not be predicted with total confidence.

Earth has benefited from volcanoes: the Earth's water and atmosphere, and consequently life on Earth, evolved from the gases produced by volcanic eruptions; rich soils have formed on the slopes of volcanoes. Volcanoes are the source of some precious gems, for example diamonds (Chapter 3) and semi-precious gems such as opal (a silica gel deposit).

Fluids associated with volcanoes (e.g. black smokers) and the last stages of cooling intrusions are the source of metal mineralisation such as gold, silver, molybdenum, copper, zinc, lead and mercury (Chapter 10).

Spas and hot springs are used for recreation and health, for example, Beppu, Japan and Baden Baden, Germany. Recreational use includes: skiing, hiking, tourism, and learning about volcanoes first-hand (Hawaii Volcanoes National Park; Crater Lake National Park; Yellowstone National Park, and others).

Miscellaneous uses of the products of volcanoes include: drilling-mud for water, gas and oil wells; kitty litter; clay filler for bread; stone-washed jeans with pumice; volcanic glass shards for polishing compounds and abrasives in toothpaste and kitchen cleansers.

4.5.2 TRIGGERING CLIMATE CHANGE

Can volcanic eruptions contribute to climatic change? If so, then the following factors are likely to be critical:

- the volumes of lava and types of gases involved;
- the timescales over which they occur;
- the temperature of the gases;
- the latitude of the eruption.

The powerful eruptions at destructive plate margins cause ash clouds that rise to great heights into the stratosphere so that dust is taken around the world on the jet streams; the particles usually fall back to Earth within a year or so. The dust can lead to a shielding effect so that some of the Sun's rays do not reach the surface of the Earth, and it cools down. After the Mt Pinatubo (Philippines) eruption in 1992, the Persian Gulf had its coldest winter on record, including snow fall. The year after the Tambora (Indonesia) eruption in 1815 was called the 'year without a summer' because of the low temperatures and continuous rain in Europe from May to October. These caused crops to fail throughout Europe resulting in social unrest in many countries. Dust in the stratosphere after the eruption of Krakatao (Indonesia) in 1883 produced vivid red sunsets in Britain, thousands of kilometres away. The gas content of these destructive plate margin volcanic eruptions varies, but many are relatively low in SO_2 compared with flood basalts. The eruption of huge volumes of flood basalts is accompanied by the release of large amounts of CO_2, water vapour and much more SO_2 than the volcanoes of destructive plate margins. SO_2 in the atmosphere can result in acid rain and also efficiently screens out sunlight. However, there are also 'greenhouse' gases trapping the outgoing radiation, so eruption of the vast volumes of lava involved in, for example, the Siberian basalts, may have an effect on climate. The

Siberian flood basalts came at the end of the Permian Period and the extinction of 90 per cent of species. Geological processes and climate interact strongly but in ways that we do not fully understand. Could several major volcanic explosions throw sufficient sun-screening SO_2 into the atmosphere to cause another Ice Age?

The Deccan Traps started to erupt at about the time of the Cretaceous–Tertiary (K–T) boundary, when there were mass extinctions (of which the dinosaurs are best known); and this may not be a coincidence. Although most geologists believe an extra-terrestrial impact on the Yucatan peninsula of Mexico was the main trigger of these extinction events, some palaeontologists are convinced that many species such as dinosaurs were already in decline because of climate change. The Deccan volcanism might have contributed to this. Geologists will continue to investigate which factor was the trigger, and which was the final straw for many years to come.

The **volume** of gases released is also important. Volcanoes at destructive plate margins are active only intermittently and over relatively short timescales of months up to years, or hundreds of years. The flood basalt eruptions were active for millions, or tens of millions of years, so their gas contribution was larger.

The temperature of eruptions may also be a factor; basalt volcanism has higher temperatures than those at destructive plate margins. Higher temperature gases over longer periods will create stronger convection currents in the atmosphere and thus may have global effects.

Lastly, the latitude of the eruption is important. Atmospheric circulation patterns (Chapter 1) mean that eruptions close to the Equator are more likely to affect the whole globe than eruptions in high latitudes, which tend to be confined to the hemisphere in which they occur.

All these factors indicate that geologists may have underestimated the contributions of continuous constructive plate margin magmatism and flood basalt eruption to climate change; they may have had much greater effects than the occasional spectacular explosive volcanoes found at destructive plate margins.

4.5.3 GEOTHERMAL POWER

The heat from magma close to the surface of the Earth can be beneficial. In Iceland most houses are centrally heated, geothermally. Their plumbing systems extract the residual heat of nearby cinder cones, using heat exchangers. Geothermal power stations extract heat from hot mud or steam associated with volcanic areas, at Larderello in Italy, the Geysers in California and Wairakei in New Zealand. A scheme for extracting geothermal energy from sources like these is shown in Figure 4.25. Geothermal energy sources are 'clean' heat sources that do not add extra CO_2 into the atmosphere. However, they are not totally renewable resources, as gradually the cinder, mud and steam cool. In Iceland, there is a constant tension between the potentially destructive power of cinder and lava being produced which might overwhelm a town, and the potential beneficial effects, of a local heat source or a lava flow that makes the harbour more sheltered than it was previously, on Heimay. Natural geological processes give the Icelanders no choice in the time, place and amount of any eruption; they have to use their ingenuity to make the best use of the rocks thrown at them.

By the 'hot dry rock' method, geothermal power can also be obtained from granite batholiths. Granites that contain a lot of radioactive potassium cool very slowly, as the decay of ^{40}K potassium to calcium and argon continues to produce heat for millions of years after crystallization is complete. An attempt was made to extract geothermal heat from the granite batholith in Cornwall near Falmouth. Boreholes were drilled in the granite down which cold water was then pumped. It flowed through the fractured granite, and was extracted as warm water from boreholes a short distance away. This is similar to the method shown in Figure 4.25, but the 'permeability' was created by fracturing the granite with explosives. This method has proved far less efficient than the other 'wet' methods mentioned above, since the temperature of the returning water soon falls, and so this experiment has been abandoned.

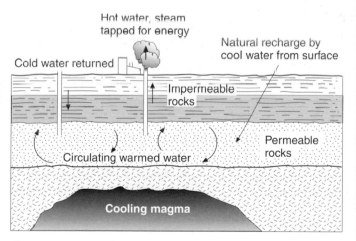

Figure 4.25 *Extraction of geothermal energy*

4.5.4 IGNEOUS ROCKS AS RESOURCES

Many igneous rocks are important as resources: as raw materials for the construction industry, or cut into thin sheets and polished for the facing material of important buildings. They can enhance our lives by their use in the modern urban environment and make a walk around a nearby town centre into an igneous field excursion.

Igneous rocks contribute to crushed rock aggregates in Britain, although at present they represent only 40–50 million tonnes (Mt) (15 per cent) of the total 250–300 Mt aggregate production in Britain. Igneous rock is also used for road construction, and for railway line ballast. In future, the proportion of igneous rock may increase as obtaining planning permission becomes more difficult for the traditional sources such as superficial gravels, which are often fairly small and close to towns. Chapter 9 will explain how one quarry in a remote granite batholith could provide continuous production for around 100 years.

Large blocks of igneous rock are also used extensively for sea defences and other civil engineering works, where their hardness, resistance to abrasion and low porosity are crucial. As a result, some beaches in the North East of England have extremely attractive exotic igneous and metamorphic rocks as part of their sea defences; they are brought from Scandinavia on barges which can off-load directly on to the beach.

Crystalline igneous rocks take a good polish, so can be used as decorative facing stones for buildings (Figures C4.2 and C4.3). Granites from Shap in Cumbria and from SW England, larvikite (a feldspar-rich rock with a shimmering appearance, named after Larvik in Norway), and gabbro have all been used on prestige buildings in many British towns since the Victorian period. Countries such as Italy and France continue to use large quantities of polished rock in buildings and, as a point of national pride, they also still use rock for cobble stones, kerb stones and paving. In Britain during the 1960s and 1970s there was a tendency to use concrete rather than real stone, largely because of local cost-cutting resulting in short-term solutions for repairs and replacement. Many towns for example, replaced Shap granite kerbstones with concrete ones, or igneous cobbles with tarmac. However the quarrying industry, architects and town planners are beginning to respond to new methods of stone cutting and mass production that reduce the cost difference between manufactured concrete and natural rocks. New developments and conservation areas now often specify the use of local and attractive rocks. These may initially cost more but they are hard-wearing and visually attractive. Perhaps more people in the building industry should be encouraged to study geology.

Polished igneous rocks are also used by monumental masons for memorials. A variety of rocks (many of which are imported) are used for their colour and texture, such as white marble and black basalt or gabbro. Frequently, masons will refer to all these rocks that take a polish as 'marble' or 'granite', whether or not a geologist would agree with this classification.

Less compact igneous rocks also have their uses. In the Auvergne of France, near Volvic, and also in Italy there are extensive quarries in the volcanic ashes of extinct volcanoes. These deposits are loose, not compacted, lithified rocks. The composition of the ash is such that, when wetted, they can be formed into blocks. They set without heat and are used as thermal insulating blocks similar to cement blocks in Britain. The ash can also be used to make water-resistant concrete, aggregate for road construction and athletic tracks.

4.6 Summary

1 The Earth's mantle is formed largely of peridotite, consisting mostly of the mineral olivine (and high pressure forms in the lower mantle).

2 Volcanic rocks crystallise at the Earth's surface and so are usually fine-grained; they rest on top of older rocks. High temperature, low viscosity basalts spread out into broad, gently sloping, shield volcanoes.

3 Basalts are characteristic of ocean ridges, where they are formed by partial melting of mantle peridotite. Basalts are composed mainly of plagioclase feldspar and pyroxene.

4 Plutonic rocks are formed deep underground; they are coarse-grained with chilled margins; they cut across older rocks. In volume, they are chiefly granites and diorites, made of feldspar, quartz and mica.

5 Fractional crystallisation is the process by which the first minerals to crystallise out from the melt leave a residual liquid of a different composition. Frequently, the first crystallising mineral is olivine, which settles to the bottom of the magma chamber to form cumulates.

6 The net result of all the processes taking place at island arcs and continental volcanoes is that throughout geological time there has been a slow and steady conversion of mantle peridotite to andesitic continental crust through a number of steps.

   (i) Partial melting of peridotite produces basaltic magmas; partial melting of basalt produces andesitic magmas.

   (ii) Andesites accumulate to form island arcs. These rocks, being of lower density, cannot be subducted back into the mantle.

   (iii) Prolonged magmatism beneath island arcs leads to remelting and progressively more siliceous magmas, which can eventually reach granitic composition.

   (iv) Island arcs accrete to form 'mini continents' and also stick to the 'sides' of existing continents.

   (v) Continuing activity adds further siliceous magmas, thus increasing the thickness of the continental crust and enlarging the 'mini continent'.

7 Magmas of granitic composition are formed by partial melting of andesitic material at destructive plate margins. Being less dense they rise through the overlying crustal rocks before solidifying into coarse-grained plutonic rocks. Only rarely do magmas of granitic composition reach the Earth's surface, where they form lavas called rhyolite, or pumice.

8 Volcanoes formed from lower-temperature, high-viscosity magma (andesitic and granitic) have steep-sided conical shapes, often with alternating layers of andesitic lavas and ashes forming a composite strato-volcano.

9 The volcanic activity at constructive plate margins is rarely hazardous and can provide sources of geothermal heat. Volcanoes at destructive plate margins are unpredictable and more explosive; hydrothermal systems associated with the volcanism can be used as heat sources.

4.7 Questions

1 Examine the photomicrographs in Figures C3.5a, C3.5b and C4.6 which show a granite, a basalt and a gabbro. Decide which is which by
   a) drawing a scale diagram of each photomicrograph, identifying the minerals present.
   b) estimating the percentage of each mineral present.
   c) deciding which is a specimen of basalt, which is gabbro and which is a granite.

2 Explain how the composition of lavas from Hawaii and Oregon, USA differ. How might the differences be explained by their plate tectonic settings? How might the explanations be used as evidence for the theory of plate tectonics?

CHAPTER 5

Sedimentary processes: at Earth's active surface

Introduction

The principle of 'the present is the key to the past' is applied by studying the broad range of sedimentary processes active today and how their products can be analysed. Analysis can be from grain size scale, through sedimentary structure scale to sedimentary sequence scale, using a variety of techniques. The results of these studies can be applied to show how the processes will be reflected in the evidence preserved in ancient rock sequences.

5.1 Case Study: What was it like at the time? – the New Red Sandstone of the Cheshire Basin

If we want to find out what an area was like when sediments were deposited, either we can go and examine exposures of the sedimentary rocks themselves to find the evidence for how they formed, or we can do a literature survey, studying the published information on the geology of an area. This Case Study shows how information taken from a range of published sources can be put together to give a picture of what an area was like when the sediments were deposited. If you do a survey like this, you will need to give full references to all the sources of information used, as has been done here.

The sequence of rocks in the area is shown in a published stratigraphic log, (Figure 5.2). It shows that rocks of the late Permian age (see Appendix 7) rest on an eroded surface of Carboniferous rocks; these are overlain in turn by a thick sequence of Triassic rocks. This Case Study looks in detail at the sequence from the Kinnerton Sandstone Formation up to the Northwich Halite Formation.

The published information on each of these formations contains evidence for the palaeoenvironment and how it changed over time. The clues about sand dunes and salt flats, rivers and shallow seas all build up a picture of a hot desert area flooded by salt water from time to time.

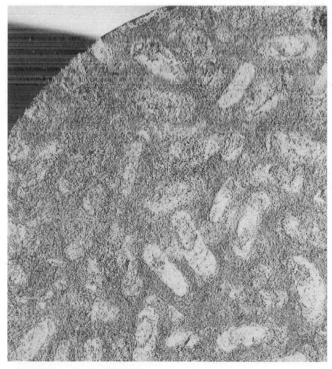

Figure 5.1 *Burrows of Diplocraterion, a trace fossil characteristic of intertidal environments*

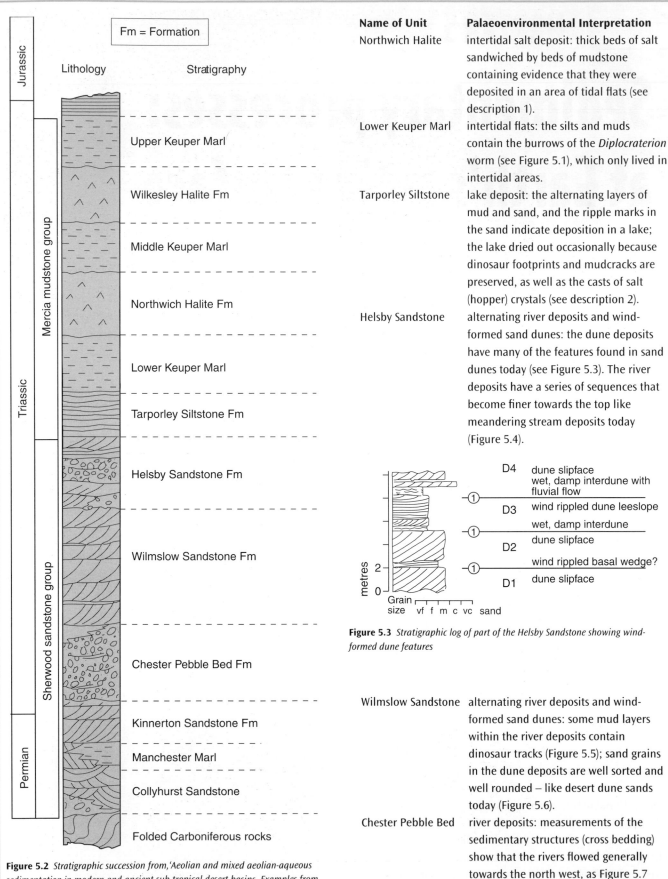

Figure 5.2 *Stratigraphic succession from, 'Aeolian and mixed aeolian-aqueous sedimentation in modern and ancient sub-tropical desert basins. Examples from the Sahara and the Permo-Triassic of NW Europe'*

Name of Unit	Palaeoenvironmental Interpretation
Northwich Halite	intertidal salt deposit: thick beds of salt sandwiched by beds of mudstone containing evidence that they were deposited in an area of tidal flats (see description 1).
Lower Keuper Marl	intertidal flats: the silts and muds contain the burrows of the *Diplocraterion* worm (see Figure 5.1), which only lived in intertidal areas.
Tarporley Siltstone	lake deposit: the alternating layers of mud and sand, and the ripple marks in the sand indicate deposition in a lake; the lake dried out occasionally because dinosaur footprints and mudcracks are preserved, as well as the casts of salt (hopper) crystals (see description 2).
Helsby Sandstone	alternating river deposits and wind-formed sand dunes: the dune deposits have many of the features found in sand dunes today (see Figure 5.3). The river deposits have a series of sequences that become finer towards the top like meandering stream deposits today (Figure 5.4).

Figure 5.3 *Stratigraphic log of part of the Helsby Sandstone showing wind-formed dune features*

Wilmslow Sandstone	alternating river deposits and wind-formed sand dunes: some mud layers within the river deposits contain dinosaur tracks (Figure 5.5); sand grains in the dune deposits are well sorted and well rounded – like desert dune sands today (Figure 5.6).
Chester Pebble Bed	river deposits: measurements of the sedimentary structures (cross bedding) show that the rivers flowed generally towards the north west, as Figure 5.7 shows.

Thickness 10-15ft

|Mud Silt | Sand |
8   6   4   2 +0 φ

Figure 5.4 *A stratigraphic log showing one of the cycles found in the Helsby Sandstone which are interpreted as meandering stream sediments*

Figure 5.5 *Cheirotherium dinosaur tracks from the siltstones in Storeton Quarry*

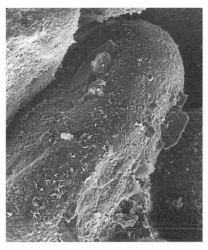

Figure 5.6 *Scanning Electron Microscope photograph. These sand grains show the typical well rounded shapes of desert sands illustrating why their porosity and permeability is high*

Figure 5.7 *Palaeocurrent data from the Chester Pebble Bed showing river flow directions from the south east towards northwest*

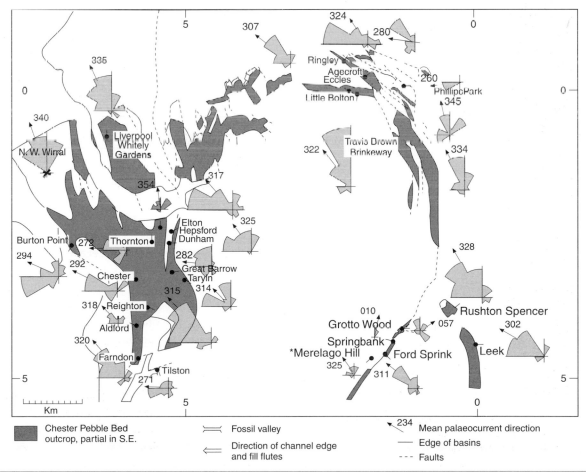

Chester Pebble Bed outcrop, partial in S.E.

Fossil valley

Direction of channel edge and fill flutes

234 Mean palaeocurrent direction

Edge of basins

- - - Faults

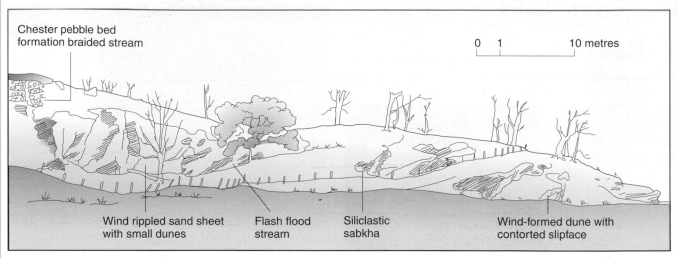

Figure 5.8 labels:
Chester pebble bed formation braided stream

0 1   10 metres

Wind rippled sand sheet with small dunes

Flash flood stream

Siliclastic sabkha

Wind-formed dune with contorted slipface

Figure 5.8 *Field diagrams of the Kinnerton Sandstone showing environmental interpretations*

Kinnerton Sandstone alternating river deposits and wind-formed sand dunes: exposures like the one shown in the field sketch (Figure 5.8) show stream deposits, salt-flat deposits and wind-formed dunes; measurements of the sedimentary structures in the dunes (wind-formed cross bedding), shown in the wind rose (Figure 5.9), indicate that the winds were easterly, as found in the Sahara desert today.

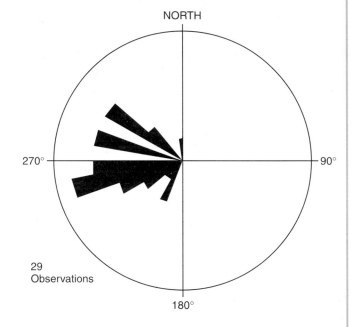

Figure 5.9 *Cross bed dip directions in wind-formed dunes indicating easterly wind*

Examples of the published data

Description 1

'. . . it consists of six or seven beds of rock-salt varying from 50 to 350 ft thick separated by beds of red mudstone, averaging 20 to 40 feet thick. Parts of each of the beds of rock-salt show well-defined banding at 2 to 4 in. intervals, marked either by paper thin mudstone or gypsum partings or by changes in size of the crystals of halite. . . .'

From 'Geology of the Country around Macclesfield, explanation of One-inch Geological Sheet 110, New Series', Evans, W. B., Wilson, A. A., Taylor, B. J. and Price, D. 1968, pub. HMSO.

Description 2

'The . . . Tarporley Siltstones consist of alternations of dark red or secondarily green shale and pink, fine-grained . . . , well sorted, ripple-bedded, ripple-marked sandstone. Mudcracks are common and some bedding planes show worm tracks and burrows . . . , and footprints of *Cheirotherium* and *Rhynchosauroides*. Other features include hopper pseudomorphs after halite . . . '

From 'Geology of the Country around Chester and Winsford, Memoir for 1:50 000 Geological Sheet 109', Earp, J. R. and Taylor, B. J. 1986. pub. HMSO.

5.2 'The present is the key to the past'

The Case Study shows how we can use information from desert environments today to understand what the Cheshire Basin area was like during Permian and Triassic times. We are using the key scientific principle that 'the present is the key to the past', which was first applied by **James Hutton** in 1788. This later became called 'The Principle of **Uniformitarianism**'. It means that the processes that we see acting on Earth's surface today must have worked in the same way in the geological past. By examining how sediments like sand and gravel are formed and laid down today, we can determine how ancient sands and gravels were deposited before they became sedimentary rocks.

The rock cycle diagram in Appendix 1 summarises the major processes involved in producing sediments and sedimentary rocks. The sedimentary processes in the cycle work at all scales from the gutter outside your door, to the sedimentary activity of the mighty Amazon River. They operate from the highest mountain ranges to the deepest oceans and from arctic to tropical climates. Some processes act in seconds while others take millions of years.

5.3 Making sediment – weathering and erosion

Sediment is the building material of all sedimentary rocks. 85 per cent of sedimentary rocks are formed from material produced by the breakdown of existing rocks into fragmental material. The fragments are known as **clasts** and so result in **clastic sediments** or clastic sedimentary rocks. Biogenic sediments, for example shell sands and peat, are produced by the activities of animals and plants. Chemical activity results in **chemical sediments**, while other types are produced by a combination of physical, biological and/or chemical processes acting together.

5.3.1 WHY ROCKS WEATHER AND ERODE

Weathering is the physical breaking up of rock into smaller pieces and the chemical breakdown of rock at the Earth's surface. Weathering involves no movement away of materials (apart from solutions). Most exposed surfaces are attacked by weathering, as you will see on local walls and buildings (Figure 5.10).

Figure 5.10 *A gatepost attacked by weathering. Chemical effects have blackened the surface, physical attack has produced cracks and loosened grains and the biological activity of mosses and lichens are attacking and weakening the surface*

Erosion is the removal of material, like the grains that have fallen away from the gatepost in Figure 5.10. It is useful to discuss weathering and erosion separately, but usually they act together: weathering loosens the grains and erosion carries them away.

Why are rocks broken down by these processes? The answer involves equilibrium and stability. Most rocks form beneath the surface. Intrusive igneous and most metamorphic rocks form at several hundred degrees Celsius and several kilometres down, while even sedimentary rocks form mostly at temperatures of up to 200 °C and depths of more than a kilometre. They are stable in these conditions; their minerals are in chemical and physical equilibrium.

Conditions are very different when the rocks become exposed at the surface. If you try to write a list of the differences, you will probably include the following. At the Earth's surface:

- the temperature is less, perhaps only 1–20 °C;
- the pressure is much lower, as there are no overlying rocks;
- there is generally much more water available;
- there is free oxygen for chemical and biological processes;
- plants and animals cause biochemical activity;
- uplift gives rock particles gravitational # potential energy;
- water, wind and ice movement transfer some of their kinetic energy to the eroded fragments as well.

Under these surface conditions, rock particles are no longer in equilibrium and so they react to produce materials that are more stable in the new circumstances.

The rock-forming minerals which are *least* prone to attack are those that formed in conditions *most* like those found at the Earth's surface. So minerals that formed at low temperatures are more stable than high-temperature minerals. Bowen's 'reaction series' of mineral crystallisation temperatures (see Figure 3.6) shows that quartz is the most stable common rock-forming mineral, which is why it is so abundant in sedimentary rocks.

The least stable minerals, olivine and calcium feldspar, are readily attacked by weathering processes and break down, mainly forming clay minerals. So clastic sedimentary rocks are made mostly of quartz and clay.

5.3.2 THE PROCESSES OF WEATHERING

There is a range of weathering processes which can be separated for convenience into chemical, physical and biological processes, shown in Figure 5.11, although they frequently act together. For example, some chemical processes have physical effects and most biological processes have chemical effects.

Although in a list like this biological processes do not seem very important, the more we find out about them, the more critical we find they are. Recent research has

shown that some rocks weather between ten and a hundred times more quickly if they have a covering of lichen. Biological processes speed up chemical and physical processes and cause reactions like chelation, that only take place organically. Vegetated soils contain high levels of CO_2 from plant respiration and decomposition. Levels of soil water CO_2 (acidity) can be ten to a hundred times those in the atmosphere and this highly acidic water plays a major role in the weathering of rocks and minerals.

Rates of weathering depend greatly on the local conditions, so that differences in temperature, humidity, chemical composition of the rainfall and the amount and types of vegetation can have great effects. Climate controls temperature and humidity and by plotting these on a graph you can outline the different types of chemical and physical weathering that take place under a range of different conditions (Figure 5.12).

In hot, wet regions chemical and biological weathering processes predominate since biological weathering is very active. In cold conditions, weathering is largely physical

Figure 5.11 *Chemical, physical and biological weathering processes*

Weathering process		Description
Chemical weathering	**Solution**	Soluble materials dissolve and are carried away in solution
	Carbonation	Rainwater containing carbon dioxide (CO2) from the air and soil reacts with carbonates to form soluble hydrogen carbonates
	Hydrolysis	Water reacts with minerals, particularly silicate minerals like feldspars, breaking them down; if the water contains CO2, more hydrogen ions (H+) are available and hydrolysis is speeded up
	Hydration	The addition of water molecules to the atomic structures of minerals
	Oxidation	The addition of oxygen to the atomic structures of minerals or a similar chemical change
	Ion exchange	Minerals rich in one ion are attacked by a solution rich in another ion and the ions exchange, e.g. Na+ can exchange for Ca2+
	Chelation	Organic compounds from soil remove metal ions from minerals
Physical weathering	**Insolation**	Heating and cooling of rocks in desert regions causes minerals to expand and contract at different rates until the rock eventually fractures
	Freezing and thawing	Water expands by 9 per cent on freezing, so fractures filled with water are prized further apart each time the water freezes until the fragment breaks off
	Crystallisation of minerals	New minerals grow in rock spaces forcing the rock apart
	Stress release	Deeply buried rocks are compressed by the pressure of the rocks above; when the overburden is removed, the rock expands to produce stress release fractures
Biological weathering	**Bacteria**	Minerals decompose much more quickly in the presence of bacteria; the bacteria produce an acidic microenvironment that allows them to remove elements directly from minerals
	Soil processes	Organic activity increases weathering rates dramatically, for example by providing CO2 for hydrolysis and carbonation, and organic compounds for chelation
	Plant roots	Plant roots growing in fractures

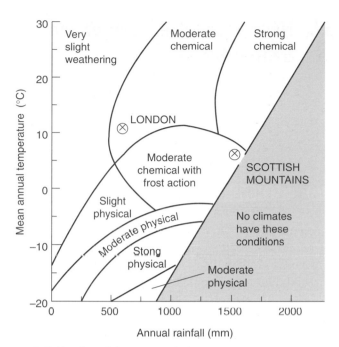

Figure 5.12 *The effects of climate on weathering*

Figure 5.14 *An Egyptian obelisk, (a) as it originally was in Egypt, and (b) as it is now in New York. Weathering rates have been much faster during the 100 years in New York than the previous 3000 years in Egypt*

and in hot, dry climates there is comparatively little weathering as Figure 5.12 shows. The dramatic increases in weathering rates that can be caused by a change in climate are shown in Figure 5.13.

Figure 5.13 *Rates of weathering in different climatic zones – measured as the thickness of material removed from bare rock surfaces over 1000 years (μm per 1000 years)*

Rock type	Cold climate	Warm humid climate
Basalt	10	100
Granite	1	10
Marble	20	200

The effects of this have been seen dramatically when Egyptian monuments from the dry desert climate of Egypt have been moved to the humid temperate climates of London or New York. Weathering rates have greatly increased, as seen in Figure 5.14.

5.3.3   SOIL FORMATION

Soil forms a thin layer, resting on the solid rock beneath. Nevertheless, it is crucial, since without soil most plant life on land could not exist and the Earth would be a very different place. Soil originates from the chemical and physical weathering of rock but a key component is the organic (biological) material from decayed plants, called

humus. It is this material that provides most of the nutrients for living plants, so they provide their own fertiliser. Since soil cannot form without plant activity, we find no soils in the geological record before plants began to colonise the land around 410 Ma ago (near the end of the Silurian period – see Appendix 7). Soils cannot form in unvegetated areas, so high-altitude mountain tops and high-latitude arctic and antarctic regions have no soil.

Soil science is complex and there are many different soil types. The character of soil depends upon a range of factors including, the parent rock, the altitude, slope, climate, vegetation cover, soil organisms and the amount of time available. Despite this, many soils are found to consist of just three main layers called **soil horizons**.

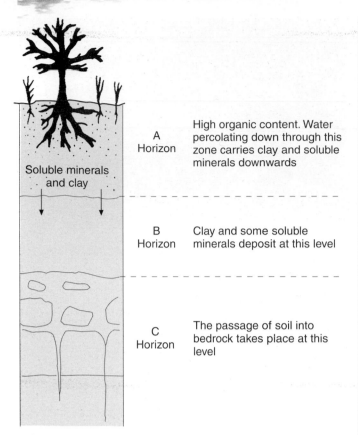

Figure 5.15 *A typical soil profile*

A Horizon — High organic content. Water percolating down through this zone carries clay and soluble minerals downwards

Soluble minerals and clay

B Horizon — Clay and some soluble minerals deposit at this level

C Horizon — The passage of soil into bedrock takes place at this level

Below the surface layer formed mainly of vegetation and humus, there is a zone from which soluble material is removed. This is known as the A horizon (Figure 5.15). Rainwater percolating down through the soil dissolves the soluble minerals (**leaching**) and carries them down to the B horizon, where some of the less soluble materials, such as iron and aluminium salts, are deposited. The more soluble constituents, which are mainly salts of sodium and calcium, are carried down through the C horizon and away through groundwater flow. Below the C horizon of slightly weathered parent rock, the unaltered bedrock itself is found.

Soil types and horizons are studied either by digging pits or by using a soil auger. The different types of soil auger are wound down into the soil and then pulled out so that the soil sequence can be seen.

There can be great variety in the character and thickness of horizons A, B and C; there may be extra layers or one of these layers might be missing. Nevertheless, wherever there is vegetation the combination of leaching and depositional processes acting on a parent rock/humus mixture produces some form of soil.

Soil protects the underlying bedrock from erosion, but where vegetation cover is removed, the soil itself will be eroded, eventually exposing the rock beneath.

5.4 Moving sediment – erosion and transportation

Weathering and erosion form clastic sediments and erosion also involves the first movement of the sediment. This movement continues through transportation.

5.4.1 MASS MOVEMENT

When material on slopes is loosened by weathering, it eventually falls under its own weight. There is a wide range of erosion processes in which gravity plays a major part and these together are called **mass movement** or **mass wasting**. A **landslide** is an example of mass wasting at speed.

Mass wasting processes can be classified according to how much the material deforms during its movement; the evidence of this deformation is preserved in the sediment that is produced. The amount of deformation is closely linked to the water content, since solid materials containing little water show little deformation. At the other end of the scale, when a mass is more water than solid material, it flows and so retains none of its original structure, as shown in Figure 5.16.

Rockfall occurs when rock or other debris is loosened by weathering and falls off a near vertical face to build up as a sloping pile at the foot of the cliff. This material is called **scree** or **talus** and usually builds up into cones. **Rockslides** occur most commonly where the rock layering dips down the face, allowing sliding to occur down the layers. Plastic clay or the lubricating effect of rainwater increase the chances of sliding.

While rockfalls and rock slides can occur rapidly and catastrophically, **creep** is a very slow process. As soil creeps down slopes, fences, walls and telegraph poles start to lean downslope, and young trees that are pushed downhill adapt by bending upwards as they grow, resulting in curved tree trunks.

When material on a slope fails along an arc-shaped plane, **rotational slips** occur. Blocks of material rotate as they slip, with the foot of the slipped material often collapsing over the end into a small slump. You can recognise rotational slips by their characteristic curved landslip scars at the top, above the surfaces of backward-tilted blocks. Many **slumps** begin as rotational slips, but once movement has begun, the material continues downslope to form lobes of highly disturbed material. Slump movement can be fast or slow, but is fairly common, particularly where cuttings have been made for new roads.

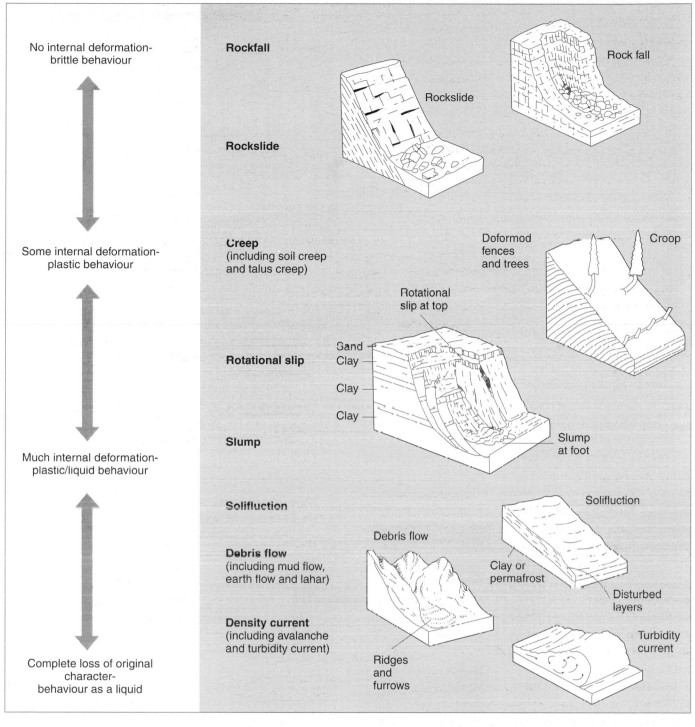

Figure 5.16 *A classification of mass wasting processes – based on amount of deformation of material*

Material can become completely waterlogged if the ground beneath is frozen (as with permafrost near glacial areas) or if it is underlain by impermeable material like clay. Then it can flow slowly on very shallow slopes indeed. This is **solifluction** and solifluction lobes and sheets are found commonly today below glaciers and near ice sheets. During solifluction the material loses most of its original structure.

Mass wasting processes that cause the greatest hazards by producing the fastest flows are debris flows and density currents. **Debris flows** are commonly triggered by very heavy rainfall or the addition of water in some other way. They include debris flows themselves, which are of coarse grade material, flows of earth and mud which are of clay grade material, and lahars of volcanic ash. All these can flow down valleys catastrophically, eroding the valley sides, carrying large boulders and even cars and buildings and causing great loss of life. Lahars are common and a major hazard near ash-producing volcanoes, since not only are eruptions often accompanied by heavy rainfall, but large volumes of water can also be released from crater lakes or by melting snow and ice.

When materials flow downhill at great speed under water, they can take in so much water that the solids are buoyed up to form **density flows**. Density flows of sediment in water are called **turbidity currents** and can move at up to 30 ms⁻¹. These flows of sand and mud can sweep down submarine slopes and out across thousands of square kilometres of ocean floor, producing the thick widespread turbidite deposits discussed on page 97.

Density currents of particles in air can also have catastrophic effects. Avalanches are flows of ice and snow particles buoyed up on air, and nuée ardentes are high-temperature density flows of volcanic ash, buoyed up by air and volcanic gases (see page 65).

Mass wasting hazards and hazard reduction are covered in more detail on page 164.

5.4.2   CARRIED BY THE FLOW – TRANSPORTATION BY AIR AND WATER

Most sediment is transported by wind or water; since these are both fluids, they carry sediment in similar ways. We can study this transport in the laboratory by simulating natural fluid flows using a flume or wave tank for water and a wind tunnel for air.

Wind blowing over dry, mixed loose sediment often removes the finer particles, depositing these as, for example, the sand dunes found at the back of a beach or the dunes found in desert areas. Coarser particles are left behind, so when the finer sand is removed from a desert area, the remaining material forms a stony desert floor.

Similar effects occur when rainwater falls on loose mixed sediment; you can investigate this yourself using a tray of sand. The first 'raindrops' will create small craters or **rain pits** in the surface. When the sediment becomes saturated, water will begin to flow over the surface in a thin sheet. The sheet soon breaks down into twisting rivulets and erodes small flat-based channels, carrying the finer sediment downstream and leaving the coarser grains behind. All these things can also be seen on a beach after rain.

If you study the sand in the tray carefully, you will also be able to see how individual sand grains move. Some of the larger grains roll while flatter ones slide; smaller grains move in a series of 'jerks' downstream. The finest mud is carried in a cloud and any material that dissolves also moves down-current, but cannot be seen. These are the ways in which sediment is transported by water, as seen in Figure 5.17. The grains that roll or slide along are carried by **traction** and the 'jerky movers' are actually

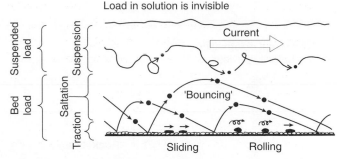

Figure 5.17 *Sediment transportation processes by water*

bouncing down current in **saltation**. All this material together is called **bedload**. The cloud of mud is sediment being carried in **suspension** and the material in **solution** is invisible. As a guide to the proportions of materials carried in these different ways by rivers, the Mississippi transports approximately 750 million tonnes of sediment in a year, of which around 7 per cent is bedload and 66 per cent is suspended load. The remaining 27 per cent, a higher proportion than you might think, is carried in solution.

Winds also transport sediment by traction and suspension, but there is no equivalent to transportation by solution in the air.

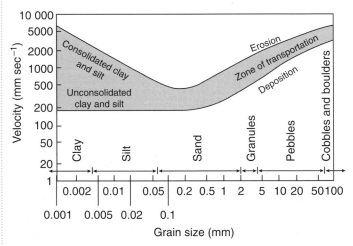

Figure 5.18 *The 'Hjulstrom curve' showing the effects of different flow rates on sediments of different sizes. The initial studies were carried out by Hjulstrom in 1935 and were published in this form by Sundborg in 1956*

The results of many flume experiments with sediments of different size are plotted in Figure 5.18. The graph shows what happens as the velocity of water is increased steadily over a flat bed of medium grain-sized sand. The first grains move at a velocity of around 500 mms⁻¹; this flow rate is the **entrainment velocity**; the first grain movement is simply erosion. Once moving, the grains will continue to be transported even if the flow rate decreases but, as the graph shows, if the flow velocity drops below 200 mms⁻¹ the grains become deposited again.

For sediment sizes larger than fine sand, the coarser the material, the greater the flow velocity needed to erode, transport and deposit the grains. However, finer sediment is all deposited at about the same slow flow rate. You can use the graph to work out the velocities at which different sizes of sediment will be eroded and deposited.

The graph also shows that silt and clay are more difficult to erode than most sand-grade material. This is because the fine grains stick together and so resist erosion.

A graph similar to the one in Figure 5.18 can be produced using a wind tunnel, although much greater speeds are needed to move sediment of a similar size in air.

During transportation, the particles rub against one another and against the bedrock. They grind down the bedrock by **abrasion**, and the particles themselves abrade one another and become ground down, in a process called **attrition**. Through attrition, weaker particles, such as micas and feldspars, become broken down and lost, while harder minerals like quartz become rounded. Grains are also under chemical attack during transport so that the less stable minerals break down, often leaving quartz.

A sediment that begins as a mixture of minerals of different grain sizes, with many of the particles being angular, is described as **immature**. After much transportation, a **mature** sediment is produced which has a mature composition (mainly quartz) and a mature texture of rounded grains that have been well sorted into certain grain sizes. Very mature sediments have usually been eroded, transported and deposited more than once.

5.4.3   WHEN THE FLOW SLOWS – DEPOSITION

As currents of wind or water slow down, they can no longer carry sediment by traction or suspension and so it is deposited. Sediments of different sizes may be left in different places, so that a river channel can contain sands in some areas, gravels in others and silts elsewhere. If fast-moving water slows abruptly, a mixture of unsorted materials can be deposited. However, if the water speed slows gradually, as happens when turbidity currents flow across an ocean floor (see Section 5.8.3), the coarser material is deposited first with finer material above. This is a **graded bed**, deposited by a single flow, coarse at the base and becoming finer upwards (see Figure C5.1f). Although graded beds are typical of turbidity currents, they can also be produced by volcanic eruptions, when mixed coarse and fine material falls through the air into water and then through the water to the bed below.

5.4.4   ICE – EROSION, TRANSPORTATION AND DEPOSITION

Glaciers and ice sheets in temperate regions are not frozen to the ground but slide across the bedrock surface. This surface is lubricated by water from melting ice at the base. If the water at the base of the ice freezes around a projecting piece of rock, it can be wrenched off by the movement of the ice in a process known as **plucking**. As a result, the base of the ice contains a large number of rock fragments of many shapes and sizes. Movement of the ice grinds these particles across the bedrock. The bedrock is ground down by abrasion and the particles themselves become ground down by attrition. This causes much more erosion than plucking and produces huge volumes of finely ground rock dust (flour).

When the ice eventually melts, the mixture of unsorted angular sediment particles and rock is often dumped as **till** in untidy heaps. Till is also commonly known as 'boulder clay', since boulders are frequently scattered through the 'clay' deposit of ground rock. If till is later eroded by wind, the fine rock dust becomes blown downwind and deposited as **loess**. This can form extensive and thick deposits beyond ice sheets.

If glacial sediment is not dumped as till, it can be carried by the melt water and become sorted into boulder layers and sand layers. The rock dust is often carried out of the area by the flowing water, but may be deposited in meltwater lakes.

In polar regions, where glaciers and ice sheets are usually frozen to the bedrock, erosion, transportation and deposition are much reduced.

5.5   Sediment to sedimentary rock – diagenesis

The processes that affect sediment after burial are called **diagenesis**. Diagenetic processes affect all sediments as they are buried progressively deeper while temperature rises and pressure increases. Eventually at depths below approximately 10 km and temperatures above 200 °C or so, diagenesis merges into low-grade metamorphism.

Diagenesis occurs because sediment, which is stable and at near chemical equilibrium conditions at the surface of the Earth, becomes unstable in the different conditions of greater pressure and temperature at depth. It therefore works in the opposite way to weathering (see page 79).

A wide range of diagenetic processes affect buried sediment and most of them cause the sediment to be bound together and **lithified** (hardened) into rock.

Figure 5.19 *The major diagenetic processes*

Diagenetic process	Description
Compaction	sediment is squeezed by the pressure of the overlying sediment; water is lost as porosity and permeability are reduced
Solution	flowing pore waters have increased power to dissolve and transport material because of the high water pressures
Pressure solution	minerals dissolve more readily at points where they are under pressure, so solution occurs where grains press into one another
Recrystallisation	some minerals, particularly calcite, change in size and shape
Replacement	one mineral becomes changed to another in a progressive, molecule-by-molecule, change
Cementation	minerals crystallise in pore spaces from circulating fluids, cementing grains together
Authigenic mineral formation	new minerals, such as clay minerals and glauconite, grow within pore spaces from circulating fluids

These processes all interact with one another, but in the Table in Figure 5.19, they are described separately. Sandstones and limestones resist compaction and so the major diagenetic processes affecting them are due to the fluids that flow through the gaps between the grains (the **pore spaces**). These include all the processes shown in the Table, apart from compaction. However, clays have such small pore spaces that liquids cannot flow through, so the major process affecting them is compaction. Diagenetic processes have been studied extensively because of the ways in which they affect the amounts of oil, gas or water that rocks can store.

Through diagenesis, sediments lithify into the sedimentary rocks defined in Appendix 3. Gravels become cemented into **conglomerates** and breccias, sands become sandstones, silts form **siltstones** and muds become either hard mudstones or softer **shales**. Clays are often compressed but do not become hardened because the fluids that might deposit cement cannot flow through. Calcium carbonate deposits become cemented into limestones or, if magnesium is present in the percolating waters the mineral **dolomite** is formed during diagenesis, the resultant rock is also called **dolomite**. Fossils made of silica may be dissolved and the silica redeposited as irregular nodules of **chert** or **flint**. Ironstone nodules also commonly grow diagenetically in shales.

If sediments that have become lithified into rocks are then uplifted and exposed, the sedimentary cycle can begin again.

5.6   On a small scale – particles and pores

Sediments and sedimentary rocks are analysed at grain size scale by considering the five main groups of properties shown in the Table in Figure 5.20.

Size, shape, orientation and packing of grains together determine the **texture** of sedimentary rocks, so a full rock description will consider composition and texture, as well as their larger scale features such as structures and sequences (see pages 90–93).

You can see the texture of coarse-grained sedimentary rocks, like conglomerates, breccias and coarse sandstones, with your naked eye, but fine sandstones and siltstones need a microscope. Nowadays, textures can also be examined on a sub-microscopic scale using a scanning electron microscope (SEM). An SEM photomicrograph can show not only the surface textures of grains and the boundaries between tiny grains, but also the types of cement and shapes of the pore spaces (see Figure 5.6).

5.6.1   COMPOSITION OF THE GRAINS AND THE NAMING OF SEDIMENTARY ROCKS

Sedimentary rock names in common usage are, unfortunately, based on several different properties: some are classified on composition, some on texture and some on a combination of these or on other properties as well. The names of the most common sedimentary rocks and their descriptions are given in Appendix 3.

A simple way of classifying sandstones by eye is that, if they are rich in quartz, they are likely to be orthoquartzites; if they contain a lot of white or pink feldspar, they are probably arkoses; dark grey-coloured sandstones often have a mud matrix, making them **greywackes**. **Orthoquartzites** have a mature composition, since minerals less stable than quartz have been lost during transportation. They usually have a mature texture too, with grains that are well rounded and well sorted, as described below. By contrast, **arkoses** and greywackes are rich in feldspar and other minerals and so have immature compositions; they are usually less well-rounded and sorted and so have immature textures as well. This is because they have undergone less attrition and breakdown during transport and have often been deposited quickly.

Figure 5.20 *Characteristics of sedimentary grains*

Characteristic		Description	Determination and importance
composition of grains		the mineralogy of the grains – see Section 5.6.1	mineral percentages are estimated with the naked eye or using thin sections under the microscope; many sedimentary rocks are named according to their composition (see Appendix 3)
texture	grain size and sorting	grain size is the mean grain size (average size of grains); sorting is a measure of the range of grain size	gravels are measured by hand, sands by sieving and silts and clays by the time they take to settle through a column of water; in rocks, grain size is determined under the microscope; size and sorting can also be assessed using comparators (Figure 5.21); mean grain size and sorting are closely related to the transportation history of the sediment; see Section 5.6.2
	grain shape	includes sphericity (closeness to a sphere shape) and roundness (amount of rounding of corners)	sphericity and roundness are assessed in hand specimen or under the microscope using a comparator (Figure 5.21); sphericity depends largely upon the physical properties of the source material, providing little evidence for the transportation history; roundness is much more valuable the more a grain is moved the rounder it becomes
	orientation of grains	long or flat particles can be oriented randomly or have a preferred orientation	determined by observation of hand specimens or thin sections; gravels can be imbricated, like tiles on a roof, and so show the flow direction of the currents that deposited them; flat lying micas and clays can affect flow of fluids through rocks in one direction
	packing	grains can be tightly packed or loosely packed	packing is reflected in porosity and permeability, which can be measured (see Section 5.6.3); oil, gas and water content of rocks is determined by their porosity and permeability

5.6.2 GRAIN SIZE AND SORTING

Sedimentary rocks are classified as sandstones, siltstones, etc. on the basis of the average or **mean grain size** of the grains. To name the rock according to grain size these measurements are compared with the grain size classification shown on the comparator diagram in Figure 5.21. This scale is applied only to clastic sediments, i.e. non-carbonate sediments. Limestone grain sizes often change during diagenesis, and so are usually described in a simpler way as coarse-, medium- or fine-grained.

Sorting is a measure of the range of grain size, with poorly-sorted sediments having grains of many different sizes and very well-sorted sediments being mainly of one grain size. Measurements of grain size are plotted on sediment-size frequency graphs, like those shown in Figure 5.22. A plot with a very narrow peak is a well-sorted sediment whilst broad peaks are produced by poorly-sorted sediments.

Winds which leave the coarser grains behind and blow finer materials far away produce dunes of well sorted sands. Well sorted sands also indicate long distances of transport by rivers, or beach conditions, where every wave sorts the sediment. In contrast, poorly sorted sediment has not travelled far or may have been deposited quickly by a waning flood or by meltwater.

Sometimes 'twin peaks' are produced when sediments from two sources are mixed together, for example, where two river tributaries join. Double peaks are also produced if sand or silt is washed into the spaces between pebbles.

5.6.3 POROSITY AND PERMEABILITY

Since geologists prospecting for oil, gas or water are more interested in the spaces between the grains than the grains themselves, porosity and permeability are critical properties.

Porosity is the amount of space in a rock measured as a percentage of the total rock. It is calculated by using the formula:

$$\% \text{ porosity} = \frac{\text{volume of total pore space}}{\text{volume of rock sample}} \times 100$$

The **primary porosity** is the result of the gaps between the grains; it is the spaces produced during the laying down of the sediment and left after diagenesis. The porosity of solid rocks increases when they later become fractured, for example in joints or faults – this is a **secondary porosity**. Secondary porosities can be vital. Some limestones, that have very low primary porosities because the pore spaces were filled by cement during diagenesis, have high secondary porosities due to jointing so that they can be used for underground water supplies.

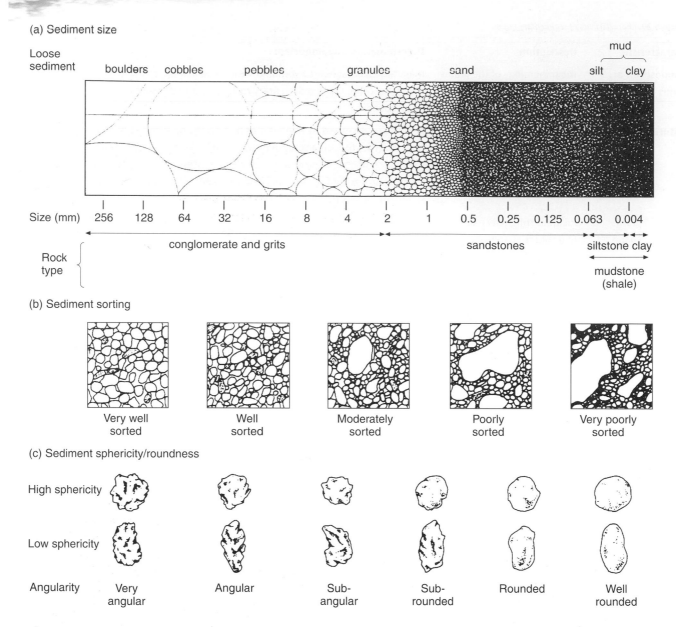

(a) Sediment size

(b) Sediment sorting

(c) Sediment sphericity/roundness

Figure 5.21 *Comparators for sediment size, sorting, sphericity and roundness*

As sediments are buried, porosity decreases due mainly to compaction and cementation during diagenesis, as shown in Figure 5.23. This indicates that clays which outcrop at the surface range in porosity between 50 and 85 per cent but at 3.5 km depth they have been so compressed that the porosity is only about 15 per cent. Although sandstones initially have lower porosities, ranging from about 17 to 57 per cent, burial reduces them less dramatically, so that they still have between 5 and 20 per cent pore space at 3.5 km depth.

Permeability is a measure of how fast fluid can flow through a rock and is given as the volume of fluid that passes through a certain cross-section of rock in a certain time (e.g. in ms^{-1}). It is an even more important property than porosity to geologists who are prospecting for oil,

gas and water. This is because while porosity indicates how much fluid a rock can hold, permeability gives a guide to how much can be extracted.

Sedimentary rocks can have a **primary permeability**, flow through the gaps between the grains, which can be measured in the laboratory. However, fractured rocks also have a **secondary permeability** which can only be assessed in the field by drilling boreholes.

Porous coarse-grained rocks usually have high permeabilities, but in fine-grained rocks like clays the pores are so small that fluids cannot pass through. So while clays have high porosities, they are usually **impermeable** – fluids cannot flow through them. You might think that this makes them of little importance to the oil or water industries but, in fact impermeable seals of clay are vital for trapping pockets of oil and gas and for guiding groundwater flows. Differences in porosities and permeabilities of common rocks are shown in Figure 5.24.

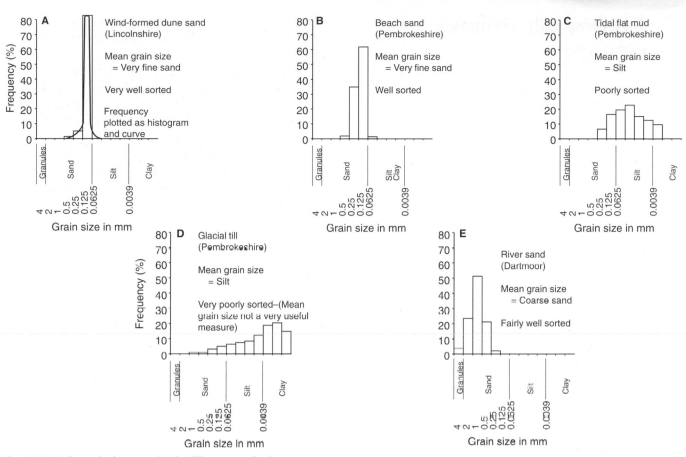

Figure 5.22 *Sediment size frequency plots for different types of sediment*

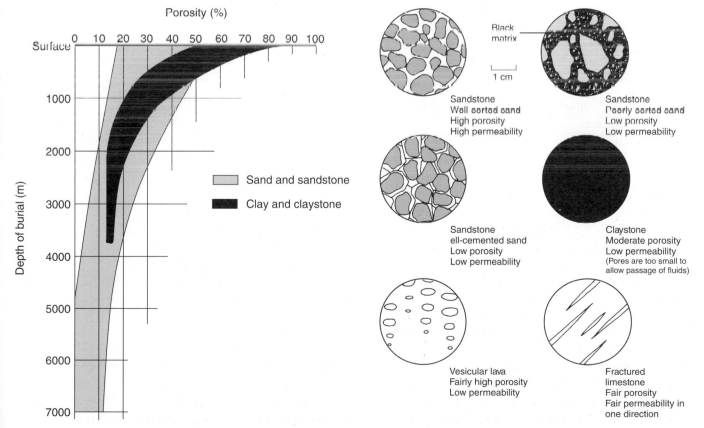

Figure 5.23 *The change in porosity with depth in sands and clays*

Figure 5.24 *Porosities and permeabilities of common rocks*

5.7 On a large scale – sediment sequences

5.7.1 CHANGING ENVIRONMENTS AND FACIES

If you go to the Wash in eastern England or the Solway Firth estuary between England and Scotland you will find a wide low-lying coastal plain fringed by marsh, sand and mud flats. This is a growing coastline because, as more and more sediment is deposited, the sea is pushed back. A detailed look shows bands of sedimentary environments parallel to the coast, as shown in Figure 5.25. Each of these bands has its characteristic sediment in terms of composition, grain size, sedimentary structures (different forms of layering), organic remains, etc. and is described as a **facies**. In **tidal flat** environments like these we can usually recognise three main bands of facies: a salt marsh facies with marsh vegetation and deep gullies, a mud flat facies further out and a rippled sand flat nearest the sea.

In such environments, it is quite easy to demonstrate how horizontal bands of sediment can produce vertical rock sequences.

Figure 5.25 shows that as sediment is deposited and the sea is moved back, the facies move outwards over time. The horizontal sequence of salt marsh, mud flat and sand flat eventually produces a vertical sequence of sediments with rippled sands at the base, muds above and salt marsh sediments on top. This type of relationship, between the plan view and the vertical sequence produced, was first recognised by **Johannes Walther** in 1894. Walther described this as his 'Law of Correlation of Facies'. As the boundaries between the facies move over time, they cross the time lines (the horizontal lines) shown in Figure 5.25. Geological boundaries that move through time are called **diachronous boundaries**.

Figure 5.25 *Facies changes on a tidal flat showing how horizontal sediment distributions can become vertical sequences according to Walther's Principle*

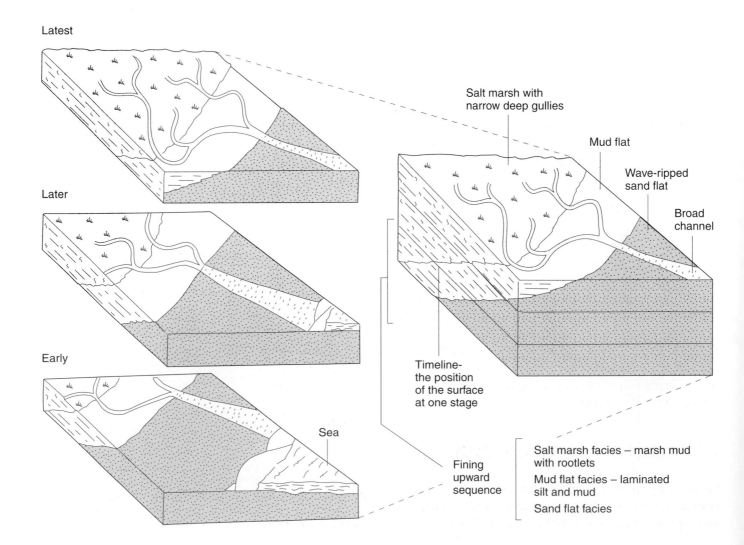

In the case of this tidal flat example, a sequence is produced in which the grain size decreases upwards from sand to fine salt marsh mud: a fining upward sequence. This, together with all the other features of the sediment, allows us to recognise similar sequences in the rock record, which are likely therefore to have been deposited in tidal flat conditions. This is how geologists apply their understanding of modern sedimentary environments to the interpretation of ancient rock sequences – the principle of Uniformitarianism ('present is the key to the past') in action.

Since Walther's 'law' does not always apply (for example, where an unconformity is present), it is better to consider his 'law' as a 'principle'. This principle is critical because geologists mostly study vertical sequences. These are either in cliff or quarry sections, in boreholes or in the way that the rocks outcrop over an area. By applying Walther's principle, these vertical sequences can be understood in terms of the plan view of the area when the sediments were being deposited.

5.7.2 STUDYING SEDIMENTARY SEQUENCES – STRATIGRAPHIC LOGGING

Sedimentary sequences are usually studied by making a record of the rock characteristics, starting at the base of the sequence and working upwards in 'stratigraphic order' (the order in which the layers were deposited). This is a **stratigraphic log** and is usually recorded on a stratigraphic log plotting sheet like the one shown in Appendix 8. A diagram summarising the main features, called a **graphic** log, is usually drawn as the information is collected.

A sheet like this will allow you to collect in a systematic way most of the important information in a rock sequence. First decide on a scale that will allow you to plot the sequence in enough detail on a reasonable number of plotting sheets. Add your scale to the right hand side of the sheet. Then begin at the bottom of the sequence and call the first layer 'Unit No. 1'; this could be just a few tens of mm thick or a metre or more of the sequence. Describe this in terms of thickness, grain size, etc. and then use the symbols and the example given to draw it at the foot of the graphic log section. Continue with Unit No. 2 upwards.

5.7.3 INTERPRETING SEDIMENTARY STRUCTURES

Sedimentary structures provide some of the most vital clues to the processes that were active when sediments were being deposited. The Table in Figure 5.26 lists some of the most important and describes how they can be interpreted.

5.7.4 ANCIENT CURRENT DIRECTIONS – PALAEOCURRENT ANALYSIS

As the Table in Figure 5.26 shows, a rock sequence may contain sedimentary structures that show the direction in which the currents were flowing when the sediments were being laid down. Similar evidence for ice flow directions can be gained by studying **glacial striations**, the scratches formed by moving ice dragging debris over bedrock. Measurements of directions like these from different localities in an area can be put together in a **palaeocurrent** (ancient current) **analysis** for a region to show overall flow directions.

Palaeocurrent data are plotted on a **current rose**, like those shown in Figure 5.27. Figure 5.27a is the plot from the measurement of 98 asymmetrical ripple marks, which shows that most were indicating current flows towards the south and south west whilst about 10 indicated

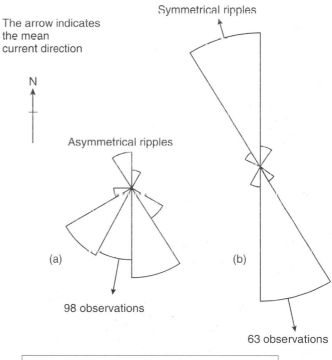

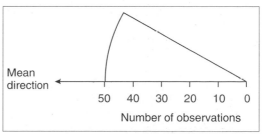

Figure 5.27 *Current roses plotted for palaeocurrent analysis taken from measurements in a modern estuary, a) for current direction data (current ripple marks) b) for current trend data (wave ripple marks)*

Figure 5.26 *Key sedimentary structures and their interpretation*

Sedimentary structure	Description	Mode of formation	Diagram/photograph
Lamination	fine layering [less than 10mm thick] in silts and muds	fine sediment settling in water under low energy, quiet conditions	Colour Figure C5.1a
Bedding	layering – individual beds are more than 10 mm thick	layers of sediment deposited at intervals under variable energy conditions	Colour Figure C5.1b
Massive sequences	thick sequences with no structures	steady deposition or a sudden sedimentary event	
Current ripple marks (asymmetrical ripple marks) (side section shows asymmetrical **cross lamination**)	ripple marks; steep slopes down current and shallow slopes upcurrent; a variety of shapes in plan view; fine sloping laminations in cross-section	first structures to form as water or wind flow increases; sand is carried up the shallow slope and deposited as a layer on the steeper slope; move downstream; ancient ripples used to indicate the flow direction of the current that formed them (palaeocurrent direction)	50mm
Subaqueous dunes (side section shows small scale **cross bedding**)	small underwater dunes similar in shape to current ripples but over 100 mm high; sloping beds in cross-section	as flow increases, ripples break down and dunes form; sediment moved up the back of the dune accumulates just over the lip and eventually collapses to form a thin layer; indicate palaeocurrent directions	500mm Avalanche Colour Figure C5.1c
Plane bedding	flat layered sand	as flow increases to high flow conditions, dunes break down to form flat beds	
Wave ripple marks (symmetrical ripple marks) (side view shows – symmetrical cross lamination)	ripple marks; equal slopes in both directions; crests are straight in plan view	in shallow water and pools waves produce small oscillating (backwards and forwards) currents; thin layers of sand are deposited when the current flows either way; indicate wave-dominated conditions (sea or large lake); ripple crests parallel the waves which parallel the coast, indicating palaeo-coastline direction	50mm
Wind-formed dunes (side view shows large scale cross bedding)	sand dunes more than one metre high; shallow slope in one direction and steeper slope in the other; crests are straight, curved or complex	formed by wind in the same way as subaqueous dunes – sand grains carried up the back accumulate at the top and eventually collapse down the face to form a cross bed; since large scale cross beds rarely form under water, they are a good indicator of wind-dominated conditions: cross beds dip in the direction the wind or the palaeo-wind was blowing	Colour Figure C5.1d
Mudcracks	cracks in mud, usually filled by sand later	mud dries out and cracks, sand is later washed into the cracks; dried mud must be a river, lake or tidal deposit	Colour C5.1 e 100mm Sand Mud
Rootlet horizons	traces of rootlet holes	vegetation puts down rootlets into the sediment; rootlets indicate fresh or brackish water conditions on land warm enough for vegetation to grow	
Bioturbation	fine sediment containing abundant burrows	burrowing organisms destroy any original layering	
Graded beds	single beds of sediment coarser at the base, becoming finer towards the top	fast-flowing currents deposit coarse sediment first and finer sediment later as they slow down; formed by underwater turbidity currents or by volcanic debris falling through water	Colour Figure C5.1f
Sole structures	structures found on the base of sandstone beds when the underlying mudstone is eroded away	as a turbidity current flows over mud, eddies hollow out 'flutes' and debris is dragged or bounced along; then it deposits sand in the depressions formed, preserving their shapes as casts; flute casts preserve current directions, groove casts just current trends; sole structures are only formed by turbidity currents	Groove cast Flute casts 50mm
Convolute bedding and other **slump structures**	small 'pillows' of sand sink into mud below producing convoluted layering; sand-stone layers slump into complex folds while surround-ing sediments are unfolded	when sloppy sands are deposited on sloppy muds underwater, the more dense sand collapses into the mud; sloppy sediments deposited on slopes can collapse downslope; slumping occurs in unstable underwater environments	10mm Sand Mud

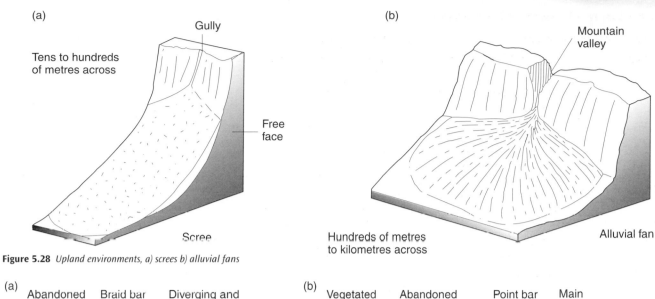

Figure 5.28 *Upland environments, a) screes b) alluvial fans*

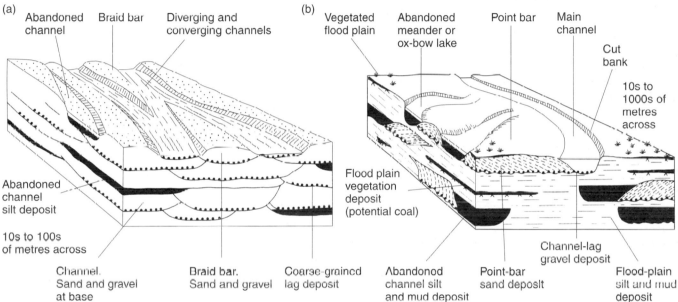

Figure 5.29 *River and stream environments, a) braided deposits b) meandering deposits*

northerly flows. The calculated **mean current direction** is shown by the large arrow, in this case, towards the south. For structures like symmetrical ripples that give only a trend (two directions, e.g. NW and SE) rather than a single current direction, the plots will be the same on either side as shown in Figure 5.27b. The data here, from 63 measurements, show that ripples were trending roughly north–south, indicating east–west movement of wave crests.

5.8 Where sediments are deposited – mountain high, ocean deep

Sediments are deposited on Earth in environments that range from the highest mountain to the deepest seas and

from the smallest puddle to the widest ocean. Each environment is affected by a range of different processes and many of these leave evidence for their activity in the sediments deposited. This evidence can be used to work out the original environments of deposition. Again, this involves applying the Principle of Uniformitarianism, since we cannot interpret how ancient sediments were deposited until we have examined the way that sedimentary environments develop today.

5.8.1 DEPOSITIONAL ENVIRONMENTS ON CONTINENTS

In upland areas, rockfall produces screes beneath cliffs (see page 82) and some of this material is eventually transported to streams. When streams flow out of mountain valleys on to lowland areas they can deposit **alluvial fans**. The sediments in both these environments (shown in Figure 5.28) have not been transported far and so are immature, with the sediment composition including some more easily weathered minerals such as feldspar and the texture being of angular grains that are poorly sorted. Screes often contain irregular bedding that dips at angles of up to 30° while alluvial fans have the sedimentary characteristics of braided stream deposits (described below) in a fan shape.

Braided streams and rivers develop where flows are very variable. Such irregular flows occur in a number of different environments, such as deserts and mountains prone to storms, ice-margin areas subject to meltwater flooding and other areas of strong seasonal variation. As currents slow after flooding, channels become progressively filled with sediment. Gravels are deposited on channel floors, followed by plane-bedded sands and later cross-bedded sands. These fill the channels and cause flows to find a new path and scour out a new channel. It is the switching from channel to channel that produces the braided pattern. Sometimes, channels can be abandoned and filled with finer sediment, as shown in Figure 5.30a. Thick sheets of braided deposits can be formed in this

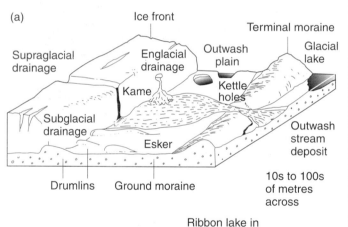

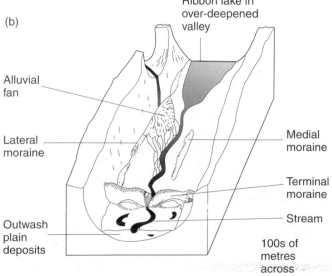

Figure 5.30 *Ice sheet environment. a) in lowland areas b) in upland valleys cut by glaciers*

way. Since the sediment has not usually been transported far, it remains fairly immature, with poor sorting, angular particles and some of the less stable minerals remaining.

Meandering streams and rivers form where currents are not overloaded with sediment, as are usually found in areas with gentler gradients than braided streams (Figure 5.29b). The currents which flow around the wide meander bends are faster on the outside than the inside. They erode sediment from the outside and usually deposit it as **point bars** on the inside of the next bend. Channels move laterally due to this erosion and deposition, cutting through previous deposits. As they move, the point bar sediments fill the old channel position; these point bar deposits have coarser sediment at the bottom and grade upwards into finer grained sands. Moving meanders can sometimes meet, when the water cuts across the junction and abandons the meander. The **abandoned meander** later becomes filled with finer sediment during and between floods. These silts and muds often become colonised by plants and are good places for fossilisation. When meandering streams do flood, the water flows beyond the channels and across the valley floor. The floods usually deposit sands near the channels and silts and muds beyond. Many layers of silts and muds can build up into thick **flood plain deposits** that dry out between floods and so may have mud cracks, rain pits, footprints and rootlet beds (if colonised by vegetation). Since flood plain deposits build up on top of point bars, the whole sequence fines upwards; series of such fining upward cycles are characteristic of meandering river environments. All these features have been used to show that the Helsby Sandstone (in the Case Study on page 76) was laid down in a meandering stream environment.

Ice brings its own sets of sedimentary environments to a region. Since the last ice sheet retreated from northern Britain only about 10 000 years ago, many signs of the ice age glaciations remain in both lowland and upland areas. Ice deposits in lowland areas are shown in Figure 5.30a. When ice melts, it leaves till, a mixture of angular pebbles and boulders in a matrix of finely ground rock (clay). The till deposited at the edge of the ice sheet as a hummocky ridge is called a **terminal moraine**, while **ground moraine** is smeared on the ground beneath the ice sheet. This is sometimes moulded by the ice into whale-backed features called **drumlins**. Meltwater can flow underneath the ice in winding channels to deposit ribbons of sand and gravel called **eskers**. Meltwater from on and within the ice flows out to build irregular deposits of sand and gravel called **kames**. Wide sweeps of meltwater flow away from the ice margin in braided **outwash deposits** and can accumulate in depressions to form glacial lakes. Such lake sediments often contain finely laminated silt layers called **varves** that

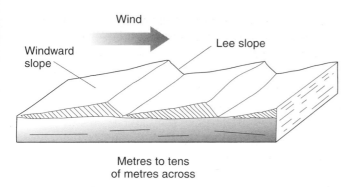

Figure 5.31 *The transverse sand dunes that form in wind-dominated environments*

usually very well sorted. **Ventifacts** or **dreikanters** are wind-faceted pebbles with three sides that also indicate wind-dominated conditions. They are formed when wind sand blasts a smooth face on one side; the pebble is then flipped over in a flood causing another side to become sand blasted. As desert lakes (**playa lakes**) dry out, evaporite minerals such as gypsum and halite are deposited. The halite crystals often have the hopper form (cubes with stepped faces) that produced casts in the Tarporley siltstone (Case Study p76). The dinosaur footprint, ripple mark and mud crack evidence all indicate a dried up desert lake environment for this siltstone formation.

have a thin, dark layer deposited in the winter and a thicker, pale layer laid down during summer.

All these features can be found in the U-shaped valleys cut by glaciers in upland areas but, in addition, piles of till can be deposited on the valley sides as **lateral moraine** and where two glaciers meet, two lateral moraines can join near the centre of the valley in a **medial moraine** (Figure 5.30b).

Arid continental areas of the Earth have sedimentary features formed by wind and by strong evaporation in addition to the fan, braided stream and lake deposits laid down during exceptional floods. Wind produces sand dunes of various types, but **transverse dunes** are the only ones that form where sediment is abundant, and so are likely to become buried and preserved (Figure 5.31); these are characterised by large-scale cross bedding. The sand dunes of the Kinnerton Sandstone (Case Study p78) are of this type. Sands in deserts have been transported great distances by wind and so are very mature. They are primarily quartz, often with a red surface-iron staining called desert varnish. The grains are well-rounded and are often pitted from impacts with other grains; they are

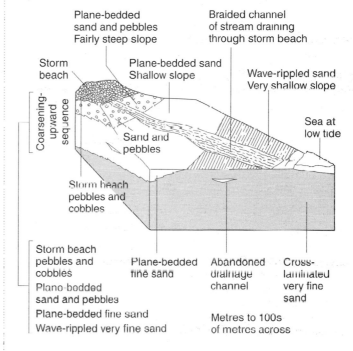

Figure 5.33 *A beach environment*

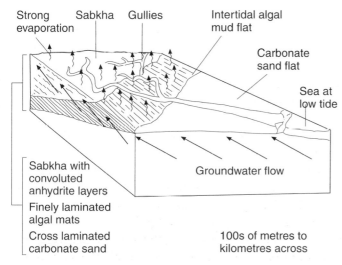

Figure 5.32 *A sabkha – an arid tidal flat environment*

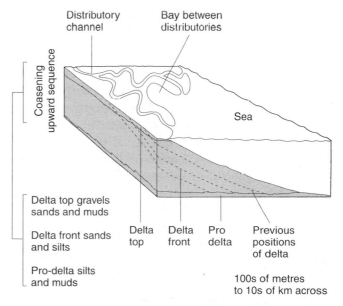

Figure 5.34 *A delta sequence*

5.8.2 DEPOSITIONAL ENVIRONMENTS ON COASTLINES

The tidal flats that develop on low-lying coastlines around Britain were used on page 90 to show how different facies move over time (Figure 5.25). These are characteristic of tidal flats in temperate conditions worldwide. However in arid areas, carbonate mud is deposited and strong evaporation causes the evaporite mineral anhydrite to grow within the sediment; layers of halite can also be laid down on the surface after an area has been flooded by the sea (Figure 5.32). Arid tidal flat deposits are known as **sabkhas** and these were the conditions in which the Northwich Halite (Case Study) was deposited.

Steeper coastlines are dominated more by waves than tides and so **beaches** form (Figure 5.33). Waves produce wave ripple marks in shallow water sands and pools and plane-bedded sands in the high energy areas where waves crash across sandy beaches. During storms, waves are even more active and are driven right to the back of sandy beaches at high tide, often creating a pebble storm beach. This produces the coarsening upward sequences characteristic of many beach deposits. Some beaches have such high energy that only rounded pebbles are deposited there. Most beach sediments are very mature, having been moved by waves many times. These mature, rounded, well-sorted sediments, that are quartz-dominated in temperate regions such as Britain, often contain much abraded shell material. Tropical beaches are usually formed entirely of shell material (which may eventually become limestones).

Deltas build out where rivers carry more sediment to the coast than the sea can remove. In quiet seas, the channels form a network pattern with a bird's-foot shape (like the Mississippi delta). In more active areas, where waves erode and redeposit the sediment in beaches along the margin of the delta, a triangular delta shape is produced (like the Nile delta) but where there are strong tides, the delta deposit develops many fingers of sediment divided by estuaries, as in the Ganges delta. These common delta shapes can be modified by vegetation, since roots slow down flows, causing deposition, and bind this sediment together, reducing erosion. All these deltas are similar in cross-section (Figure 5.34) with a **pro-delta** of mainly mud and silt at the foot, an active sloping **delta front** formed mainly of sand and a **delta top** that has a range of environments. The channels that meander across the tops of deltas are similar to meandering stream channels, except that the 'flood' happens twice a day during high tide. The bays between the channels are like tidal flats, but may become colonised by vegetation as meandering river floodplain deposits do. In tropical conditions, the vegetation may be very luxuriant and abundant and, because its area is usually waterlogged as

well, swampy conditions develop, like the ones in which thick coal sequences accumulated during late Carboniferous times in Britain.

Limestone formation dominated early Carboniferous times in Britain. Limestone-forming conditions are found today off tropical and subtropical coastlines where seas are clear (no mud is being brought into the area by rivers). This is because the lime deposits that will form limestone are largely produced by life in the sea – and life is abundant when seas are warm, shallow and clear. Under these conditions, sunlight can penetrate to reasonable depths allowing plants to photosynthesise and grow to produce the food and oxygen that animals need. Shallow water currents also play their part in transporting food and oxygen around the area. The result is prolific life.

Some tropical coastlines have an offshore barrier that absorbs much of the wave energy from the open sea, allowing a quiet, shallow lagoon to form between the barrier and the shore. The barrier is either a bank of carbonate sand or a reef, and reefs today have frameworks mostly built of coral. A variety of different organisms encrust the coral of the reef and live in all the nooks and crannies; many of these have hard parts made of calcium carbonate. If they end up on beaches or in sand banks when they die, they become ground down into carbonate sand. Sand banks are not only made of biological debris but may also be formed of **ooids**. These are spheres of calcium carbonate around 1 mm in diameter, the carbonate being deposited as the mineral aragonite. As they are rolled around by waves and currents in the warm strongly evaporating sea water, more aragonite precipitates on the outside causing them to grow. If they

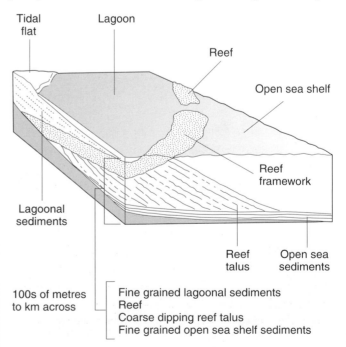

Figure 5.35 *A reef sequence*

are eventually preserved in a limestone deposit, this is an **oolitic limestone**; in most oolitic limestones the aragonite has altered to its more stable mineral form of calcite.

Within the quiet conditions of the lagoon, fine carbonate mud is deposited. This is largely aragonite from calcareous algae, and is released and breaks down when the algae dies. The lagoon mud contains organic material, the food supply for many burrowing and surface living animals. These usually destroy any original lamination as they burrow and chew. The mud may eventually become fine limestone.

Outside the reef or sand bank, reef debris or material from the sand banks accumulates on the sea floor and this builds up over time. The reef or sand bank can build upwards and outwards over this sediment so that the lagoon becomes steadily wider, as shown in Figure 5.36.

One type of environment that has accumulated unusual sequences of sediment over geological time is the **barred basin**. This is a sea that has a narrow opening and often also has a lip or shelf at the entrance that restricts flow of water in and out of the enclosed bay so that water currents only affect the surface waters. Such basins range in size from the Mediterranean Sea down to a Norwegian fjord or smaller.

In the Black Sea, for example, there is plenty of life at the surface but lack of circulation and oxygen at depth means that black stinking muds are deposited there (the rotten egg gas, hydrogen sulphide H_2S, forms in oxygen-poor conditions, reducing conditions). Because circulation is reduced, such basins are called **confined basins** (see Figure 5.36a). Most of the bacteria that cause decay cannot live without oxygen, so the decay of organic material is slowed down or stopped. Not only are these conditions excellent for fossilising any organism carried there after death, but such sediments also form the source rocks for oil and may eventually become oil shales.

In arid conditions, strong evaporation from barred basins causes continuous inflow of sea water and the formation of an **evaporite basin** (Figure 5.36b). The ions in the water become concentrated until first gypsum ($CaSO_4.2H_2O$) or anhydrite ($CaSO_4$) crystallises out and is deposited, then halite (NaCl) and finally potassium and magnesium salts such as sylvite (KCl). Flow of dense brine over the lip ensures that there is more gypsum/anhydrite and less potassium and magnesium salts than you would expect from an evaporating body of sea water. The continuous inflow of sea water can produce great thicknesses of evaporite minerals over time. There are no such environments on Earth today, but these conditions did produce the thick salt deposits that accumulated in the north east of England during Permian times.

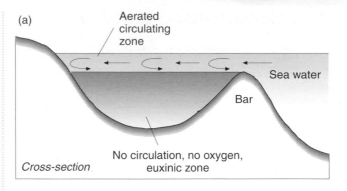

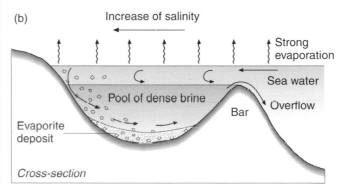

Figure 5.36 *Barred basin environments, a) a confined basin b) an evaporite basin*

5.8.3 DEPOSITIONAL ENVIRONMENTS OFFSHORE

The sediments found in shallow seas come from rivers and coasts. In tropical areas where there are few rivers they are largely carbonate sands and muds; in other regions they are mostly clastic sediments. They are redistributed by waves and tides to form a range of sedimentary structures and bodies of various sizes. The shallow seas off Britain today are affected by tidal currents and by waves down to 200 m. In high energy areas, erosion exposes bedrock or gravels deposited by ice in the past. There are broad sweeps of sand across many areas of sea floor and mud is being deposited in the quieter regions. We see the same variety in ancient shallow sea deposits, with irregular sheet sands being deposited in some areas and thick muds and clays in others. Ancient **marine sheet sands** can be distinguished because they often contain the green mineral **glauconite** which only forms in shallow marine conditions.

Deeper sea areas are often dominated by **turbidity currents**. These form due to the build-up of sand and mud at the edge of the continental shelf. When an earthquake causes this material to slide, it takes in so much water that it becomes a density current of sediment-laden water that can flow at speeds of up to 30 ms⁻¹ down and out across the ocean floor (see page 84). As the current flows across the ocean floor mud, eddies scour hollows called **flutes** and drag debris across to produce grooves. Then sand

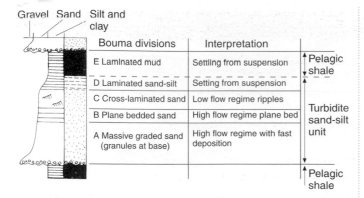

Figure 5.37 *The Bouma sequence of turbidite deposits*

begins to settle out and fills the hollows to make casts of these depressions which will later become **sole structures**. The sediment continues to settle as the current slows to produce **turbidite** sediment sequences, first recognised by Bouma and now known as a **Bouma sequence** (Figure 5.37). Massive sand grades up through plane-bedded sand to rippled sand, then to laminated silt followed by mud. Continued sediment build-up and earthquakes cause many more turbidity currents and layer upon layer of turbidite beds, thick and thin. In this way, huge thicknesses can build up covering vast areas of ocean floor. Most ocean trenches and depressions are at least partly filled by turbidite deposits.

Turbidites do not reach the deep ocean far from continental margins and so the only sediment found here is the fine material that settles slowly from suspension. Some ocean floors areas are covered by **deep sea clays**: these are either red clays that originated as fine silt eroded from deserts or green clays formed from volcanic ash. Where planktonic life is abundant near the surface, dead micro-organisms can accumulate on the sea floor in huge numbers forming **deep sea oozes**. Some are carbonate oozes formed of the hard parts of micro-organisms like foraminifera (see page 121) but these dissolve at depths below around 4 km, the calcite compensation depth. Other oozes are formed of the siliceous hard parts of organisms like radiolaria and diatoms. Where ocean floor sedimentation is very slow, **manganese nodules** can grow. These rounded lumps rich in iron, magnesium and other metals may one day be economic to mine.

One sedimentary environment that has not so far been described is that in which chalk was deposited. This very fine white calcium carbonate deposit is made of the microscopic platelets of calcareous algae. The great area and volume of chalk deposited in Cretaceous times shows that huge algal blooms must have affected many sea areas. The platelets settled from suspension in very quiet mud-free conditions, but some evidence shows that the seas in which this happened may not have been particularly deep. Siliceous organisms that were deposited at the same time later dissolved and the silica crystallised out during diagenesis as nodules of flint.

5.9 Summary

1. Sedimentary rocks are investigated by applying the principle 'the present is the key to the past'. Thus ancient sediments are interpreted in terms of modern sedimentary processes.
2. Rocks weather because they were formed in circumstances that differ from the cool, low pressure, high energy conditions of the Earth's surface; they are unstable under such conditions.
3. During weathering and erosion, rocks are attacked by a potent mixture of interacting physical, chemical and biological processes.
4. Sediments are moved by a range of water, wind, ice and gravitational processes that impart their own characteristics to the sediment. When the transporting medium loses energy, sediment is deposited.
5. When sediments become lithified into rocks, the main processes affecting coarser sediments such as sands, some limestones, etc. is cementation, while finer sediments like muds mainly undergo compaction.
6. Detailed study of sedimentary rocks on a grain size scale involves determination of the composition, size and sorting, shape, orientation, packing of the particles and the porosity/permeability produced.
8. Important methods used to analyse sedimentary sequences include stratigraphic logging and palaeocurrent analysis.
7. A systematic study of modern sedimentary environments allows the geologist to build up a picture of the key characteristics of the body of sediment that is likely to be deposited. This model can then be used to interpret ancient sedimentary sequences.

5.10 Questions

1   How would you expect the composition and texture of the following sands to differ?
    a coastal dune sand; a glacial outwash plain sand; a tropical island beach sand.

2   Examine Figure 5.25 which shows how diachronous sequences might develop. Draw the block diagram that might come next in the sequence.

3   If cross-bedded sandstone was exposed in a quarry, what evidence might show that it was deposited: a) by wind, b) in a braided stream environment, c) on a beach, d) in a delta?

4   What changes would you expect to see if you moved from rock exposures interpreted as off-reef limestones, through a palaeo-reef into a lagoonal facies and eventually into a sequence interpreted as a tropical tidal flat?

5   What factors might affect the porosity and permeability of a mixed limestone, sandstone, shale sequence discovered on top of a natural gas source rock?

6   If you were asked to interpret the conditions under which a dipping sedimentary sequence was deposited which is now exposed in a cliff section several hundred metres long; what observations would you make; how would you record the observations; how would you ensure systematic collection of data; what specimens would you take; what laboratory identifications and tests would you carry out on the specimens and how would you ensure your safety in the field?

CHAPTER 6

Fossils: interpreting life forms from the past

Introduction

Fossils are the remains, or traces, of plants or animals including any signs of past life, for example footprints, burrows and feeding trails. **Palaeontology** is the study of fossils. Most palaeontologists (geologists who study fossils) use the rule of thumb that fossils are prehistoric (before written history began), and so are at least 10 000 years old. Younger remains are not fossils but are archaeological remains.

One of the earliest uses of fossils in geology was to work out the relative ages of rocks, that is, in what order a sequence of strata was laid down, but age dating is now also done by radiometric means (Chapter 11). One modern use of fossils is the study of the communities of ancient plants and animals, to determine the environment in which they lived. The study of groups of organisms and their environment is ecology (or, when studying fossils, **palaeoecology**). Fossils can tell us, for example, about the surface of the Earth long ago, whether a particular place was a swamp or river, or covered by deep or shallow sea. This is called **palaeoenvironmental** analysis and can assist the reconstruction of the geography and climates of times past.

Through examining the remains of animals and plants that existed long ago, it is clear that most are very different from those living today. In some cases they became *extinct*, they died out completely; whereas other types changed and, in time, *evolved* into new forms. By comparing early fossils with later ones we can see how they have altered through time, and so learn more about the processes of evolution. We can also speculate on how evolutionary changes might be linked to environmental conditions.

6.2   Fossils as evidence of past life

Fossils are the most direct evidence for past life. Not all fossils are bones and shells, which are **body fossils**; the remains of activity such as footprints, tracks or burrows are called **trace fossils**. Remains of what an animal ate and excreted (faecal pellets) may also be fossilised and can provide valuable evidence about the organisms that produced them. The three principle sources of information about a fossil's mode of life are: its form, its nearest living relatives and the enclosing sediment.

6.2.1   TYPES OF FOSSILS

Fossils range in size from being too small to be seen with an optical microscope to dinosaur bones several metres long. Appendix 4 shows a biological classification of life forms and Appendix 5 contains descriptions of some fossil groups, their modes of life and living environments.

6.2.2   THE SHAPE EVIDENCE

The shape, or morphology, of an animal's shell or its skeleton often reflects its way of life: for example animals that have wings usually fly. We can also get many clues about how and where fossil animals lived by looking at modern animals. In Chapter 5 you saw how the environment of deposition of sedimentary rocks could be interpreted by looking at modern sediments. This idea, that the present is the key to the past, is equally true for fossils.

When we find features in a fossil of which there is no modern equivalent, there is difficulty interpreting the fossil's original mode of life. In this situation, knowing

6.1   Case Study: Lucy

Figure 6.1 shows the remains of 'Lucy', an adult female who lived three and a half million years ago in the Afar region of Ethiopia in Africa. Some palaeontologists think she is a direct ancestor to humans – one of your ancestors. Lucy was named after The Beatles' song 'Lucy in the Sky with Diamonds' which was playing when the bones were first brought back to the expedition camp site. Try using the scale in Figure 6.1 to work out the approximate length of Lucy's thigh bone. You can then use this figure to work out Lucy's height, since in humans the thigh bone is about a quarter of the height.

There are many scientific questions that can be asked about Lucy:

- How should she be classified: as human or as ape?
- How do we know she was female and adult?
- Did she walk on two legs or four?
- How did she live?
- What was the environment she lived in?
- What did she eat?
- What do her bones tell us about how apes and humans evolved?
- What factors caused this evolution?
- How did she die?
- How has she been preserved and why are some of her bones missing?
- How can we tell how long ago she lived?

A palaeontologist would ask similar questions about any fossil. What evidence would you look for to answer them? Some of the questions can be answered directly from the bones of Lucy that were preserved.

Although all the evidence is not visible in Figure 6.1, careful study revealed that.

Lucy was very small, only about one metre high (as her thigh is about 25 cm) but we know she was an adult because she had

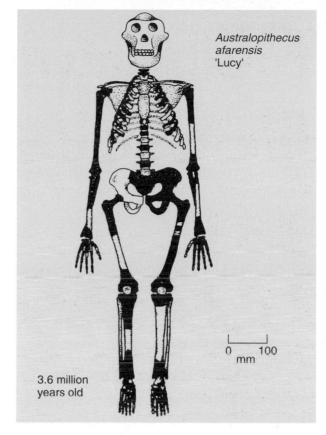

Figure 6.1 *The bones of 'Lucy'. The bones marked in solid black are those that have been found*

wisdom teeth. Since the hole in the pelvis is proportionately larger in females than in males (because babies are born through the hole) Lucy must have been female.

We can be fairly sure of the answers to some of the questions above but others we shall probably never know, such as the cause of her death.

about the community and environment in which the creature lived gives extra important evidence.

6.2.3   LIVING RELATIVES

Another clue to the way of life of a fossil is the lifestyle of its living relatives. All modern spiders are predators, so we assume that fossil spiders were predators too. All modern echinoids (sea urchins) and brachiopods are marine so we think that all fossils of these two groups were marine, too. For example, the internal parts of the ammonite shown in Figure 6.2b (ammonites became

extinct at the Cretaceous–Tertiary boundary) are thought to resemble those of a modern 'equivalent', the *Nautilus* shown in Figure 6.2a. This is because we believe that ammonites lived in the same way as the *Nautilus* does today.

We can understand Lucy's way of life better by comparing her bones with those of her nearest living relatives: apes and humans. We know Lucy walked upright because when we compare her knee and hip joints with those of apes and humans, we find that they are much more like those of humans. Microscopic scratch marks on the teeth of monkeys and humans reflect the food they eat. Examination of Lucy's teeth suggests she

ot of grass seeds and nuts. Vital clues like these help
to paint a picture of the life that Lucy lived.

6.2.4 ENVIRONMENTAL CLUES

The environment in which an animal or plant lives is
called its **habitat** and a huge range of different habitats
exist on Earth. Most of the animals you see live on the
land and it might be tempting to think that many of them
will one day be fossils. However land animals are rarely
preserved as fossils since sediments are not often
deposited on land. Mammals such as Lucy, or reptiles like
the dinosaurs, are found very rarely compared to marine
groups like shellfish. Figure 6.3 shows the life habitats of
some marine organisms.

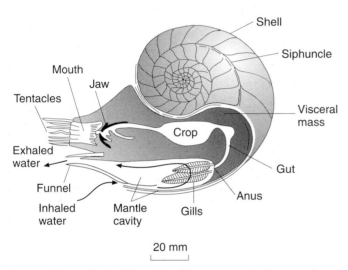

Figure 6.2(a) *Nautilus, the living relative of the ammonites, that became extinct at
the KT boundary. The earliest nautiloid shells were straight. They were the most
efficient predators in the sea (before fish) and some grew to be 5 m long. Straight
Nautiloids became extinct*

Figure 6.2(b) *A Jurassic ammonite, Pleuroceras. The shell is coiled in one plane
and filled with gas, for buoyancy. The last chambers contained some gas and also
some water that the animal could expel through a siphuncle. This allowed
movement up and down in the water. The thin shell was strengthened by partitions
(septa) to resist pressures of vertical movement and which were further
strengthened by corrugations, radial ribs*

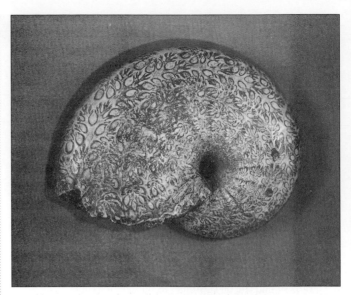

Figure 6.2(c) *A Triassic ammonite Phylloceras. Here the shell has been removed
and the surface polished. The septa are attached to the shell at the suture line,
which is a refolded pattern, showing that the internal chambers are complex
shapes*

Animals are adapted to the environments in which
they live but they also choose them to some extent, and
transform them to their advantage. Organisms living in
the open sea are either swimmers or they float. Predators,
scavengers and grazers move around to find their food so
they are all active. Filter feeders extract the small food
particles which are suspended in the water by sucking in
the water, filtering out the food and then squirting out the
water. **Sessile** (fixed) and **planktonic** (floating) animals
largely rely on this method of feeding. Deposit feeders eat
sediment and extract nutrients from it; worms and some
sea urchins are examples of deposit feeders.

If geologists are to make deductions about the
environment from the fossils, it is important to know
whether the fossils lived in that area or whether they have
been brought in by currents from elsewhere. A **life
assemblage** is a group of fossils which are all thought to
have lived together. Burrowers are often preserved where
they lived and coral reefs often contain a great variety of
animals which lived together. A **death assemblage** is one
where the fossil remains have all been brought together
by water movement. They are often all of about the same
size and may show signs of abrasion. Often death
assemblages contain fossils from several living
environments.

6.2.5 NAMING AND GROUPING FOSSILS

To build up information about past environments, fossils
are first described and classified; then the relationships
with other fossils are examined. Since fossils relate closely

to biology, palaeontologists use the same classification system as biologists. The organisms are sorted into groups on the basis of their characteristics such as whether they have backbones, shells, legs, muscle scars, hair, claws, leaves etc.

Modern organisms are divided into at least five major **kingdoms**, shown in Appendix 4. Four of these represent multicellular life: animals, green plants, multicellular algae and the fungi. The fifth contains unicellular life, the **protistans** and unicellular algae. All of these are **eukaryotes**, that is they contain cells with a discrete nucleus and a complex internal structure. A further group is the **prokaryotes**. These are simpler, smaller, single-celled organisms including 'bacteria' (single-celled organisms without a discrete nucleus) and blue-green bacteria (cyanobacteria) formerly called blue-green algae. Some biologists consider this last group embraces two or three further kingdoms, but as these creatures do not feature strongly in the fossil record, we will consider all unicellular organisms as one kingdom.

Each kingdom is subdivided into major groups called **phyla** (singular 'phylum'). The phyla are further divided into progressively smaller units: **classes**, **orders**, **families**, **genera**, and **species**, each nestling within the other as shown in Figure 6.4.

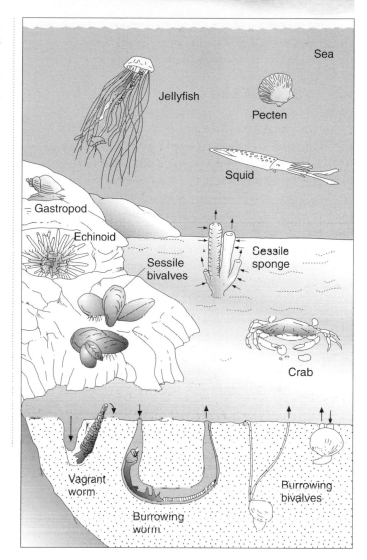

Figure 6.3 *The life habits of some marine invertebrates. Living on the sediment surface (epifauna) some animals are fixed in place (sessile), such as bivalves, but others move around (are vagrant) such as crabs, sponges, gastropods and echinoids. Those living in the sediment (infauna) include vagrant and burrowing worms, and shallow and deep burrowing bivalves. In the seawater, some animals drift with currents (pelagic) e.g. planktonic jellyfish, and some are active swimmers (nektonic), such as squid (a cephalopod) and bivalves (e.g. Pecten)*

Figure 6.4 *The classification of humans (Homo sapiens) and a cockle*

Division	Classification of humans			Classification of cockles	
	Name	Key characteristics (sometimes the 'translation' of the word in column 2)		Name	Characteristics
Kingdom	Animalia	animal		Animalia	animal
Phylum	Chordata	possessing nerve cord down the back		Mollusca	soft bodies and hard shell
sub phylum	Vertebrata	nerve cord surrounded by a bony spine			
Class	Mammalia	nurse their young; often have hair		Bivalvia	two valves
subclass				Heterodonta	
Order	Primates	have nails, not claws		Veneroida	
sub order	Anthropoidea	have an opposable thumb; no tail			
Family	Hominidae	upright walk			
Genus	*Homo*	(hu)man		*Cerastoderma*	cockle
species	*sapiens*	sensible		*edule*	

Note: By convention, the genus and species are written in italics (or in handwriting they are underlined) and the genus name has a capital letter, while the species name begins with a small letter.

Humans belong to the kingdom Animalia, the phylum chordata, the class Mammalia etc. – we are animals, chordates, vertebrates, mammals, primates, anthropoids and hominids that are called *Homo sapiens*. All organisms, both living and fossil, are named in this way; all have two parts to their final name – the genus name and the species name.

Our species is *Homo sapiens* and there are two types of fossil humans with skeletons which are only slightly different from ours. These are assigned to different species: *Homo erectus* and *Homo habilis*. However, because of Lucy's height, relative arm length and very different head shape, she is allotted to a different genus, *Australopithecus,* but she belongs to the same family, the Hominidae. The same sorts of argument are used for deciding the classification of all fossils, though for some, such as the invertebrate bivalve related to the modern cockle, the most practicable level of classification is the superfamily.

The phylum Chordata contains all those fossils which have backbones: fish, amphibians, reptiles including dinosaurs, and mammals. For some people these are regarded as the most interesting fossils but are very rarely found. The fossils you are most likely to find are those without backbones: these belong to several different phyla but are collectively referred to as **invertebrates**. They include all the shell fossils, corals, all the crawling animals like trilobites and worms, and all microscopic animals.

The broad classification of all major organisms is shown in Appendix 4.

6.2.6 PROBLEMS OF CLASSIFYING FOSSILS

It is more difficult to classify fossils than living organisms – but why should this be? When animals die, the soft tissues usually rot and only the hard parts, that is the shell or skeleton, remain to become fossils. Fossils are fitted into the classification on the basis of the similarity of their remains to those of modern animals. Even the interpretation of a fossil's internal organs is often done through comparison with modern life. Since palaeontologists usually only have hard parts to study, there may be controversy as to where fossils fit into the biological classification, as many different types may have visually similar hard parts.

The fundamental unit of biological classification is the species. In biological terms, all members of a species must be able to interbreed and produce fertile offspring, but classification may be done using, for example, bird song

or behaviour. These features do not fossilise well, so we have to use different criteria for defining fossil species.

There are other problems when assigning fossils to groups.

Male and female individuals may look sufficiently different, for example in size, to be identified as different species (Figure 6.5a). This is known as **sexual dimorphism**. Also, juveniles may look different (in modern species, for example, tadpoles look different from adult frogs) and can be misidentified. Most arthropods (shelled animals) discard their shells periodically in order to grow, and may change their form gradually during this process, as the trilobites in Figure 6.5b show.

Disconnected parts, for example of large plants, may be given different names (called **form species**). This happened with the Carboniferous tree *Lepidodendron*, where the root systems (*Stigmaria*) were considered different from the stem (*Lepidodendron*) and the reproductive bodies (*Lepistrobus*) until all were found fossilised together (Figure 6.5c).

Environmental factors can influence and affect the size and shape of creatures, so that the same type of animal in a slightly different habitat may be identified as a different species. The depth of water and turbulence have been found to affect the form taken by coral such that, when fossilised, these might be mistaken for separate species.

6.3 Snapshots from the past

We can get a 'feel' for how life on Earth has changed and the range of different types of animals to be found at different stages of geological time by looking at the types of organisms found in marine environments at those times. But first, a few words to introduce geological timescales.

6.3.1 THE GEOLOGICAL COLUMN: AN INDISPENSABLE FRAMEWORK

As the science of geology developed, geologists needed a widely accepted framework for relating geological sequences from different times to each other. The framework devised is called the standard geological column shown in Appendix 7. Dates in millions of years (Ma) have also been added relatively recently and the methods used to determine dates in years will be explained in Chapter 11.

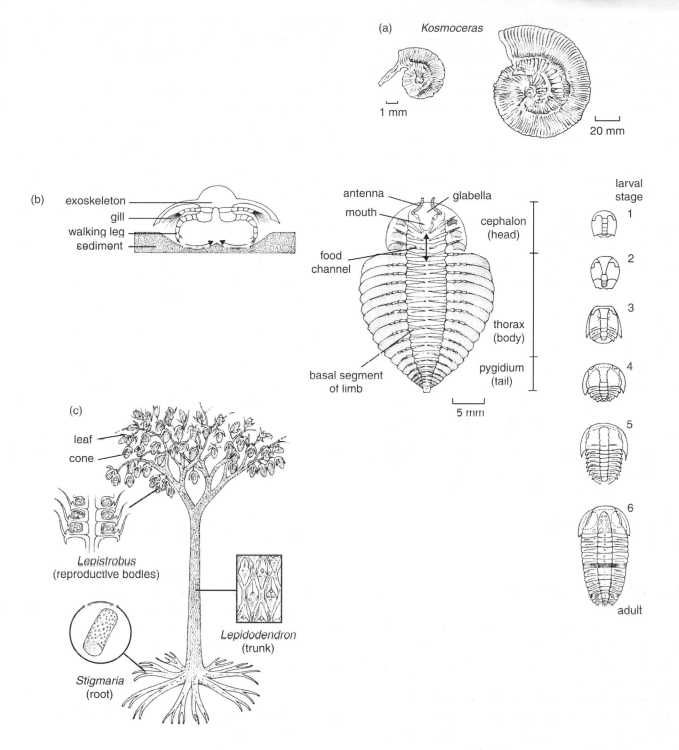

Figure 6.5 *Fossils showing dimorphism, developmental series and form species: (a) The Jurassic ammonite genus Kosmoceras, consisting of a large and a small form. These were originally identified as different species. It is still unclear whether the larger is male, or female; (b) The form of a Cambrian trilobite and the developmental series of moults of the Cambrian trilobite, Sao hirsuta, from the earliest larval stage (smallest) to full adult (largest); (c) Carboniferous tree Lepidodendron, showing the roots (Stigmoria), trunk (Lepidodendron) and reproductive bodies (Lepistrobus) which were named separately*

Figure 6.6 *Silurian organisms: (a) Crinoid Gissocrinus goniodactylus. Crinoids are plant-like animals usually sessile (fixed in position). In life the skeleton was covered by flesh and when the animal died the flesh usually rotted and the calcite skeleton broke into many disc or rod-like segments; (b) Brachiopod. Brachiopods show bilateral symmetry, where the plane of symmetry cuts through the two valves with each half of the valve being a mirror image of the other; (c) Graptolite. Graptolites changed their form through a two-branched 'tuning fork' in the Ordovician (left of Figure), 'cups' on both sides near the Ordovician–Silurian boundary (centre) and single branched varieties through the Silurian into the Devonian (right of Figure)*

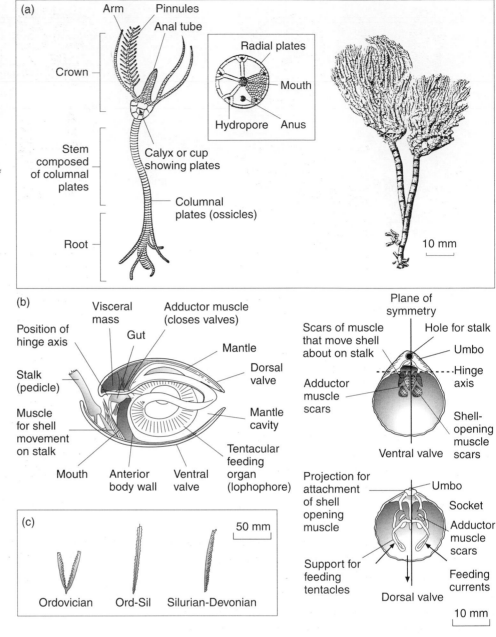

Most of the geological column is divided into three major units of time, known as **Eras**. These are subdivided into **Periods**, which are the usual way of referring to age. So, the Jurassic ammonite shown in Figure 6.5a must have lived during the Jurassic Period, 208 to 145 Ma ago. At first sight, the names appear a little daunting, but since they form the dating framework used by all geologists it is worth learning them and the order in which they occur. If you find it hard to learn the actual names, try making up a mnemonic as an aid, e.g. "**P**rehistoric **C**amels **O**rdinarily **S**it **D**own . . .".

6.3.2 SILURIAN SEAS – THE ENGLISH MIDLANDS

Around 420 Ma ago, the West Midlands area that now includes such fossil localities as Wenlock Edge and Dudley were warm shallow seas. Several different types of organisms including corals and algae built small reef-like structures on the sea floor. The main coral types were tabulate corals, dominated by series of horizontal 'floors' called tabulae. Crinoids or sea lilies also lived in the reef. These animals looked like plants, with roots and a head, but the head was made of tentacles that could trap prey. The most common shellfish in the reef were brachiopods animals with two shells – one larger than the other – that lived in several different areas of the reef, like bivalves do today. The trilobites that crawled and swam around the reefs had already had a long and successful geological

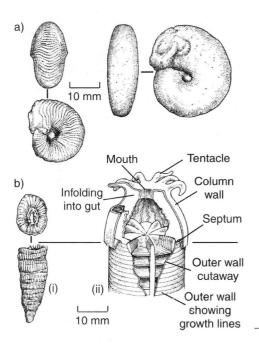

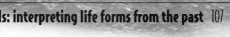

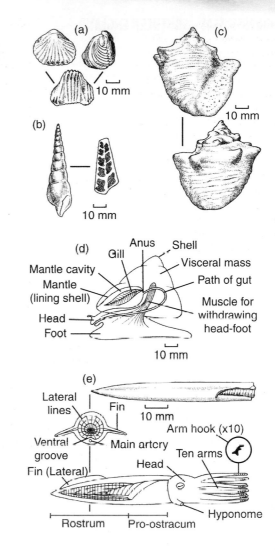

Figure 6.7 (a) arboniferous goniatites, an early form of ammonite. (b) Carboniferous coral, a rugose or solitary coral, and the anatomy of a coral. The animal's soft parts are in the top section and are usually not preserved

Figure 6.8 Jurassic animals: (a) Jurassic brachiopod Tetrarhynchia tetraedra; (b) Jurassic gastropods Melanioptyxis altararis with longitudinal section through; (c) Purpuroidea morissea; (d) The morphology of a gastropod; (e) Belemnite Cylindroteuthis puzosiana (×0.5) and the morphology of a belemnite, a cephalopod

history spanning more than 150 Ma (Figure 6.5b). Graptolites must also have lived in the area, but they are not found commonly in shallow sea deposits because they were very fragile and often broken up after death. They, too, already had a long history. Earlier times were dominated by the four- and two-branched graptolite forms, while the graptolite population of Silurian seas was dominated by the single-branched type (Figure 6.6c). Swimming shelled cephalopods related to the living *Nautilus* (Figure 6.2a) also lived in the area, some with curved shells and others with straight ice-cream-cone like shells. Figure 6.6 shows fossil types common at the time and C6.1 is a reconstruction of a fossil shallow-sea community.

6.3.3 CARBONIFEROUS SEAS AND MARGINS IN BRITAIN

Some 70 Ma later, around 350 Ma ago in early Carboniferous times, several parts of Britain still had reef-dominated shallow seas, and an excellent example is found in the Peak District. The reefs still contained crinoids, brachiopods and corals, but the predominant corals were now rugose corals, characterised by radiating vertical partitions called septa (Figure 6.7b). Trilobites had dwindled and graptolites become extinct. Relatives of the cephalopod *Nautilus* still swam in the area, but a new group called the ammonoids, were more common

(Figure 6.7). All ammonoids had spiral catherine wheel-like shells divided into a series of chambers by partitions. The early ammonoids found at this time were called goniatites and had nearly straight partitions that formed a simple pattern where they met the outer shell. The pattern is called a **suture line** and is used to distinguish different ammonoid types (Figure 6.2c). Bivalves were more common. Figure C6.2 shows a reconstruction of a Carboniferous shallow sea community.

Elsewhere in Britain, lush tropical vegetation on land (Figure C6.5) supported various invertebrates, and the first reptiles. Meanwhile, in what is now the southern hemisphere, Australia and South Africa were experiencing a period of glaciation!

6.3.4   JURASSIC SEAS – SOUTHERN ENGLAND

The Jurassic period was between around 208 and 145 Ma ago. Good examples of the sediments and fossils deposited at that time are found in the Dorset area of southern England. Both tabulate and rugose corals had become extinct and had been succeeded by the type of coral found today, scleractinian corals. Different forms of brachiopod were found and bivalves were more common (Figure 6.8). Huge numbers of cephalopods swam near the surface of the sea; the most common were the ammonites. A wide range of different ammonite types is found and they sometimes littered the sea floor in their thousands. Another common type of cephalopod was the belemnite, which had hard parts that were bullet-shaped (Figure 6.8).

Meanwhile, at the shoreline, dinosaurs, amphibians and other creatures would feed and, overhead, there were flying reptiles (pterosaurs). An artist's impression of a Jurassic shallow sea is shown in Figure C6.3.

6.3.5   CRETACEOUS SEAS – SOUTH-EASTERN ENGLAND

The Cretaceous followed the Jurassic, and began about 140 Ma ago. The sea was warm but was deeper and muddier than in the Jurassic. One animal that became much more common was the irregular echinoderm *Micraster*. The evolution of this burrowing sea urchin is described in some detail in section 6.4.4. Brachiopods and bivalves and a range of different types of ammonite are found, although the latter, with many other species, were to become extinct at the end of the Cretaceous. Typical fossils of these Cretaceous seas are shown in Figure 6.9 and a colour reconstruction in Figure C6.4.

6.4   Preservation – how organisms can become fossilised

What are the chances of the animals and plants in the reconstructions becoming fossils? How do plants and animals become changed into fossils?

There are some 250 000 species of fossil plants and animals known but this compares with the more than 14 000 000 species of plants and animals known to be alive on Earth today. We will never know the number of species that have ever lived, including those being discovered now and those from the geological past, but it must be many tens, possibly hundreds of millions. We can calculate that the sample of 250 000 fossil species is just 1.8

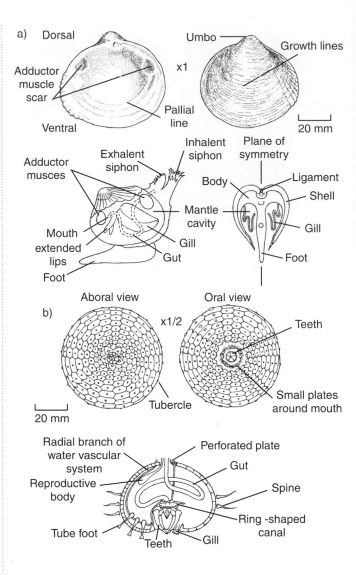

Figure 6.9 *Cretaceous marine animals: (a) Bivalve, Protocardia hillana and the anatomy of a burrowing bivalve. The plane of symmetry lies between the two valves, as shown. The valves are connected by a ligament. These animals moved by contracting the adductor muscles to close the valves and extend the foot. The siphon was extended to draw in water and food particles. The pallial line marks the innermost of the calcareous layers of the shell.*
(b) Echinoid anatomy. Because of their calcite exoskeleton, echinoderms are abundant in the fossil record. To move, the echinoid first extends its tube feet, which have suction cups at the ends. It is also supported by spines. Some species lived on the surface, but others burrowed into the sediment

per cent of the number of species alive today. It is likely to be less than 0.25 per cent of all species that have ever lived. One palaeontologist put it this way: 'to a first approximation, all species are extinct'. A species may survive for a few million years, but it is unusual for a species to survive for more than 30 Ma. This means that not only is the fossil record very poor and patchy, it is also highly biased towards those organisms most likely to be preserved. Those least likely to be preserved probably never have been. So, what factors increase the likelihood

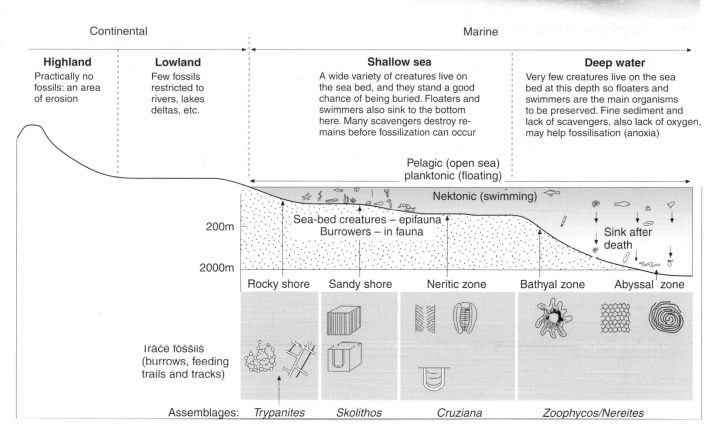

Figure 6.10 *Environments and the likelihood of preservation in each*

of fossilisation? What characteristics increase preservation potential?

6.4.1 PRESERVATION POTENTIAL

The soft parts (the soft internal organs, that is all except the shell, bones and teeth) of animals are only preserved under very exceptional conditions because they usually rot away or are eaten by scavengers after death. Even where there is no oxygen (anaerobic conditions), bacteria destroy soft tissues. The hard parts, such as shells or bones, are most likely to be preserved if they are buried quickly. In the sea, a dead animal may be covered rapidly with sediment and thus have a good chance of fossilisation. Land areas are not usually sites of deposition but of erosion, so the chances of preservation are poor; the shell or bones of the dead animal will remain on the surface and will weather away, be broken, scattered or eaten by scavengers. Lucy's skeleton was not complete and it is likely that animals had removed some of the bones before they became buried by sediment.

One of the environments where animals are most commonly preserved is in soft sediment at the bottom of lakes or on the sea bed, especially where the water contains little or no oxygen. Animals which swim or float in the upper oxygenated water sink to the bottom after they have died. If there are no scavengers to eat or scatter the remains, no water movement to cause abrasion or breakage, no oxygen to cause rapid decay but sediment to cover them, they are likely to be fossilised. Despite this, the most fossiliferous rocks are those deposited in environments where there is lots of life and where there is a reasonable chance of preservation, that is, in shallow warm seas. These are above the carbonate compensation depth at which calcite begins to dissolve. Figure 6.10 shows different environments and the likelihood of preservation in each.

The chances of preservation are also affected by the type of material making up the hard parts. In some rocks of Jurassic age (208–145 Ma) it is possible to find the complete shells of brachiopods and oysters but only hollows where the shells of gastropods and burrowing bivalves had been. This is because the brachiopods and oysters had shells made of calcite, the stable variety of calcium carbonate, whereas the gastropods and burrowing bivalves had shells made from aragonite, a less stable form of calcium carbonate, which is more easily dissolved.

The type of sediment that animals are buried in also affects their chances of preservation as fossils. Sandstones are permeable and tend to have acidic waters percolating through them which will dissolve the shells. In clays and limestones, the water is not acid and the shells are less likely to be dissolved. The hard parts of animals rarely remain unchanged; they are chemically altered by percolating waters or by the heating resulting from burial.

All these considerations are put together as the 'preservation potential' of an organism. Those that had hard parts made of stable material, that lived in quiet environments in large numbers where burial in fine sediment was likely, have high preservation potential and

Figure 6.11 *The major fossilisation processes*

Group of processes	Process and result	Frequency
Preservation with little alteration	freezing; animal becomes deep frozen in ice	very unusual
	mummification; animal dries out in arid areas	very unusual
	organism is preserved in anaerobic peat bog	very unusual, apart from microscopic spores and pollen
	body falls into anaerobic tar pit and becomes sealed in	very unusual
	animal becomes sealed into sticky pine tree resin that becomes hard amber	very unusual
	burial of calcite ($CaCO_3$) remains in fine-grained sediments; preserves hard parts of many invertebrates and Palaeozoic corals	common
	burial of aragonite ($CaCO_3$) remains in fine-grained sediments; preserves hard parts of molluscs and scleractinian corals	common, after Mesozoic
	burial of calcium phosphate ($CaPO_4$) remains in fine-grained sediments; preserves brachiopod hard parts and vertebrate bones and teeth	fairly common
	burial of silica (SiO_2 – in its microcrystalline form) remains in fine-grained sediments; preserves sponge and some microfossil hard parts	fairly common, after Cenozoic
Altered in fossilisation	carbonisation (anaerobic environments); organic soft parts become preserved as carbon films	very unusual
	carbonisation; heat due to deep burial, changes plant cellulose to a film of carbon; chitin skeletons of arthropods and graptolites altered to carbon	fairly rare
	permineralisation – minerals deposited in pore spaces of skeleton (also called petrification); porous skeletons become solid mineral (often $CaCO_3$, rarely SiO_2, glauconite, iron compounds, etc.)	fairly rare
	recrystallisation; porous skeletons usually become solid	fairly rare
	replacement; aragonite replaced by its more stable polymorph calcite; other materials replaced by different minerals e.g. calcite by iron pyrites, calcite by silica, dolomite, etc.	very common
Preservation as moulds or casts	mould formation; depressions left by soft parts or when hard parts e.g. shells, are dissolved away; moulds of outsides of shells are called external moulds, of insides of shells, are internal moulds	common
	cast formation; casts tend to stick out of the rock when the mould is removed; casts may retain great detail of the outer surface of the specimen, but all internal detail is lost	fairly common
Traces of animal activities	tracks and trails are preserved as moulds or casts preserving details of how the animal moved	trails common, tracks rare
	burrows in which soft or hard bodied organisms lived are preserved; in soft sediment they deform layers	fairly common
	coprolites (fossilised faeces); details of the diet and structure of the gut may be preserved	uncommon
	boring is into hard rock and cuts through layers; animals bore to make holes in which to live or during predation; tooth marks indicate predation	uncommon

are frequently found as fossils. On the other hand, those that had no hard parts and lived in active environments have low preservation potential so they are rarely found as fossils.

6.4.2 FOSSILISATION PROCESSES

The major processes of fossilisation are shown in Figure 6.11. Those in which the soft parts are well preserved are very uncommon, whereas hard parts are preserved in a wide range of fossil types.

6.4.3 EXCEPTIONAL PRESERVATION

Occasionally, fossils may be found in a state of 'exceptional preservation', that is, a great deal of detail can be seen. This is usually because the fossilisation process was fast: for example imagine a fly being trapped in resin, or an animal being engulfed in a tar pit. When many different animals covering a larger area are found,

these sites are called **lagerstätten** and are very rare; only 59 examples have so far been discovered worldwide, for the whole of geological time since the Cambrian (545 Ma). They are, however, very important, because in these circumstances the form of soft tissue is often preserved. This means that internal organs and the outline of whole organisms without hard parts, such as a jellyfish, can be seen.

One of the most famous localities is the Burgess Shale, a dark-coloured, fine-grained Cambrian deposit, now high in the Rocky Mountains of Canada, but originally a deep marine deposit. It has all the hallmarks of exceptional preservation: rapid burial, no oxygen, no scavengers or burrowing organisms, and a chemical environment in which minerals were able to grow and replace the soft tissues as they decayed. The result is that a huge number of weird and wonderful creatures have now been found, most with no hard parts and with their soft organs beautifully preserved. Many of these are unlike any organisms alive today or known from the geological record. Other creatures are very early examples of animals that later evolved to play an important part in life on

Figure 6.12 *Fossils from the Burgess Shale. Arthropods with hard exoskeletons and paired legs crawled on the surface. These were the ancestors of animals such as trilobites. Other sessile animals such as sponges were suspension feeders. Many soft-bodied creatures such as burrowing and creeping worms have also been preserved*

Earth. Without the Burgess Shale and its fauna (Figure 6.12), we would have no idea of the diversity of life in middle Cambrian seas.

Other sites producing fossils with exceptional preservation are the Santana Formation (Cretaceous) in Brazil and the Green River Formation (Eocene) in Wyoming, USA. The pale cream coloured limestones contain, in particular, fishes with the scales intact. Preservation was so fast in the Santana Formation that the remains of muscle fibres can be seen. Some horizons contain so many dead animals that they have been interpreted as having been caused by periodic catastrophic changes in water conditions causing mass mortality.

In Southern Germany, the Solnhofen limestone, of Jurassic age (208–145 Ma), is a lagerstätten, from which many large and varied fossils have been found since the 1850s. The limestone was used to make plates for printing, hence its name the Lithographic Limestone. One quarry has produced three of only eight known examples of *Archaeopteryx*. This animal has the first identified feathers, so is interpreted as the ancestor of birds and is thought to have lived in shrubs on islands in the Solnhofen lagoon (most of the other Solnhofen fossils are marine). Birds with feathers have also been identified from the Santana Formation, which is younger, but both fossil assemblages existed before the extinction of the dinosaurs.

6.5 The origin and evolution of life

How did life begin? How has life evolved and what causes extinction? These are questions that have created heated debate that continues among palaeontologists and biologists.

6.5.1 HOW IT ALL BEGAN

There are many millions of different species living today but all of them have the same basic organic chemical building blocks. Elephants, insects, plants, fungi and bacteria are all made of two kinds of large molecules, proteins and nucleic acids. These are common to all forms of life, so a starting point was to assume that they were also present in the earliest forms of life, and experiments were devised to try to create these organic molecules from inorganic ones.

Experiments by **Miller** and **Urey** in the 1950s showed that electric sparks and ultraviolet (u.v.) light passed through a mixture of inorganic gases such as methane CH_4, ammonia NH_3 and water H_2O, produce a variety of more complex organic molecules including amino acids and sugars. The idea was that if these gases with their organic molecules are then condensed and heated, they can join together producing cell-like organic structures. Other experiments used different gases and also produced amino acids. However, all these investigations assumed that the atmosphere contained hydrogen, whereas modern thought is that, because of its low relative atomic mass, it escaped from Earth's gravity and was lost to space.

The Earth's early atmosphere, formed by volcanic emissions, is thought to have been a mixture of carbon dioxide, CO_2, nitrogen N_2, and sulphur dioxide SO_2, with some water H_2O, and a deficiency of gaseous oxygen. This would be the composition from an early, outgassing Earth. Methane CH_4, and ammonia NH_3, may have been present, but the amounts and importance of these are uncertain.

Examination of meteorites showed that they contained organic molecules that could have been a catalyst for life, early in Earth's history. However, just because experiments and observations show that something *can* happen doesn't prove that it *has* happened that way, and there is a huge gulf between the creation of organic molecules and the formation of a living cell with an enclosing cell membrane which is capable of reproduction.

Life may have existed before 4100 Ma, but frequent bombardment from space by meteorites and the violence of volcanism would have made it difficult to maintain continuously. Indeed, it is possible that life may have begun several times on the young Earth. In recent experiments clay particles exposed to u.v. radiation in a CO_2 atmosphere have catalysed the formation of complex organic molecules, which would then fall into the water beneath. Modern ideas centre on early life (before 2.2×10^3 Ma) existing in water beneath a reducing (oxygen-free) atmosphere. The organisms metabolised ('ate') hydrogen from water, and iron, living totally without oxygen. Some sulphur-eating (and methane-eating) bacteria are heat-loving, living at temperatures far in excess of 100 °C. This has given support to the idea that the 'black smoker' sites at constructive plate margins provide all the ingredients for early life. Other workers have suggested life began in hot, sulphur-rich pools near volcanoes or at hydrothermal sites in shallow seas.

The earliest forms of life must have been complex molecules which had the ability to grow and subdivide. These early organisms were single cells with no organisation of the materials within the cell, or recognisable nucleus, called prokaryotes. Geologists looking at rocks from 3×10^3 Ma ago recognised structures that were similar to those made by modern micro-organisms, blue-green bacteria. These are single-celled organisms with no clear nucleus, that reproduce by simple division. The formations they produced are mounds of finely layered material that resemble algal mats found in shallow water. They have modern counterparts called **stromatolites**. One of the important discoveries was that these organisms were photosynthesisers, that is they 'fed' on CO_2 and hydrogen from water. They gave out oxygen as a 'waste product' and after some while it began to accumulate slowly in the atmosphere.

Ultraviolet light can break the bonds of the O_2 molecule into individual atoms that can combine with other O_2 molecules to form O_3, **ozone**. Ozone then began to build up in a layer in the outer atmosphere and this absorbed incoming u.v. light and protected surface life from this cell-damaging radiation. Before the free oxygen built up to one to three per cent, there would have been insufficient ozone for the layer to be protective. Modern blue-green bacteria are the most resistant of all organisms to damage by u.v. radiation. Their ancient counterparts would have relied on this resistance to survive, and it appears that they were the most common life form for 2000 Ma.

The development of a nucleus that contained the genetic material was a further step forward, forming larger, more complex organisms called eukaryotes. It has been suggested by **Lynn Margulis**, a biologist/geologist, that these organisms developed as a symbiosis (living together) of two bacteria, one providing the nucleus and a living space within the cell wall for others. This is because some organelles (subcellular functioning units) called chloroplasts resemble the simple photosynthesising bacteria. This step forward allowed cells to become far larger, more complex and able to produce energy in the chloroplasts.

The best described Precambrian fossils are the **Ediacaran fauna** from the Flinders Range in Australia. They are all soft-bodied animals, similar to jellyfish, soft corals and sea pens; however tracks, trails and burrows indicate that there may have also been worms similar to modern forms and one animal had developed a gut system. Similar fauna, of the same age or earlier, have recently been discovered in South Africa, China and Russia.

When atmospheric oxygen passed the 1 per cent of present level it became possible for organisms to respire (oxidise substances to provide energy) **aerobically** and this lead to more complex organisms than had been possible through simple anaerobic respiration. However, the multicellular organisms did not replace the single-celled ones, which remain at the bottom of all food chains, often acting as decomposers. Although the first steps towards life took thousands of millions of years, the evolution from eukaryotes to all modern invertebrate phyla took only 100 million years and culminated during the Cambrian Period, in the 'Cambrian explosion'. Figure 6.13 shows the main groups of plants and animals from the Cambrian to the present. The early development of life is shown in Appendix 7.

6.5.2 DEVELOPMENT OVER TIME: EVOLUTION

Many systems evolve: galaxies, languages, patterns of transport. **Biological evolution** is the process in which changes to an organism's characteristics are passed on from parent to offspring.

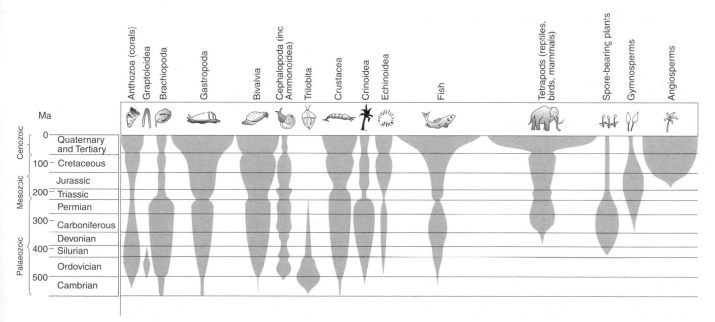

Figure 6.13 *The main groups of fossils and plants. These, however, represent only part of the biota as most life is microscopic and not classified on this diagram*

Darwin's name is closely connected with the development of the theory of evolution. His evidence was based largely on the study of plants and animals alive at the time; he used some fossils but there were no sequences of fossils available that could illustrate the theory of evolution in detail. Nowadays, some of the best evidence for evolution comes from very detailed study of the changes in fossils over time, for example trilobites during the Cambrian Period, or ammonites during the Jurassic Period.

6.5.3 THEORIES OF EVOLUTION

On the basis of the available evidence, the originators of evolutionary theory, **Charles Darwin** and **Russell Wallace**, believed that gradual change was how all evolution took place, one species slowly changing into another form, by natural selection. This is called **phyletic gradualism**. However, it now seems that this phyletic gradualism is very uncommon and cannot account for the huge number of species that have evolved within geological timescales. Usually a species appears suddenly in the fossil record. It was originally thought that these 'sudden appearances' happened because the intervening layers of sediment between were not preserved and so the 'missing links' in the fossil sequence were not preserved either.

A more recent idea, by among others **Stephen Jay Gould**, is called **punctuated equilibrium**. Here it is thought that a group of interbreeding animals stays the same for a length of time (called **stasis**). Meanwhile near the edge of the region in which the species is found, e.g. on an island or other isolated area, a change takes place among a small group of the animals and a new species evolves. This is more successful than the original species, so that when the two species come into contact again, the new one quickly takes over the living environment (the ecological niche) of the other and becomes established. This happens almost instantly in geological time.

Modern examples similar to punctuated equilibrium are common. For example, the grey squirrel from North America was introduced into Britain and except in Northern Britain has now almost wiped out the original red squirrel population. It does this not by killing the red squirrels, but by more effectively competing for food and occupying their niche. This change has taken place within tens of years, much too short a time interval to be seen in the geological record.

More recently, ideas have centred on environmental pressures and the interactions between life and the environment as factors in evolution; species are affected

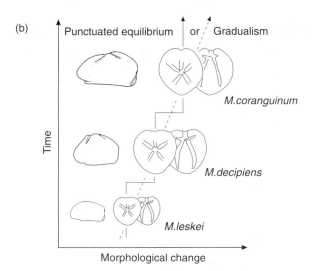

Figure 6.14(b) *Patterns of evolution in three species of Cretaceous echinoderm, Micraster. Note that through time the test gets larger, broader and taller, the anterior groove deepens and the mouth moves forward. Gradualism is interpreted by the dotted line and punctuated equilibrium by the stepped solid line*

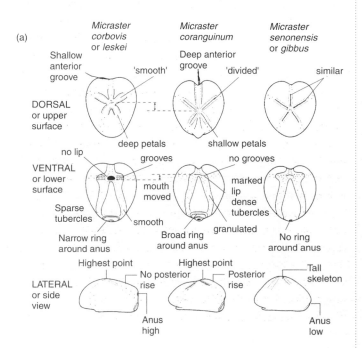

Figure 6.14(a) *Views of three species of Cretaceous echinoderm, Micraster*

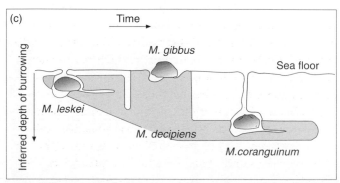

Figure 6.14(c) *An interpretation of the evolution of Micraster in terms of changing burrowing depth. Micraster leskei is thought to be a shallower burrower and Micraster coranguinum, a deep burrower with Micraster decipiens as an intermediate form*

by predation and the success of competitors. One idea was that as the environment changed, for example, the sea becoming warmer, species had to evolve in order to survive, or move to more suitable conditions (called habitat tracking), where the sea was less warm. This seems a logical line of reasoning. However, close examination of fossil evidence indicates that greatest change of form occurs when environments are constant. So modern thinking is that change takes place when species 'take risks' to gain advantage during a period of environmental stability.

A study was published in 1987, of the tail (pygidium) shape of 15 000 Cambrian trilobites representing 3 Ma, interpreted by its author as phyletic gradualism. However, when the data were studied by Gould, he and his co-workers interpreted the gradual change as nothing much happening over the 3 million years i.e. stasis! What experts agreed was the need to debate how the evolutionary process works in nature; it can be argued that it is much more complicated than simple natural selection at organism level, as some biologists believe.

6.5.4 EVOLUTION OF *MICRASTER* AND *GRYPHAEA*: MICROEVOLUTION

When punctuated equilibrium was proposed in the 1970s, much of the evidence for gradual evolution was re-examined. One of the best known examples previously given as evidence for gradual evolution was the change in form of the sea urchin *Micraster*. In one study, hundreds of these fossils were collected from the Chalk and the position in the sequence of strata noted. The results are shown in Figure 6.14b which shows how the test (shell) shape changed over time. The dotted line on the diagram shows the original interpretation as gradual evolution. However, careful collecting of specimens from different sites that represent the times between the different species seems to show that the new species appeared suddenly, indicated by the solid line, supporting punctuated equilibrium. Studies of the form and mode of life of modern heart-urchins resulted in the interpretation of the shape of fossil *Micraster* with burrowing depth, as shown in Figure 6.14c. The changes are thought to be adaptations as, through time, *Micraster* began to burrow to a greater depth. Several ideas might explain this: that the sediment type changed or a new food source was available, or it was to escape predators such as burrowing gastropods. It appears that gradual change in shape occurred, but periodically there were abrupt changes that can be interpreted as punctuational.

A more complex picture has recently appeared when the evolution of the bivalve *Gryphaea*, was re-examined. It

has been suggested that earlier interpretations were not valid because there had been no biologically appropriate standard used, so comparisons were being made of animals at different stages of development. An increase in shell size had been interpreted as gradual change (phyletic gradualism). However, this is now thought to be because the animals higher in the succession grew quicker and lived longer. Other features such as the thinning of the shell and changes in its coiling, formerly interpreted as increasing stepwise (punctuated equilibrium) also have to be re-examined, as older specimens would be expected to show more coiling. One study indicates that while size increased with time, coiling was little changed. *Gryphaea* show periods of stasis in shape, and also of continuous evolution. A few years ago, a book such as this would have presented a simple story for the evolution of *Gryphaea*, but reality and nature are rarely simple and the evolution of this bivalve fits neither the punctuated equilibrium nor the phyletic gradualism models and is a topic of current research.

6.5.5 EVOLUTION OF THE HORSE: MACROEVOLUTION

Thousands of fossil horse remains have been found, mostly in North America, and their overall evolution over the past 50 million years is clear. The earliest horses were the size of a sheepdog, had four toes, lived in the forest and ate the leaves of bushes. As North America became warmer and drier, the forest was replaced by savannah grassland and the horse had to adapt to survive, or migrate. It changed from a typical small forest animal to a large grassland beast, shown schematically in Figure 6.15. One key adaptation was an increase in leg size which allowed the animal to run faster, to escape from predators. The teeth and jaw also changed to allow the horse to deal with the tough grasses that developed during the Miocene (50 Ma ago). The teeth developed ridges, and became longer and more complex. The horse has been evolving for the last 50 million years from the early horses about 25 cm in height to the horses of today, on average 1.5 m high. Since this time span represents about 15 million generations you can calculate the average increase in height per generation.

The evolution of the horse is an excellent example of how changes in the environment led to evolutionary change. However, it was not simple linear change, since at times many species of horse existed together, many types evolved only to become extinct, including in their original home, North America. Overall, however, there was a net increase in size and a decrease in the number of toes.

6.5.6 CONVERGENT EVOLUTION

When animals from different groups come to live in the same habitat they often evolve to look alike. This is **convergent evolution**. Bats, birds and the flying reptile *Pterodactyl* all developed forelimbs into wings for flying; but they had major differences and only birds have feathers. Whales which are mammals, *Ichthyosaurs* which were marine reptiles and sharks all have similar body forms due to adoption of a similar way of life. Similarly, brachiopods and bivalves have exhibited many examples of convergence in the past but probably the most bizarre was when members of both these groups lived in coral reefs and grew to look like large solitary corals to avoid predators.

6.5.7 EVOLUTION OF PLANTS

Most of our discussion of fossils has been about animals, and particularly marine animals. However, the contribution of land plants to life on Earth cannot be overlooked; plants use carbon dioxide to create carbohydrates for energy, incorporating carbon into their cell walls and giving out oxygen. Before plants evolved the continents were barren, except, perhaps at margins of seas and rivers. Without plants there could be no land animals such as Lucy. Also, plants such as trees live far longer than marine animals and produce large, multi-layered communities. The evolution of life on to land was one of the most significant steps in the evolution of life on Earth.

Bacterial mats and fungi may have existed at the water's edge of rivers and lakes in the late Precambrian. The major late colonisation of the land by green plants began in the Silurian, from 410 Ma. The first plants were similar to mosses and liverworts, without true roots or a rigid cell structure. Land plants needed to develop a support structure to overcome the effects of gravity, which aquatic plants do not need, and a waxy coat to protect the plant from drying out. The first plants evolved close to the ground where the air is relatively still. However, those that were taller had advantages for scattering their spores in the moving currents of air. So, strengthened cell walls developed in the stem that allowed the plant to grow taller and a valve (vascular) system of plumbing moved water up the stem and carbohydrate down to the body. Also, plants needed small

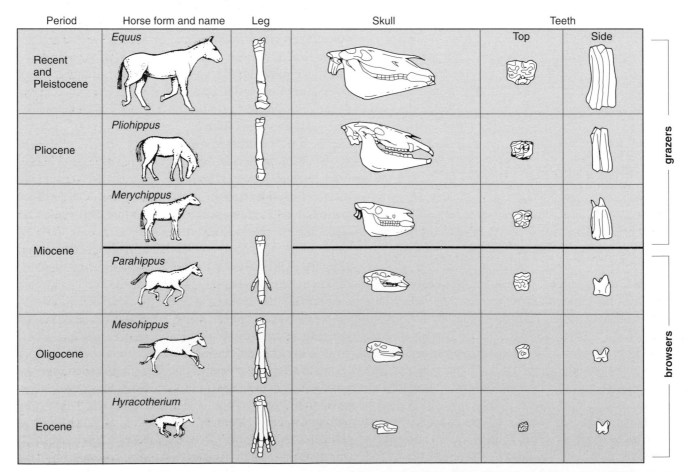

Figure 6.15 *Evolution of the horse. The skulls and teeth are drawn to scale and the legs to a standard length. The changes in the skull and teeth are related to the change from forest browsing to grassland grazing*

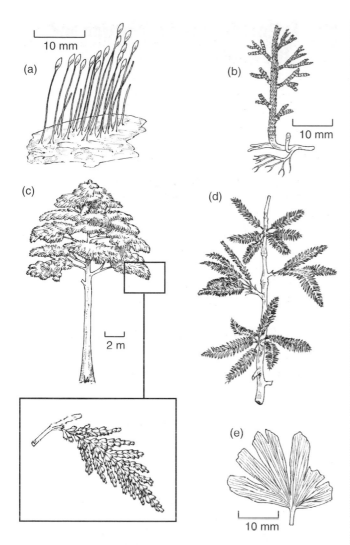

Figure 6.16 *(a) An early Devonian plant (about 2 cm tall) Sporogenites exuberons. The spores are contained in the sac on the top of the stem. The Figure is a reconstruction of the plant from fossil remains. (b) Asteroxylon mackei, Devonian, about 30 cm tall. An outgrowth from the stem functioned as a small leaf. This plant grew by extending the rhizome and putting up vertical shoots for reproduction. Plants such as the modern ground elder grow in a similar way. (c) A reconstruction of the Devonian-Carboniferous tree Archaeopteris. It had wood containing lignin and similar to that of modern conifers and so was identifed as being that of a gymnosperm (seed-bearing) plant. However, the foliage was similar to that of ferns (reproduction by spores). These were described together in the same plant, giving rise to a group of progymnosperms. These were a significant advance, as the large tree would have replaced its leaves many times, drawing carbon out of the atmosphere. (d) The Cretaceous plant Nilssoniocladus, that grew in the Arctic. It has been interpreted as a deciduous cycad. This was because the stem has side shoots with scars where leaves have been shed and mats of intact Nilssonia leaves suggest that all the leaves were shed at the same time. Modern cycads are squat and palm-like and do not shed their leaves annually. (e) Jurassic leaf Ginkgo huttoni*

holes (stomata) to take in air and expel oxygen and water (transpiration).

The first plants were non-flowering and reproduced either by alternate sterile and spore-producing generations, or by wind-blown pollen but were restricted to damp sites, close to water. Reconstructions of some early plants can be seen as in Figure 6.16.

One of the best known flora is that of the Carboniferous swamp forest, which has similarities with modern tropical forest. Tree ferns, lycophytes (club mosses) and trees dominate, with large insects and amphibians using the plants as their habitat. Leaves and trees of the Carboniferous forest, reconstructed in Figure C6.5, that became preserved in boggy ground eventually formed coal. The importance of these plants is that they drew down CO_2 until it reached a very low level in the atmosphere, contributing to lower global temperatures. Many of the Carboniferous plants have modern counterparts, though they may not closely resemble their ancestors. Lycophytes, *Lepidodendron* for example, formed towering trees in the Carboniferous forest but their modern relatives, club mosses, are tiny creeping plants. These have adapted to survive the various habitat and environment changes during the last 300 million years. Later in the Carboniferous and early Permian in Europe/North America, lycophytes declined as the climate became drier. This may have been because the roots of *Lepidodendron* (*Stigmaria*) were adapted to soft waterlogged sediment, not more compact, drier soils. However further east, in China, patterns of vegetation and climate remained much the same until the Permian, so large swamp deposits that were to become coal accumulated in rocks of Permian age.

The seed-bearing **gymnosperm** plants developed during the late Palaeozoic and Mesozoic and include groups such as conifers, ginkgos and cycads. These plants had female seeds containing food with a tough coat for protection. This method was a further advance on spores, as seeds could survive being submerged in water, or be dormant for long periods of drought, cold or other environmental disaster. Consequently, gymnosperms could colonise drier and higher land areas. Lycophytes gave way to conifers, the most successful of the gymnosperms, which today contains the largest living organism of all time, the 110 m tall redwood (*Sequoia sempervirens*).

In higher latitudes during the late Carboniferous to late Permian, extensive forests existed, dominated by deciduous trees with tongue-shaped leaves, called **glossopterids**. The annual leaf-fall accumulated in swamps and eventually formed peat that is now coal, in Australia, which has extensive Permian coal deposits.

Flowering plants (**angiosperms**) developed 100 Ma ago, during the Cretaceous. Deciduous angiosperms had large, thin leaves similar to modern plane trees and these leaves are often found whole as fossils, even in sandstones. The reproduction of flowering plants was more successful than wind-pollination, as attracting, for example, insects for pollination is less chancy. Also the seeds were fully enclosed and so protected. It has been suggested that flowering plants developed as a response to trees that were periodically flattened by herds of plant-eating dinosaurs. Flowering plants germinate quickly and can take advantage of the light when trees aren't present. One hundred million years later, most of the food plants used by humans are angiosperms. However, flowering plants did not replace other types, they lived alongside conifers, ginkgos and horsetails and continue to do so.

The various innovations in form that mark the stages of plant development are shown in Figure 6.17.

Seeds and pollen grains are often found as fossils, because of their tough cell walls, when the plants to which they belonged are merely unidentifiable carbon films. At the Cretaceous–Tertiary boundary in Alaska, varied pollens below the boundary were replaced by ferns above it; these are known to be the first colonising plants, for example on new volcanic rocks, or after major eruptions such as Mount St Helens. Thus they can indicate a period of intense change that killed other plant species.

6.6 Extinction, mass extinction and afterwards

Animals and plants often evolve so that they are specialised, that is they become very good at surviving in particular environments. The disadvantage is that if that environment changes rapidly or disappears and the organism is unable to move or adapt quickly, it dies out. Extinction has been a universal process since life began. Oceanic species survive, on average, longer than land types, but it is unusual for a species to last for more than 30 Ma. Figure 6.13 showed how the size of groups of related organisms have varied through geological time, with the width of the bars being an approximation of the abundance of fossil families. It can be seen from Figure 6.13 that all graptolites became extinct in the Devonian, and trilobites became extinct at the end of the Permian.

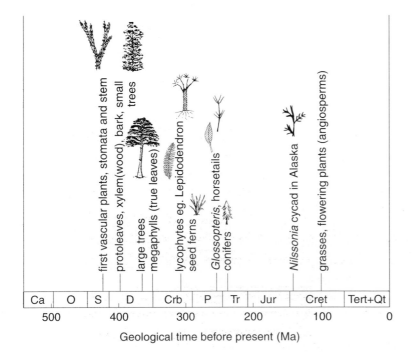

Figure 6.17 *The changes in the development of plants, from the first plants with ducts for fluids (vascular system), through the development of lignin (wood). The latter development allowed plants to grow taller (trees) with a larger canopy, thus drawing down more CO₂ to form organic carbon. True leaves which could be shed annually (deciduous) allowed a dormant period during unfavourable conditions, of cold or drought. This enabled plants to radiate into sub-polar regions*

6.6.1 PATTERNS OF MASS EXTINCTION

The diversity of life is a measure of all the groups of organisms alive at a particular time. A graph can show how the range of life forms has changed by plotting the number of fossil families against time, as shown in Figure 6.18a. This shows a steady increase in types of organisms from the Cambrian to the Ordovician, but then a drop in diversity before the Silurian, when the graph climbs steeply again. Each drop on the graph is a time when large numbers of families died out, with the greatest of these being at the end of the Permian when around half the families and 96 per cent of all species on Earth became extinct in a geologically short time (about 8 million years). Four other times of major mass extinction are also seen on the graph, including one at the end Cretaceous, when the dinosaurs, the ammonites and several other groups became extinct. What great change could possibly have caused these great mass extinctions?

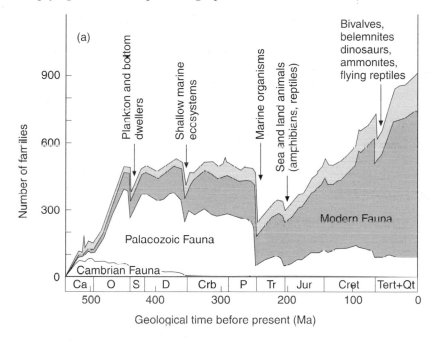

Figure 6.18(a) *Changes in the diversity of life in the last 600 Ma showing five major extinction episodes and the fauna in each that were most affected. The area at the top represents those families known only from sites of exceptional preservation. The main area is based on skeletal hard parts and comprise three evolutionary faunas: Cambrian, Palaeozoic and Modern*

Figure 6.18(b) *Examples of the three evolutionary faunas: Cambrian, Palaeozoic and Modern*

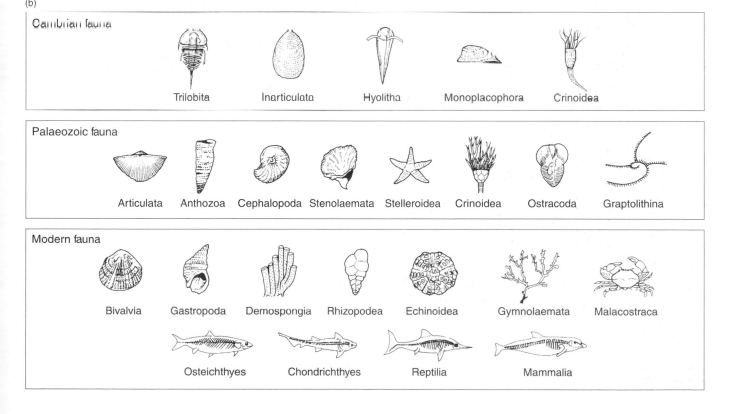

6.6.2 HYPOTHESES FOR MASS EXTINCTIONS

A wide range of different hypotheses has been put forward that might explain these devastating changes to life on our planet.

Some geologists suggest that mass extinction is linked to *sea level variation*, particularly **marine regression**, when sea level falls, for example because of a decline in sea floor spreading and a reduction in the size of ocean ridge mountains. During marine regression, many broad shallow sea areas are reduced in size or become land. This would trigger the oxidation (rotting) of marine organic matter exposed at the surface, causing a rise in atmospheric carbon dioxide and an overall increase in temperature (global warming). There would be a decrease in atmospheric oxygen and lack of oxygen in the oceans (anoxia). It is suggested that all these factors led to ecological instability and extinctions. Marine regression is thought to have been a major factor in the Permian mass extinction, together with the eruption of flood basalts in Siberia adding more CO_2 and further contributing to climate change.

Glaciation has also been suggested as a mechanism. At the end of the Ordovician, organisms including groups of trilobites (bottom-dwelling) and graptolites (planktonic) became extinct. This has been connected to a vast ice-sheet at that time, on a large super-continent called Gondwana, causing sea levels to fall and changes to ocean basin size, ocean chemistry and climate.

A third hypothesis relates to *volcanicity*. In large volcanic eruptions, huge volumes of volcanic gas and ash are expelled into the upper atmosphere. More of the Sun's radiation than normal is reflected back into space and a period of intense cooling of the Earth results in a 'volcanic winter'. Photosynthesis would cease causing food chain collapse as plants and then animals die. Huge amounts of basalt were erupted in India at the end of the Cretaceous during 68–63 Ma, which is why some geologists link this to the extinctions (Figure 4.24).

These hypotheses all involve geological factors that trigger climate change which causes ecological instability by disruption of the food chains and habitats.

A fourth idea being seriously considered is the *extra-terrestrial impact* hypothesis. It is suggested that an asteroid hit the Earth at the end of the Cretaceous, causing global fires and ejecting huge amounts of dust into the upper atmosphere. The time of the impact is marked by a clay layer that is iridium-rich worldwide. The metal iridium is very rare on Earth but is common in meteorites and other extra terrestrial bodies. The fires and dust would have had the same effect as volcanic ash in the atmosphere and could give rise to an 'impact winter'.
However, this would be followed by warming as organic material decomposed, giving out carbon dioxide.

In 1990, the Chixulub impact crater, 200 km in diameter and dated at 65 Ma was discovered (Chapter 1). Figure 6.19 shows some of the evidence for great tsunamis that affected the shoreline of the time and glassy spherules have been found.

Close examination of the fossil record shows that many marine species were in decline or extinct before the time of the impact, while other groups continued on unchanged. None of this evidence means that the impact (now considered an established fact) was unimportant; the ecosystems were under severe stress before the impact, supported by climate evidence that shows that temperature was rising to its highest level in the last 400 Ma. The impact may have been a 'final straw'.

Studies of the five major periods of mass extinction indicate that there was no single cause. In several, climatic change is involved, with associated sea level and habitat changes. Extraterrestrial impact has been implicated in the extinctions at the Cretaceous–Tertiary (K–T) boundary, and there are suggestions of impacts associated with the Triassic–Jurassic boundary.

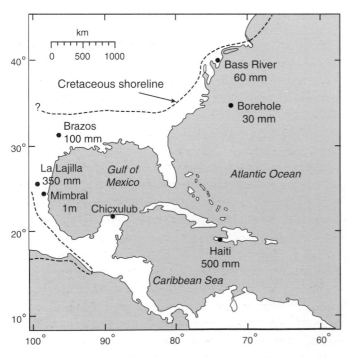

Figure 6.19 *Evidence for late Cretaceous impact on the Gulf of Mexico at Chixulub: location and thickness of identified spherule layers in marine setting*

6.6.3 PATTERNS OF EVOLUTION

After mass extinctions, **radiations** occur, when groups of animals or plants evolve in a short period of time into many different new species. This may be due to the development of some special feature; this gives the organism a significant advantage that can allow it to spread rapidly into many habitats which were previously unoccupied or, before the extinction, were occupied by another group. This is **adaptive radiation**. Examples include the radiation of bivalves after they developed siphons, the radiation of plants after the development of seeds, and the radiation following the evolution of the first mammals. In each case there was rapid evolution as the plants and animals spread and adapted successfully into new habitats.

6.7 Uses of fossils and assemblages

Some fossils and groups of fossils provide very valuable evidence for Earth processes in the past.

6.7.1 DETERMINING THE AGE OF ROCKS

Geologists have been able to work out the order of formation of strata by the fossils they contain. The changes in plants and animals during evolution has caused sedimentary sequences from different times to contain different fossils. This changing sequence of fossils is called the **faunal succession**. On the basis of this, strata have been grouped into major time units called periods (see Geological Column Appendix 7). More detailed examination of the fossil succession allows each period to be subdivided into **zones**, each zone being characterised by a particular fossil or group of fossils. Working out the relative age is one of the most important uses of fossils and is dealt with in detail in Chapter 11. We can find the relative age of many hominids from fossils found with them but rarely the actual age, in years. The age of Lucy's remains was found by dating lava and ash flows close to where she was discovered.

6.7.2 ENVIRONMENTS OF THE PAST

The aim of **palaeoenvironmental** studies is to use fossils and sediments to build up a picture of the Earth's surface at any one time, to find out for instance where there were hills and rivers, shallow seas and lagoons. This helps to define the extent and location of the continental masses, the deep oceans and how these have changed over time. Once this has been done, it is easier to predict, where for example, hydrocarbons might be found, so oil companies spend a great deal of time and money doing palaeoenvironmental analysis.

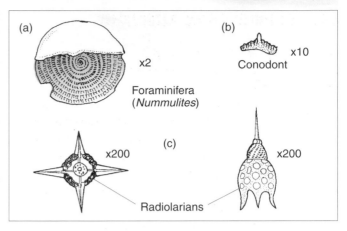

Figure 6.20 *A selection of microfossils (a) A large, foraminifera (marine organism) called Nummulites. This organism had a CaCo₃ test (shell) with internal chambers and formed limestones of Eocene age in the Mediterranean. These were used to build the pyramids of Egypt; (b) Conondonts were tiny jawless vertebrates that grew together to grasp and grind food. Their main use is as a palaeotemperature indicator in metamorphic rocks as they change colour with temperature; (c) Radiolarians are one-celled plankton that have exoskeletons made of silica (SiO₂). They live on bacteria and phytoplankton and live at all depths in the ocean, though frequently in the topmost layers, with symbiotic algae*

Colonial corals are good and precise indicators of past environments. Modern corals live in quite restricted conditions; they only live in the sea in shallow, warm, clear water within the Tropics. Since it is very likely that corals had the same requirements in the past, the finding of corals in Carboniferous rocks in Britain means that either the world has cooled down or Britain was once within the Tropics.

Foraminifera (Figure 6.20) are microfossils that lived in the plankton near the sea surface and accumulated in great numbers on the sea floor when they died. Different groups of foraminifera have adapted to a range of living conditions, and this can also have great value. Some live in brackish water (less salt than the sea) while others live in very salt water, so they give excellent evidence for different salinities in the past. We can judge water depth by comparing the ratio of benthic forms (living on the sea floor) to planktonic forms: a greater proportion of benthic forms are found in shallow water sediments. Different types also live in different shallow water environments, so we can use foraminifera to distinguish lagoons from tidal mud flats and from deeper mud deposits. Some forms are associated with sandy areas near reefs while another group is found in high energy sandy regions. When you add this information to the importance of foraminifera in dating rocks, you can see why the study of microfossils has become such an important part of palaeontology today.

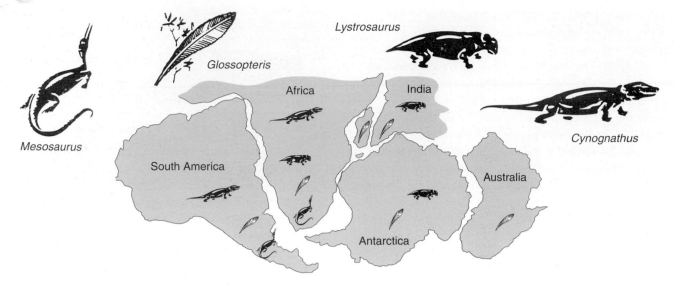

Figure 6.21 *Permian/Triassic fossils used as evidence for plate tectonic movement; their distributions are best explained if the southern continents were once together in a supercontinent called Gondwana.* Mesosaurus: *the tail and feet suggest a strong swimmer, while the 'crocodile-like' snout and teeth indicate predation on fish or crustaceons. A glossopteris leaf.* Lystrosaurus: *early work interpreted this animal like a hippopotamus, living close to streams and watering holes, although more recently it has been thought of as having parallels with the modern pig.* Cynognathus *('dog-tooth') has small sharp incisors at the front of the mouth with large canine teeth indicating a carnivore. Teeth along the cheeks are broader, for tearing flesh from bones. They could breathe and chew at the same time*

6.7.3 PALAEOGEOGRAPHY

Fossils have been used to chart the movements of the continents, giving vital clues during the early work on continental drift and still provide evidence for the theory of plate tectonics. Figure 6.21 shows a map based on the work of **Alfred Wegener** who assembled a great deal of evidence supporting the hypothesis. It shows how the distributions of *Mesosaurus*, a reptile found only in freshwater swamp deposits, the plant *Glossopteris* and land-living reptiles such as *Lystrosaurus* and *Cynognathus*, can only be properly explained if the southern continents were all connected to one another as a super continent, Gondwana. The fact that *Glossopteris* was a polar plant indicates that the supercontinent was much closer to the south pole than the southern continents are today.

The way that brachiopod communities and trilobites helped in the reconstruction of the geography of the ancient Iapetus Ocean is discussed in Chapter 12.

6.7.4 PALAEOTEMPERATURE

Fossils can give several lines of evidence for the temperatures in the past and climate change.

For example, if we dig through the peat in some parts of eastern England and examine the pollen at different levels, we find that the earliest levels contain only pollen from scrub birch such as is presently found in Arctic Norway. Higher up the sequence, pine pollen becomes abundant representing the climate currently found in southern Scandinavia. Towards the top the proportion of oak and hazel increase suggesting a temperate climate like we have today. This sequence indicates the vegetation changed in response to a warming of the land after the end of the last glaciation.

Foraminifera are found in many fossil communities, but are particularly valuable to us where they accumulated slowly in deeper sea areas because then they can contain a complete record of sedimentation, unbroken by periods of erosion. Some species are particularly sensitive to temperature – an excellent example being the type that coils to the right in warm sea conditions but coils to the left when the sea becomes colder. This temperature information is reinforced because foraminifera contain more 'heavy' oxygen (^{18}O) in their shells when they live in warm conditions and less when seas are cold, so an excellent guide to temperature is obtained from measuring how the ratio of heavy oxygen to normal oxygen ($^{18}O:^{16}O$) changes over time. This evidence has provided a detailed picture of how global temperatures changed during the glaciations (cold periods) and interglacials (warm periods) of the most recent ice age (the Pleistocene glaciations). This is shown in Appendix 7.

Plants are also useful climatic indicators, for example leaf size gives information about temperature and rainfall. The ratio of saw-edged leaves (cooler climates) to smooth edged-leaves (warmer) can be used to calculate mean temperature; the number of stomata and 'drip tips' can be used to indicate wet or dry climates.

6.8 Summary

1 The fossil record is biased towards marine organisms with hard parts; land animals, soft-bodied animals and single-celled organisms are under-represented.

2 Sites of exceptional preservation provide unique insights into communities of organisms and internal organs.

3 Life began in single-celled organisms without nuclei (prokaryotes), in the Archaean. Eukaryotes and multicellular organisms developed in the Proterozoic and were followed by the 'Cambrian explosion'.

4 The early atmosphere contained no oxygen, which was first produced as a result of photosynthesis by cyanobacteria, which could withstand strong ultraviolet radiation. Aerobic respiration became possible when oxygen had built to 1 per cent of present levels.

5 Plants colonised the land after the Silurian, drawing down CO_2 and giving out oxygen.

6 Land animals developed after the protective ozone layer formed in the stratosphere.

7 There are several theories of evolution, including natural selection, punctuated equilibrium and complex interactions with environmental factors.

8 Species have become extinct throughout geological time. There have been five periods of major mass extinction, when many families became extinct. Theories to explain mass extinctions include sea level or climate change, volcanicity and extra-terrestrial impact.

9 Fossils are used for rock correlation and give insights into palaeogeographical reconstruction and palaeoclimates.

6.9 Questions

1 What type of fossil are you most likely to find, vertebrate or invertebrate? Why?

2 Different types of trilobites evolved different types of eyes to suit the environment they lived in. Can you match the types of eyes to the environment:

very large	burrowing in mud
on stalks	living in poorly lit water
none	living almost submerged beneath sediment

3 Which of the following are life assemblages and which are death assemblages. Why?
  a) group of trilobite head shields
  b) a mixture of marine and non-marine shells all of the same age
  c) a group of graptolites in black shales
  d) a group of *Gryphea* shells (Jurassic) in Pleistocene gravels
  e) a group of oyster shells all resting on each other

4 Describe how the following might have become fossilised: (a) a Cretaceous echinoid made of flint; (b) the body shape of a Jurassic *Icthyosaurus* preserved as a dark film around its skeleton on a bedding plane; (c) the internal and external moulds of gastropods in Jurassic Portland Limestone; (d) the casts of deep sea feeding trails on the base of Silurian turbidite sandstone beds; (e) an Eocene shark's tooth preserved in clay.

5 If an organism were found to show a steady increase in size through a series of beds, what different theories might be put forward to account for this finding?

6 How might the evolution of the horse (Figure 6.15) be used in discussing the close links between the evolution of environments and organisms?

7 a) The 'Lucy' Case Study on page 101 lists a number of scientific questions about her. Which of these might eventually be answered and how?
  b) How might these questions be answered for a well-preserved Silurian coral?

CHAPTER 7

Metamorphism: transformation by heat and pressure

Introduction

Tectonic processes introduce a range of changes in crustal rocks. Depending on the type of plate margin involved, the rocks may be subjected to unusual conditions of temperature and pressure; for example, by deep burial within a collision zone, or heating by rising magma over a subduction zone. Altered physical conditions result in the breakdown of previously stable minerals and the growth of new ones: **metamorphism**. The process takes place without melting, in the solid state, and usually without loss or addition of elements from outside the 'system' i.e. it is an isochemical, or closed system. When the rocks are once again exposed at the surface, their history can be discovered in the metamorphic changes they preserve.

7.1   Case Study: the outer limits

Much of our understanding of large scale metamorphic processes came originally from studies in Scotland. Since then, we have been able to discover the causes of these processes in terms of plate tectonics. These have shown that during late Precambrian and Cambrian times a major ocean separated northern Britain from what was to become England and Wales. This was the **'Iapetus'** Ocean, named after the father of Atlantis in mythology. The northern shores of the ocean were affected in just the same ways as continental margins are today – acquiring a thick mantle of sediments derived from erosion, in this case, from land-masses to the north and west. This peaceful scenario was, however, about to be changed by a series of plate tectonic events loosely described as the **Caledonian Orogeny**, a major mountain building episode.

The onset of subduction in the Iapetus Ocean resulted in the formation of major island arc systems. Continued closure of the ocean led to the collision and **over-thrusting** of the island arc on to the continent. The evidence for all this was not left undisturbed: the ocean continued to close until a full continent–continent collision occurred. It welded a proto-Scotland (at that time part of the American continent) on to England which formed part of another continent. The sedimentary rocks of the continental margin were caught in that titanic collision and severely deformed. They now crop out in the Scottish Highlands over a wide area of northern Scotland. Given the subsequent long and dramatic history of these rocks, how do we know that they were regionally metamorphosed during that Caledonian event?

Our understanding of these rocks is mostly thanks to the brilliant and methodical science of **George Barrow**. By a painstaking analysis of the mineral content of fine-grained meta-sedimentary rocks in the region, he recognised that the existence of certain **index minerals** indicates the highest temperature reached by the rock. As some of these diagnostic minerals remain stable at higher temperatures, it is their first appearance on their outer limits that enables a new division to be drawn on the map.

This revolutionary zonal mapping technique, which provides us with so much information on the geological history of this crucial area, is surprisingly not the result of the latest technical breakthroughs in mineral analysis but was put forward by Barrow more than a hundred years ago in 1893. His map (Figure 7.1), published in an excursion guide for the Geologists' Association in 1912, clearly demonstrates the sequence of **'Barrow zones'** marking the first appearance of each diagnostic index mineral. In order of increasing metamorphism, the index

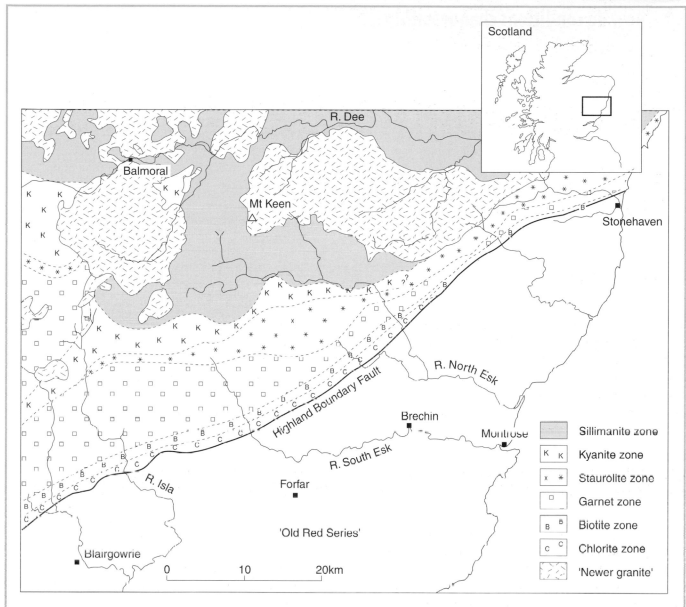

Figure 7.1 *Metamorphic zoning of the eastern Highlands based on the sketch map of G. M. Barrow published in 1912. The Highland Boundary Fault divides unmetamorphosed Devonian rocks in the SE from the metasediments to the NW. The zones mark the first appearance of metamorphic minerals indicating progressively higher metamorphism towards the NW*

minerals are chlorite, biotite, garnet, staurolite, kyanite and sillimanite. These palaeo-temperature indicators run roughly parallel to a major fault that forms the escarpment between the Scottish Highlands and the northern side of the Midland Valley of Scotland, called the Highland Boundary Fault.

The rocks immediately to the north west of the Highland Boundary Fault contain the metamorphic mineral chlorite. The metamorphism occurred at relatively low temperatures and is referred to as **low-grade**. Approximately one kilometre to the NW the first appearance of biotite is noted in the metamorphosed sediments. Biotite *and* chlorite are both present in the biotite zone but it is that first occurrence of biotite that defines the boundary between the biotite and chlorite zones. Rocks further to the NW contain progressively higher

temperature (**higher grade**) metamorphic minerals producing a broadly linear pattern of zones.

The presence of unmetamorphosed Devonian rocks in the Highlands (Barrow's 'Old Red Series') demonstrates that the **regional metamorphism** occurred prior to the Devonian. Only the Caledonian Orogeny that came after the original sediments were deposited, but before the Devonian could have caused the metamorphic changes of the sediments.

Barrow also showed that there was no connection between the metamorphism of the sediments and the intrusion of granites in the area, as he stated: "the position of the zones in the south eastern Highlands proves there can be no connection between them and the Newer Granites, which are also shown on the map".

7.2 How do conditions change within the crust?

Two physical changes which are familiar are that pressure increases with depth and that temperatures also increase as you go down, as shown by a geothermal gradient plot (see page 34). The weight of the overlying rock clearly provides a reasonably predictable increase in pressure; the temperature rise is less intuitively obvious, but the arrival of molten rock from the depths provides a substantial hint that temperatures are higher there than at the surface.

When the actual rise of temperature with depth is measured near the surface and plotted, it gives a reasonably straight line with a slope which can be used to predict temperatures at greater depths. This geothermal gradient is approximately 25 °Ckm^{-1} within continental lithosphere and this gradient has been long established. Rocks from the Archaean in the early Precambrian suggest that, even then, the gradient was between 20 and 25 °Ckm^{-1}.

Oceanic lithosphere shows wild variations of geothermal gradient. Values are predictably high at ridges where the asthenosphere is closest to the surface; by contrast, values as low as 10 °Ckm^{-1} occur at trenches because during subduction, the gradient is depressed by the cooling effect of the relatively cold slab as it is carried down into the mantle.

An important physical property of rocks needs to be taken into consideration – the fact that they are very poor conductors of heat – probably poor enough to be classed as insulators by physicists. The transfer of heat from the mantle can be made many times more efficient if the heat is transferred by **convection** (transporting heat within rising magma) rather than by **conduction**. Any region in which magma moves towards, or up to, the surface will show abnormally high geothermal gradients.

Pressure increases with depth at a rate of about 30 MPakm^{-1} in the continental crust. This can be worked out by calculating the mass of rock involved using an average density.

At the base of the continental crust the temperature is in the region of 900 °C, and it should come as no surprise that minerals stable at those temperatures and pressures are not stable at the surface; conversely, if rocks created near the surface are moved to greater depths, their component minerals may undergo changes to adjust to the new physical conditions. These changes of mineralogy and mineral form are the response to metamorphic processes.

So pressure and temperature increase with depth, and if molten rock is finding its way towards the surface, temperature will increase rapidly towards the intrusive body of magma. In this way, temperatures can vary horizontally as well as vertically. It is the task of the geologist to identify the sensitive mineral adaptations that accompany and identify such changes.

Pressure, too, can show lateral variations. Stresses with all sorts of directions and values result from the various interactions of plate tectonic margins, for example, stresses increase dramatically when two continents collide! Metamorphic minerals allow us to unpick the evidence for past geological activity; this is especially useful when the obvious evidence, such as a mountain range like the Himalaya, has been removed by erosion from the scene of the crime.

In the early stages of sedimentary rock formation, increases in pressure and temperature produce changes such as de-watering and compaction. These changes do not result in the formation of new minerals and are called diagenesis (see page 85). At the other end of the scale, when temperatures are high enough, rocks melt. At this stage, we are out of the realms of metamorphism and into igneous processes. Metamorphic processes occur over a

Figure 7.2 *The relationship of metamorphic processes to diagenesis and igneous processes.*

Approximate temperature °C	Process	Approximate depth km	Result	Example
20	surface processes	0	sedimentation ↓	sand ↓
100	diagenetic processes	5	diagenesis ↓	sandstone ↓
200	metamorphic processes	10–30	metamorphism ↓	metaquartzite ↓
650		35–40	partial melting ↓	migmatite ↓
800–1200	igneous processes	50–100	magma formation	granite

range of temperatures and pressures that are between those found at a depth of approximately 8 km (c. 200 °C and 220 MPa) and the depths at which melting occurs: at around 35 to 40 km (see Figure 7.2). As usual in a natural science, it is hard to be exact because the type of rock and variations in crustal heat flow exert strong influences on this scheme.

Metamorphism happens to both sedimentary *and* igneous rocks – as you can see in the diagram of the rock cycle (Appendix 1). The effects on igneous rocks can be very subtle and less easy to see in hand specimens; as a result, many examples in metamorphic studies are based on changes in sedimentary rocks.

If we look only at variations in the two physical variables, temperature and pressure, there are a small number of combinations which can usefully be tied in with geological 'environments', for example:

- low pressure/high temperature: places where heat flow is high at or near the surface, associated with igneous activity;

- high pressure/high temperature: deep within the crust in a plate collision zone;

- high pressure/low temperature: where tectonic stresses are high and temperatures low; for example at a subduction zone.

7.3 What happens to rocks during changes of temperature and pressure?

The effect on rocks of temperature and pressure changes depends on several factors:

- the original composition of the rock;
- the amount by which the physical conditions of temperature and pressure change;
- the presence of pore fluids;
- the length of time during which the new conditions are experienced.

Some minerals have a smaller stability field than others – small changes in conditions may lead to their breakdown. The breakdown products are then reconstituted to make new minerals stable under the new conditions.

The changes in mineral form and chemistry are usually slow. This means that we are able to find records of physical conditions still preserved at the surface by rocks which have been tectonically thrust up or exhumed by erosion following mountain-building episodes. If there

were instant responses to temperature and pressure we would find only minerals stable in surface conditions, of less than 50 °C and one atmosphere, no record of previous metamorphism would be preserved and a whole branch of geology would never have developed. A recent estimate for the growth of metamorphic garnets showed they had been increasing in diameter by 1.4 mm every million years for ten million years – a tricky experiment to repeat in the laboratory. The reaction rate depends largely on the temperature and it is calculated that a 1 mm rim of the metamorphic mineral wollastonite that grew on a quartz grain in 50 years at 800 °C would take 400 000 years at 600 °C.

Metamorphic rocks are generally divided into those that have been principally affected only by increased temperatures during **contact metamorphism**, and those that also preserve evidence of increased pressures. These two classes of metamorphic rocks are described in the next two sections following a general consideration of the conditions that give rise to them. As you have seen in previous chapters the shape and relationship of grains within a rock are described as the texture; metamorphic rocks have either a foliated ('layered'/banded) or non-foliated (random) texture.

Until now, we have blithely assumed that pressure increases with depth as a result of the increasing mass of rock involved. This is referred to as the **lithostatic pressure** ($\rho \times g \times$ depth). We have also casually referred to lateral pressures due to the horizontal movement of the lithospheric plates. Pressure influences metamorphism in two important ways: one involves fluids, the other applies when there are large differences in the stresses acting in different directions.

The pressure in the crust is made up of the confining pressure and the pressure exerted by fluids in the pore spaces (the **hydrostatic pressure**). Fluids trapped within sediments and subjected to compaction are further pressurised as the temperatures increase with burial. These **metamorphic fluids**, chiefly water and CO_2, act to promote recrystallisation. The composition of the fluid may even determine the pressure and temperature at which metamorphic reactions occur. A good example of this is in carbonate rocks, where CO_2 is produced during reactions and enriches the fluid. High concentrations make it more difficult for the reactions that produce CO_2 to proceed. Another common reaction involves dehydration, which proceeds much more readily when H_2O is scarce.

Lithostatic pressure is like hydrostatic pressure i.e. it acts equally in all directions (more or less). Somewhat surprisingly, once depths of a few kilometres are reached, lateral stresses are within a few per cent of vertical stresses, but these will not result in deformation.

Deformation requires unequal (**differential**) stresses which have a clear effect on the textures of metamorphic rock.

Many of the minerals sensitive to pressure increases are platy with flat crystal shapes (e.g. micas). As a response to increased pressure, a platy mineral regrows perpendicular to the maximum stress rather than parallel to it. If enough of these minerals grow with that same orientation, then the rock becomes anisotropic (its properties are not the same in every direction). It is weaker in the plane parallel to those plates (Figure 7.3). As a result, it may split along such planes and the alignment of minerals gives the rock a **foliation** (the term comes from the Latin meaning leaf). Foliated rocks are found wherever there is a large difference in the stresses in the different directions. This stress differential is essential for the formation of foliation: in situations of equally increased stresses, but not differential stress, the new minerals form with random orientations.

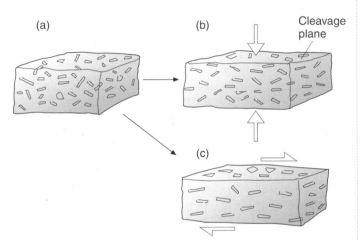

Figure 7.3 *Diagram to show the regrowth of micas and formation of foliation: (a) Platy minerals are oriented randomly in the unmetamorphosed rock; (b) High differential stress results in growth of platy minerals at right angles to maximum stress direction. The alignment of minerals means that the metamorphosed rock is weaker in the plane of cleavage; (c) A similar alignment of minerals can be caused by high shear stresses*

7.4 Contact metamorphism: the development of non-foliated textures

Metamorphism is usually an isochemical process, that is, the same elements are re-combined in the solid state to make either the existing minerals in different forms (**recrystallisation**) or new minerals not seen in the unmetamorphosed rock. This emphasises the importance of the original composition of a rock since metamorphism cannot produce minerals out of thin air. It can, however, make permanent changes to the proportions of elements present by driving off any volatiles produced. The most

obvious of these is that water is driven out of the system by increased temperatures (dehydration) and, less obviously, carbon dioxide may be released (decarbonation).

To illustrate this, let us consider the effects of the heat from a nearby igneous intrusion on limestone. We are familiar with Michelangelo's use of **marble** as a material for sculpture, but he could not have used it successfully were it not an isotropic material. The original limestone would have had many planes of weakness due to its mode of deposition; imagine trying to chisel out some delicate feature and coming across a large bivalve shell! The calcium carbonate of the limestone was recrystallised during metamorphism into a uniform texture. Looked at carefully with a lens, you can often see recrystallised, interlocking grains the size of sugar granules – hence the name **sugary** or **saccharoidal texture**.

The various calcium carbonate components of the limestone (calcite and aragonite) recrystallised into a pure marble, which isn't surprising. However, if the limestone were not pure to start with, then various other elements are free to recombine. If the original rock were, for example, a dolomite, then the increased heat would release carbon dioxide and leave magnesium oxide (periclase) within the marble.

$$\text{dolomite} \rightarrow \text{marble} + \text{periclase} + \text{carbon dioxide}$$
$$CaMg(CO_3)_2 \rightarrow CaCO_3 + MgO + CO_2$$

In this and similar reactions, if the carbon dioxide is lost from the system it is difficult to reverse the reaction.

Another example of a simple chemical system recrystallising is when a pure quartz sandstone is metamorphosed into a **metaquartzite** with interlocking quartz grains in a sugary texture.

One texture seen often in an igneous rock is when large crystals have grown in an otherwise fine-grained matrix. The metamorphic equivalents of these large crystals are called **porphyroblasts** (Figure 7.4b). Such large crystals growing, in this case, as a result of elevated temperatures, are useful evidence because they allow the field identification of metamorphic zones. A good example is the **metamorphic aureole** around the Skiddaw granite which crops out in the Lake District. Approaching from beyond the aureole, the first noticeable change in the country rocks is the appearance of dark spots in the slates. As water is driven off, new minerals begin to grow in patches giving rise to spotted rocks. Any metamorphic rock with a spotted appearance may be said to have a **maculose texture**. Closer to the granite, where temperatures have been higher, the new minerals are large enough to identify. For example andalusite, a mineral that is light in colour with a characteristic square

Figure C2.1 *Xenoliths of peridotite (composed mainly of green olivine) from a depth of 60 km, contained within basalt lava. The large olivine xenolith is approximately 80mm across.*

Figure C3.1 *A crystal of a variety of gypsum (CaSO$_4$.2H$_2$0) called selenite. This mineral shows rhombohedral cleavage, similar to that of calcite.*

Figure C3.2 *A large biotite mica cystal, showing a well-developed single cleavage direction*

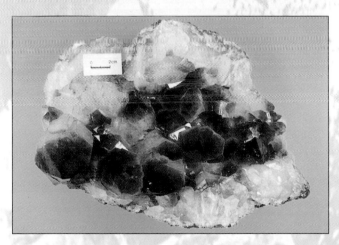

Figure C3.3 *Amethyst, a purple variety of quartz. These crystals show good crystal form, as they have grown in a void in a lava flow.*

Figure C3.4 *Two samples of iron pyrites (FeS$_2$). The left-hand sample shows intergrown cubes of the mineral. The right-hand example shows more complex shapes, and also the characteristic striations that crystals of pyrites often display.*

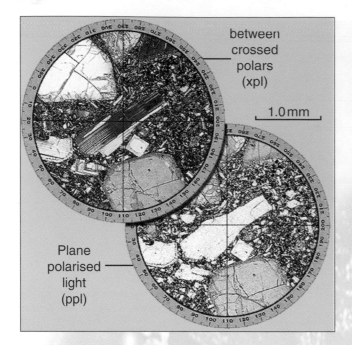

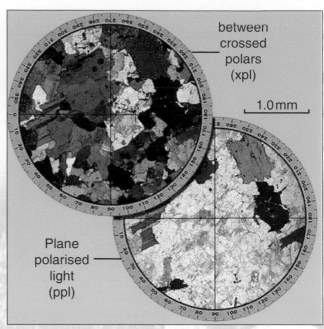

Figure C3.5a *Large, well-formed crystals of pyroxene show as brightly coloured mineral (xpl) in this thin section of pophyritic basalt. The large crystal in the centre is plagioclase feldspar, as are the small grey crystals in the groundmass.*

Figure C3.5b *Biotite mica crystals under the polarising microscope show a pale yellow - brown in plane polarised light (bottom right-hand view). The crystals change colour from pale yellow in E-W orientation, to dark brown in N-S orientation, as the stage is rotated. Micas have a 'flaky' shape, with cleavage often visible.*

Figure C3.6a *Simple twinning in orthoclase feldspar (xpl) shown in the large crystal in the top right-hand of the microscope view, and lamellar twinning in the crystal at the bottom left-hand of the illustration. The brightly coloured minerals are olivine and pyroxene.*

Figure C.3.6b *Lamellar twinning in plagioclase feldspar, shown in the crystals in the bottom left-hand quadrant of the microscope view (xpl). Quartz is shown in the right-hand quadrant edge, its crystals showing different shades of uniform grey, with no twinning.*

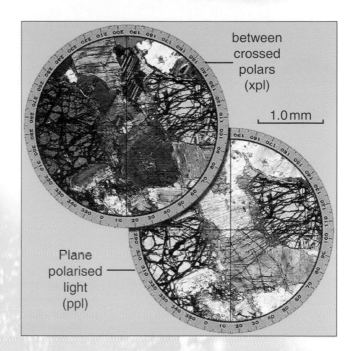

Figure C4.1 *Photomicrographs of two similar igneous rocks. Both contain feldspar: in the finer-grained sample the feldspar comprises the majority of the rock, with lamellar twinning visible in the crystals. In the coarser-grained sample the pale crydstals showing greys in xpl are feldspar. The brightly coloured crystals with thick, irregular black lines crossing them are olivine; the brightly coloured crystals with paler, regular lines at 90° are pyroxene. The main difference between the photomicrographs is the grain/crystal size of the rocks.*

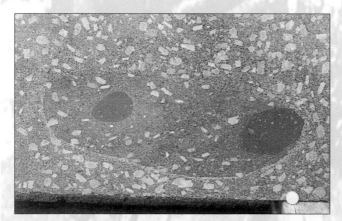

Figure C4.2 *A slab of granite containing a xenolith. The angular shape indicates that this is a piece of country rock, possibly sedimentary, that is being assimilated into the magma (fine layers are visible in the xenolith).*

Figure C4.4 *A piece of obsidian, a black, glassy rock formed by the rapid cooling of a silica-rich lava. Note the curved (conchoidal) fracture.*

Figure C4.3 *A piece of Shap granite containing autoliths. The rounded dark shapes with feldspar crystals inside a larger 'blob' also containing feldspars indicate that this material was liquid, so this illustrates magma mixing.*

Figure C4.5 *Igneous building materials a) The walls of this house are built of basalt but the 'coins' (edge pieces) are Carboniferous sandstone.*

Figure C5.1a *(left)* Lamination, fine layering in sedimentary rocks. The lamination in this Carboniferous sandstone shows that it was laid down under quiet current conditions.

Figure C5.1b *(above)* Bedding, sedimentary layers more than 10mm thick. Bedding in this Carboniferous Coal Measure cyclothem sequence is shown by colour differences in the beds. Individual beds are visible in the yellow sandstones, with the small overhangs indicating bedding planes. Mudstone and coal form darker layers. Cyclic changes in cyclothem sequences, illustrated in Figure 9.4, reflect changes in the environment during deposition.

Figure C5.1c *(left)* Small scale cross bedding, sands deposited as sloping layers on the downcurrent side of small underwater dunes. They show that these sands were laid down in water and indicate the palaeocurrent direction, the flow direction of the depositing current.

Figure C5.1e Mudcracks, fossil mudcracks that were later filled by sand. These Triassic cracks from Herault in the South of France show that, after the mud was deposited, it must have been exposed to the air and dried out. The lens cap is 5cm in diameter.

Figure C5.1d *(above right)* Large scale cross bedding, large scale slopping layers formed on the downwind side of wind-formed dunes. Note the size of the person in the foreground. This Permian dune sequence from a quarry in the north of England shows that the area was dominated by desert dunes at the time of deposition.

Figure C5.1f *(right)* Graded bedding, a single bed of sediment in which grains are coarse at the base and become finer upwards. This specimen of Aberystwyth Grits from Mid Wales shows a laminated sediment with a graded bed above. Since grading in the specimen becomes finer towards the top, the specimen is the correct 'way up' (see other 'way up' structures in Figure 11.4)

Figure C6.1 *Reconstruction of a Silurian shallow sea fossil community.*
1 *Crinoids (Pariechocrinus moniliformis);* **2** *Corals;* **3** *Corals (Favosites);* **4** *Trilobite (Calymene);* **5** *Brachiopods;* **6** *Trilobite (Dalmanites);* **7** *Gastropod (Poleumita);* **8** *Bryozoa;* **9** *Coral (Heliolites)*

Figure C6.2 *Carboniferous shallow sea fossil community.*
1 *Crinoids (Woodocrinus);* **2** *Sharks (Sphenodontus);* **3** *Colonial corals (Lonsdaelia);* **4** *Solitary corals (Caninia);* **5** *Colonial coral (Lithostrotion verticale);* **6** *Brachiopod (Productus);* **7** *Gastropod (Straparollus pentangulus);* **8** *Spirifer (a brachiopod).*

Figure C6.3 *Jurassic shallow sea and land community.*
1 Megalosaurus; 2 Sauropods (Cetiosaurus); 3 Forest of gingkos and conifers; 4 Cycads; 5 Pterodactyls; 6 Ichthyosaurs; 7 Belemnites; 8 Ammonites.

Figure C6.4 *Cretaceous marine community.*
1 Teleost fish; 2 Shark; 3 Sponges (Ventriculites); 4 Echinoids (Cidaris); 5 Echinoid (Micraster); 6 Brachiopod (Inoceramus); 7 Lobsters (Palaeastacus);
8 Gastropod (Natica); 9 Echinoid (Echinocorys); 10 Sponges (Pachinion).

Figure C6.5 *Reconstruction of a Carboniferous coal forest.*
1 *Lepidodendron;* **2** *Calamites;* **3** *Amphibian (Megalocephalus);*
4 *Giant dragonfly (Meganeura);* **5** *Tree ferns.*

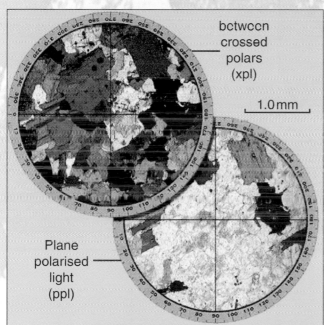

between crossed polars (xpl)

1.0 mm

Plane polarised light (ppl)

Figure C7.2a & b *High grade metamorphic rocks* **a)** *(above) A piece of gneiss with alternate light (felsic) and dark (mafic) bands, called gneiss minutiae.* **b)** *(below) Larger scale segregation with large 'augen' ('eyes') containing red garnet. This rock is called augen gneiss.*

Figure C10.1
Haematite (Fe$_2$O$_3$) an ore of iron. This specimen is about 30cm across.

Extracts from the BGS Thematic set of Maps 'Applied Geology of the Wigan Area' *Scale 1:25 000*

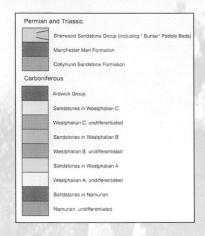

Permian and Triassic

Sherwood Sandstone Group (including " Bunter" Pebble Beds)

Manchester Marl Formation

Collyhurst Sandstone Formation

Carboniferous

Ardwick Group

Sandstones in Westphalian C

Westphalian C, undifferentiated

Sandstones in Westphalian B

Westphalian B, undifferentiated

Sandstones in Westphalian A

Westphalian A, undifferentiated

Sandstones in Namurian

Namurian, undifferentiated

C8.1 Map 1 *Bedrock geology*

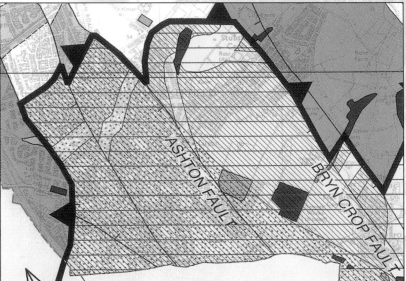

C8.2 Map 2 *Key geological factors relevant to planning and development*

A. ABANDONED SHALLOW MINE WORKINGS

A1 Abandoned shallow mine workings are unlikely:
Areas where no coal seams are believed to occur within 30m of the surface.

A2 Abandoned shallow mine workings are possible:
Areas where coal is believed to occur within 30m of the surface, but no evidence was found during the study of seams having been worked locally within the fault block, although they are known to have been mined elsewhere in the Borough.

A3 Abandoned shallow mine workings are possible and proven:
Areas where coal is believed to occur within 30m of the surface and evidence was found of seams having been worked within the fault block.

For the location of shafts and known shallow workings see Map 9 and for more details see volume 1 chapters 10 and 11; volume 2 chapter 7.

B. PAST AND PRESENT INDUSTRIAL POTENTIAL FOR CONTAMINATED LAND
Careful investigation is required at and near these sites to determine the suitability of these areas for future development

B1 Past and present industrial uses of land which may be associated with contamination
(May contain or be associated with B2 landfill sites)

B2 Landfill sites:
(May be on or associated with B1 industrial sites)
More details are given on Maps 7,6; volume 1 chapters 12,13 and 14; volume 2 chapters 5 and 6

C. POTENTIAL FOR GROUNDWATER CONTAMINATION

C1 Total catchment zone

C2 Principal recharge areas

C3 Areas with significant water source protection zones

C4 Public water supply boreholes
More details are given by Map 4; volume 1 chapter 9; volume 2 chapter 4

D. MINERAL RESOURCES

D1 Open cast working of coal may be possible, subject to planning permission, in areas within the exposed coalfield north of the Permo Triassic outcrop.

D2 Sand and Gravel from superficial deposits of glacial origin.

D3 Sand from exposed bedrock deposits of weak sandstone or where the cover of superficial deposits is not too great.

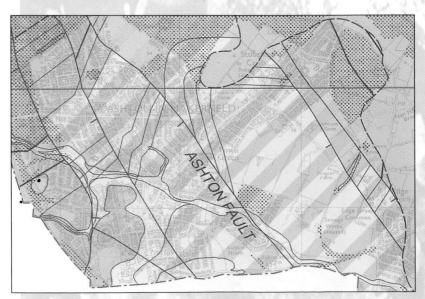

C8.3 Map 3 *Engineering geology*

ENGINEERING UNIT		GEOLOGY UNIT
ROCKS		
SANDSTONE	"STRONG"	COAL MEASURES SANDSTONE
	"WEAK"	COLLEYHURST & SHERWOOD SSTS PEBBLE BEDS
MUDSTONE	"STRONG"	COAL MEASURES MUDSTONE
	"WEAK"	MANCHESTER MARL
SOILS		
MIXED COHESIVE/ NONCOHESIVE	STIFF/DENSE	TILL (BOULDER CLAY)
	SOFT/LOOSE	LAMINATED CLAY ALLUVIUM

NONCOHESIVE	FINE		SHIRDLEY HILL SAND
		COARSE	GLACIAL SAND; GRAVEL OUTWASH GRAVEL
ORGANIC			PEAT
HIGHLY VARIABLE MIXED			MADE GROUND FILL

(a)

(i)

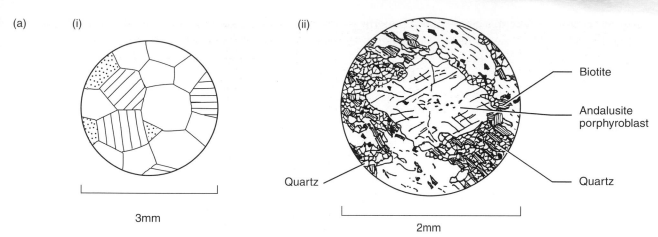

3mm

(ii)

Biotite

Andalusite
porphyroblast

Quartz

Quartz

2mm

Figure 7.4(a) *Common contact metamorphic textures found in the Skiddaw granite zones*

(i) Idealised granoblastic texture typical of recrystallisation due to metamorphism in a hornfels. The grains interlock, are nearly all the same size and crystal boundaries are frequently at 120°

(ii) A porphyroblast of andalusite such as can be found in the hornfels zone immediately around the Skiddaw granite intrusion, Lake District. Quartz grains show the granoblastic texture and the original slaty cleavage is still visible as a preferred orientation of biotite and muscovite

(b)

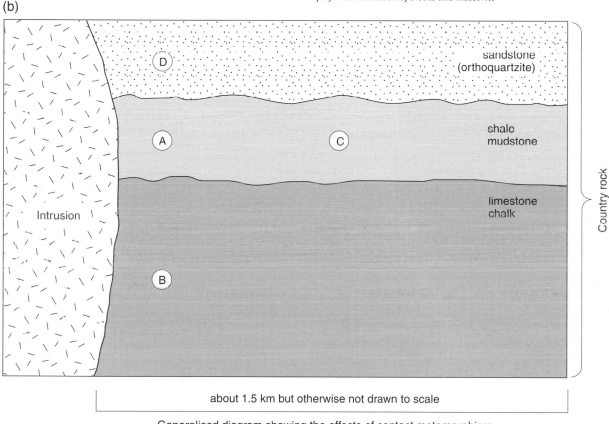

sandstone
(orthoquartzite)

shale
mudstone

limestone
chalk

Country rock

Intrusion

about 1.5 km but otherwise not drawn to scale

Generalised diagram showing the effects of contact metamorphism

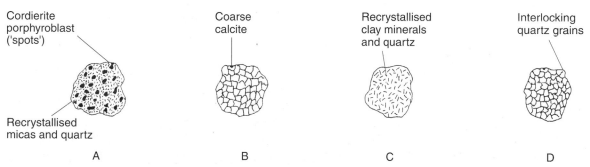

Cordierite
porphyroblast
('spots')

Recrystallised
micas and quartz

Coarse
calcite

Recrystallised
clay minerals
and quartz

Interlocking
quartz grains

A

B

C

D

Figure 7.4(b) *Contact metamorphism of sedimentary rocks and identification of metamorphic textures*

cross section and occasionally with a cross-shaped pattern of inclusions (Figure 7.4a(i)). These characteristics make it easy to identify – a user-friendly mineral!

In the inner zone of the metamorphic aureole, the original rock has totally recrystallised to a **granoblastic texture** (Figure 7.4a(i)). The rock is called **hornfels** and contains tiny equidimensional interlocking grains of quartz, andalusite, cordierite and micas, with no preferred orientation.

Contact metamorphism, otherwise known as **thermal metamorphism**, can produce broad metamorphic aureoles in the country rocks surrounding large igneous masses and narrow baked margins adjacent to small intrusions such as dykes and sills. The size of the metamorphic zone depends upon the amount of heat contained by the intrusion.

7.5 The development of foliated textures

Foliated textures are the result of the effects of increased temperature and pressure; they occur over a range of temperatures, but critically they are a response to a substantial differential stress. They are common in areas of high tectonic stress such as destructive plate margins and are found over wide swathes of country. However, they are also present on a much more restricted scale near zones of major fault movement.

The rocks most 'sensitive' to differential stress are mudstones, which contain a high proportion of platy minerals (**phyllosilicates**). These are generally fine-grained and the grains have a large surface area to volume ratio which increases reaction rates. Such fine-grained sediments show rapid changes in mineralogy as pressure increases and so provide a good record of past tectonic regimes.

The first changes that occur under high stresses and relatively low temperatures produce a partial recrystallisation of small quartz grains and a growth of new platy clay minerals in a direction perpendicular to the maximum stress (Figure C7.1). This gives the rock a well-defined **slaty cleavage** along which it can be split much more easily than across those planes. The presence of this cleavage is what distinguishes a slate from a shale. The original bedding or laminations of the sediment may still be visible, often at an angle to the more obvious cleavage. When fossils are present in such rocks they can provide an indication of the amount of deformation that has taken place. Occasionally, colour-changes caused by reduction of the iron staining in the parent muds may

provide a measurable strain marker, the original sphere now being compressed to an oval shape.

At higher pressures and temperatures (Figure 7.5 see page 131), recrystallisation is more pronounced. Clay minerals are replaced by aligned muscovite and chlorite, both platy minerals. The resulting rock, a **phyllite**, is silky to the touch, green or grey in colour and has a distinct sheen caused by reflections off myriad tiny muscovite crystals.

With increasing temperature and pressure, medium to coarse-grained recrystallisation results in a wavy foliation called **schistosity**. The minerals are large enough to identify with a lens or good eyesight, and the rocks, now termed **schists**, are named for the abundant metamorphic minerals they contain, e.g. **chlorite schist**, or the higher temperature **biotite schist**.

As pressures and temperatures increase further, the coarse grains of paler minerals (quartz and feldspar) tend to segregate in crude bands between the darker layers, rich in biotite, muscovite or garnet. These alternate dark and light layers are called **gneissose banding** (Figure C7.2).

Banded **gneisses** are unmistakable, but the mechanisms of their formation are complex; the bands may be the result of the partial melting of low melting point quartz and feldspar that then separate from the higher melting point darker minerals. At higher temperatures still, the degree of melting increases and the characteristic banding of gneisses is lost. The resulting rock looks as if it were a badly-stirred mixture of felsic and more mafic rock. It is termed a **migmatite** and is on the verge of becoming a migrating melt, which takes us into the realms of igneous processes.

7.6 Geothermometers and geobarometers: the Al₂SiO₅ polymorphs

The minerals formed during metamorphism depend to a large extent on the temperatures and pressures reached. However, they are also controlled by the parent rock-type and are influenced by a host of other factors, such as the presence of particular minerals. To help in the study of metamorphic processes and the metamorphic history of rocks, simple systems with only a few variables have been extensively tested in laboratory conditions. Figure 7.6 shows the stability fields of the three minerals, **kyanite**, **sillimanite** and **andalusite**. They are polymorphs, i.e. they have the same chemical formula (Al_2SiO_5) but different crystal structures and so different physical properties, e.g. crystal form.

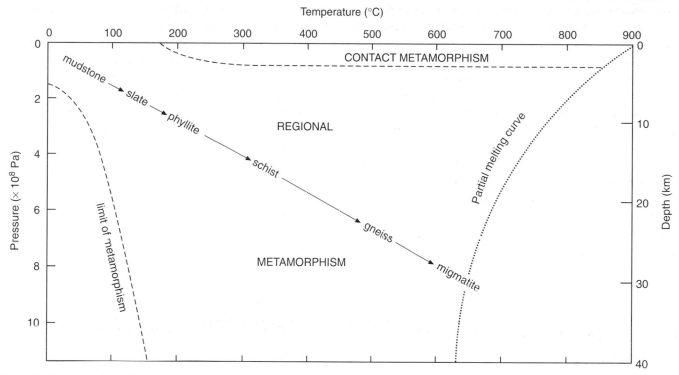

Figure 7.5 *Diagram showing the increasing pressures and temperatures involved in the slate / phyllite / schist / gneiss / migmatite progression, showing the relative positions of conditions that can produce a progression of metamorphic rocks from a fine-grained sediment*

When a critical temperature or pressure is exceeded, one polymorph changes into another; only at the triple point where the three stability fields meet, at 500 °C and 4×10^8 Pa, can all three polymorphs be found together. The Figure is one example of how the conditions under which these minerals were formed can be estimated for real metamorphic situations. To establish the temperatures (geothermometry) and pressures (geobarometry) more precisely, many different mineral reactions have had to be determined experimentally.

7.7 Dynamic metamorphism

As you might reasonably expect, when one section of the Earth's crust moves in relation to another, there are profound, if localised, alterations to the fabric of the parent-rock. This only involves a rearrangement of the components already present in the parent-rock, and is largely a matter of breaking the rock up into smaller pieces in the vicinity of fault planes or shear zones, a process called **cataclasis**. The recognition of the products of dynamic metamorphism help the geologist to determine the structural history of a region.

The product of this metamorphism depends on the depth at which faulting occurs (higher load pressures and temperatures increase the possibility of ductile

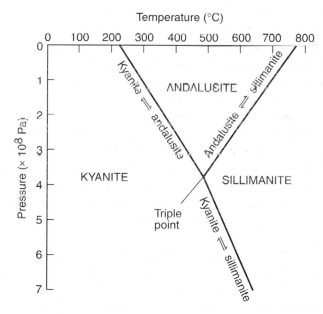

Figure 7.6 *Pressure temperature dependence of the Al_2SiO_5 polymorphs*

deformation), and the amount of relative movement (a nappe moving several tens of kilometres can do a more thorough job of destroying the original fabric than a fault moving a metre or so).

At shallow levels in the crust, brittle fracture dominates and the zone of fault movement is characterised by angular fragments of rock (**fault breccia**) set in a finer-grained matrix produced by the grinding of rock on rock (**fault gouge**). In the early stages of a fault's history it acts frequently as an easy pathway for groundwater and so becomes a site for the crystallisation of minerals such as calcite or quartz which can cement the fault breccia after movement has ended (Figure 7.7).

At deeper levels, where ductile deformation is more important, the shearing action of fault movement produces a fine-grained metamorphic rock consisting of lens-shaped fragments in a streaky, very fine-grained matrix (Figure 7.8). This material is so obviously different from the undeformed country rock that it is given the name **mylonite** (from the Greek for mill – *mulon*). The alignment of the sheared rock particles can give a rough foliation to the rock and the fine matrix may show signs of recrystallisation. An example in Switzerland marks the basal plane of a nappe which has moved 35 km in 10 Ma. The effects of the movement of a 2.5 km thick nappe over this large distance has been to produce a mylonite with foliation parallel to the direction of movement in a distinct layer only a few metres in thickness. In Britain, the Moine Thrust of north west Scotland is associated with an intensely deformed rock layer which probably resulted from earlier shear movement at depth.

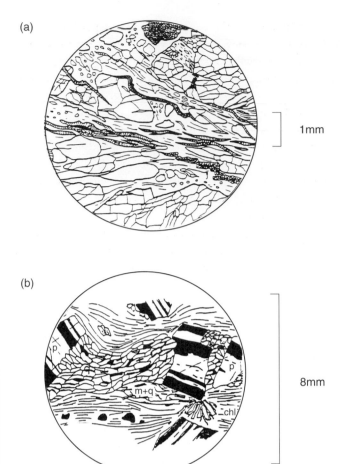

(a)

1mm

(b)

8mm

Figure 7.8 *Drawings of thin sections of mylonite: (a) A thin section of the Lochstein Mylonite found below the Glarus Nappe in Switzerland. The extensive movement of the 2.5 km thick nappe has resulted in clear foliation in the mylonite. It is composed of calcite crystals and fragmented veins; (b) A large plagioclase feldspar crystal (p) has been extended during the deformation, quartz has been recrystallised in the fractures. The foliation in this mylonite is shown by the alignment of muscovite (m) and chlorite (chl)*

7.8 Contact metasomatism: breaking the 'rules' of metamorphism

In this process the metamorphic rules established so far in this chapter are broken. This is metamorphism accompanied by the introduction or removal of *new* elements or ions – the process is no longer isochemical. These additions to the system are brought in by hot fluids in the vicinity of intrusions; they may supply ions from the late stages of crystallisation of the igneous intrusion or merely pick them up as they pass through the country rocks. The process of changing the mineral composition of rocks in this way is called **metasomatism**. The loss or gain of components means that we are now dealing with an open system, as opposed to the closed systems (nothing added or taken away) of most metamorphic processes.

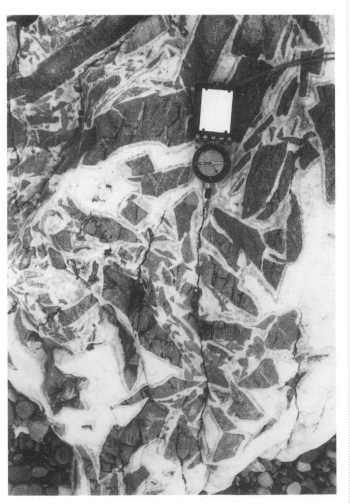

Figure 7.7 *Fault breccia created in Carboniferous limestone at Ogmore-by-Sea*

The fluids are able to affect rocks at surprisingly large distances from the source. This is graphically illustrated by the tendency for the metamorphic aureoles (areas affected by metamorphism) around granitic intrusions to be larger than those around gabbroic intrusions of the same volume. As the gabbroic magma was intruded at temperatures several hundred degrees higher than the granite, the gabbro should have a wider influence. It is the abundance of fluids associated with granitic instrusions that makes the difference. This is another reminder that rocks are poor conductors of heat, which is more efficiently carried by fluids.

The hydrothermal circulation set up on the flanks of ocean ridges (see page 60) and responsible for 25 per cent of all heat energy lost from the interior of the planet, is an economically important example of metasomatism. Sea water enters the oceanic crust with ease because the pillow basalts and sheeted dykes are highly jointed, and become part of an active circulation pattern. The basalts through which the hot fluids pass are changed appreciably by metasomatism. They have often lost calcium and silicon to the fluids but gained magnesium from the sea water.

The effect of the fluids from granitic magmas on limestones can produce an interesting range of metasomatic rocks called **skarns**. These are of economic interest as they often contain ores as oxides or sulphides (e.g. magnetite or chalcopyrite), and also frequently contain a bewildering array of magnesium, calcium, boron and manganese silicates.

7.9 Plate tectonics and metamorphic rocks

The study of metamorphic rocks allows us to recognise the effects of past plate-tectonic events. These effects are concentrated near plate boundaries, and so produce metamorphic rocks in belts a few hundred kilometres wide but often thousands of kilometres in length. These extensive areas are said to be **regionally metamorphosed**, and usually contain foliated rocks. The metamorphic belts are recognisable as the roots of ancient mountain belts, occurring even in the deeply eroded ancient shield areas such as the Precambrian of the African continent. It is assumed that similar metamorphic rocks underlie most of the sediments covering less-deeply eroded continents, so these rocks are not rare. Because in regional metamorphism, both movement and heating are involved, the metamorphism is also referred to as **dynamothermal**.

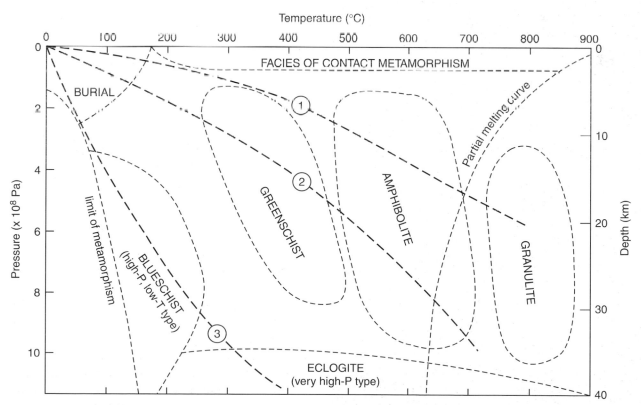

Figure 7.9 *Some of the metamorphic facies named after characteristic minerals or rock types. The paths labelled 1, 2, 3 represent the P/T conditions found (1) at volcanic arcs such as above a subduction zone (2) within a continental plate and (3) the upper part of a subduction zone, near the trench*

Plate margins where spreading, or merely strike-slip, movement is taking place do not produce startling metamorphism. The subtle effects of extension of the lithosphere and the associated high geothermal gradient are still the subject of heated debate. A long-lasting metamorphic record is only produced at convergent margins.

The most striking example is that of the paired metamorphic belts produced by subduction zones. At the trench, the geothermal gradient is exceptionally low and is accompanied by high tectonic forces. The unique combination of high pressure and low temperatures results in the formation of characteristic metamorphic minerals making up the **blueschist facies** (Figure 7.9). The 'blue' refers to the presence of the sodium-rich amphibole called glaucophane, which is easily recognisable in thin section, giving a navy-blue colour to the rock. The subduction also results in the release of water into the overlying asthenosphere and a consequent increase in melting above the slab. The rising melt, which can eventually give rise to the volcanoes of the island arc, transports heat efficiently to the surface. This results in a belt of high temperature/low pressure metamorphism. If parallel belts of these distinct facies are found in rocks, the past influence of a subduction zone can be recognised.

By comparing Figure 7.9 and Figure 7.5 you will see how the wide variety of temperature and pressure conditions experienced by the different rock types have been classified according to an important metamorphic mineral or group of minerals typifying these conditions. In this way, **metamorphic facies** are recognised. For example, rocks of the **greenschist** metamorphic facies are likely to contain chlorite indicating relatively low temperature and pressure conditions as chlorite breaks down above about 800 MPa or 500 °C.

chlorite + quartz → talc + garnet + H_2O

Higher pressures and temperatures could result in **amphibolite facies** rocks. Within this pressure and temperature range, metamorphosed mafic igneous rocks are composed largely of the common amphibole mineral hornblende. Basalt subjected to very high pressures without the usual high temperatures can result in an **eclogite** rock containing the minerals pyroxene and garnet. These may be associated with blueschists. The other extreme high grade metamorphic facies is **granulite**. This is characteristic of rocks subjected to extremely high temperatures. No hydrous minerals such as micas or amphiboles are present but rocks may contain pyroxene, garnet, kyanite or sillimanite and can be foliated.

All types of convergent margin generate a variety of metamorphic rocks. The continent–continent collision which gives rise to a mountain chain presents a serious challenge to the geologist. One of the difficulties is that the rocks involved may include previously metamorphosed 'basement'! The Alpine–Himalayan chain has provided a wealth of evidence for European geologists, and the Alps have now been sub-divided into a series of metamorphic belts reminiscent of the Barrow zones of NE Scotland. These range from merely folded, unmetamorphosed rocks on the outer flanks of the mountains to zones of extreme high pressure metamorphism (3000 MPa equivalent to depths of 100 km) within the chain where subduction followed by uplift took place. The regional metamorphism took place over a considerable time period. The earliest event was in the Late Cretaceous (90 to 65 Ma), the latest in the Oligocene or Miocene (38 to 5 Ma). Despite the fact that geologists have been studying this spectacular collision zone for the past 100 years, it is only recently that the metamorphic mapping has been completed. Interpretation of Alpine metamorphic history and its correlation with all the other geological evidence is still a matter of hot debate.

As well as causing regional metamorphism, plate tectonic processes are the major cause of tectonic activity, as studied in the following chapter.

7.10 Summary

1 Metamorphism is the result of two physical changes, those of temperature and pressure.

2 Increases of temperature with depth can be plotted as geothermal gradients.

3 Metamorphism by pressure requires differential stress and is not simply the result of increasing depth of burial.

4 Contact metamorphism occurs when temperatures are high but pressures are relatively low, in the vicinity of igneous intrusions.

5 Regional metamorphism and the foliated rocks that result are caused by increased pressure and temperature.

6 An idea of the conditions that produced metamorphism can be gauged by using mineral geothermometers and geobarometers, in particular the aluminium silicate minerals.

7 Dynamic metamorphism results from the grinding and breaking of rocks adjacent to major fault planes.

8 While most metamorphic processes are isochemical, involving no change in chemistry, when elements are added or removed by fluids, the processes are called metasomatic.

9 Plate tectonic processes are ultimately responsible for the effects preserved in metamorphic rocks

7.11 Questions

1 If the upper continental crustal rocks have an average density of 2800 kg m^{-3}, what would be the pressure at 100 metres, 1 km and 35 km depth? Recall that the acceleration due to gravity is approximately 10 metres sec^{-2} and that pressure is a force (equal to mass times acceleration) per unit area.

   Answer: A column of rock with a cross sectional area of 1 m^2 and 100 m depth has a mass of 2.8×10^5 kg, giving a pressure of 2.8×10^6 N m^{-2} or 2.8 MPa. Ten times that depth gives 28 MPa and at 35 km, the base of the continental crust is under a pressure of approximately 1000 MPa – roughly equivalent to 10 000 times atmospheric pressure.

2 Plot graphs using the data from the Table in Figure 7.10 for temperatures attained at increasing distances from various plutons. These vary according to their size and their original temperature which depends on the chemistry of the intrusive magma.

Figure 7.10 *A comparison of the change in temperature of country rocks with distance from an intrusion. Intrusions of different magma temperature and size are given at a depth of 5 km below the surface where the original country rock temperature was 150 °C*

Magma type	Magma temperature (°C)	Intrusion diameter (km)	Temp at contact 0 km (°C)	Temp at 0.5 km away from contact (°C)	Temp at 1.0 km away from contact (°C)	Temp at 2.5 km away from contact (°C)
gabbro	1200	5	875	775	700	550
syenite	900	5	700	625	550	450
granite	800	5	650	575	500	425
granite	800	1	650	460	330	150

3 If hornfels is a metamorphic rock requiring a temperature of around 500 °C to form, use the plots from the exercise above to estimate the relative sizes of the zones in which it could be found around the plutons.

4 Garnets that grow during regional metamorphic processes sometimes contain inclusions that follow the lines of the original layering of the rock. The garnets may have inclusions reflecting parallel straight layers while the surrounding rock contains highly folded layers. How is this possible?

5 How is marble formed during regional metamorphism likely to differ from marble formed during contact metamorphism?

6 At Knockan in north west Scotland, there is an escarpment in which the top of the scarp is formed of regionally metamorphosed schists which overlie unmetamorphosed sediments; a zone of shattered rock is found between the two. How might this be explained? What might have been the original causes of this phenomenon?

7 In some parts of the Scottish Highlands, granite plutons are surrounded by areas of migmatites which are in turn surrounded by gneisses and schists. How might this situation have developed?

CHAPTER 8

Tectonic processes: folding, faulting, deformation

Introduction

Tectonic processes are linked to the plate movements which occur in the outer layers of the Earth. The forces involved deform (bend and/or break) rocks in the Earth's crust. Small plate movements can be observed today but there is evidence in the rocks that, over long periods of time, deformation on an enormous scale has occurred.

The key questions and puzzles to be solved by the geologist are:

- how do rocks deform?
- why do rocks deform in different ways?
- what kinds of structures are produced?

This chapter looks at the different types of structures produced by tectonic processes. It also shows how an understanding of rock deformation is linked to landscape features and how people live.

8.1   Case study – The view from the air

Figure 8.1(a) *Oblique aerial photograph of plunging Sheep Mountain anticline in Wyoming*

Aerial photographs can show the effects of rock deformation on a regional scale. Figure 8.1a is an aerial photograph of Sheep Mountain in Wyoming, USA and shows one of the effects of large-scale compression of rocks. The rock layers were once horizontal, but compression has bent the layers to produce the complex pattern you can see.

Erosion has removed the rock sequence that once arched over the top leaving the sloping beds visible on either side. The harder rocks remain to form ridges in the centre of the structure. This folding can be seen so clearly because, in the arid climate of Wyoming, little vegetation or soil has formed to obscure the rock structure.

Figure 8.1b shows a different type of deformation. Here, the rocks have fractured along the San Andreas Fault line in California. Dramatic movement occurred near here on 17 January 1994 when an earthquake hit Los Angeles. The following day, newspapers around the world reported that a million people were without lights or heating, there were over 100 fires, up to 1000 buildings were damaged, there was flooding linked to damaged water mains and at least 24 people were feared killed.

Such regional scale deformation is the result of the enormous stresses developed by plate tectonic movement. The results can be seen not only on this large scale, but right down to the microscopic scale in the bending and fracturing of individual minerals in rocks.

Figure 8.1(b) *Aerial view of the San Andreas Fault as it crosses the Carrizo Plain some 450 km south of San Francisco. Note the elevated Elkhorn Scarp to the left of the picture*

8.2 How rocks deform

The fractured rocks left after earthquakes, like the one that hit Los Angeles in 1994, show that the Earth's surface responds in different ways to large-scale forces deeper in the Earth. Figure 8.2 shows a steep slope (**scarp**) with a height of 7 metres produced when rocks fractured and slipped, forming a **fault** during an earthquake that

Figure 8.2 *Fault scarp formed as a result of the earthquake that struck Maddison River Canyon on 17th August 1959*

occurred near Maddison River Canyon, in Montana, USA, in 1959. Although fault scarps are sometimes produced by recent earthquakes, most deformation in the crust takes place too slowly or too far down to be observed.

Faults and **folds** (bent layers of rock, like the ones shown in Figure 8.1a) are the two main types of structures produced when rocks deform in the Earth's crust. The forces (**stresses**) which cause **deformation** (change in shape and/or volume) of the rock are shown in Figure 8.3. There are three types of stresses that commonly act on rocks. These are **compressional**, **tensional** and **shear** stresses.

8.3 Why do rocks deform in different ways?

8.3.1 BRITTLE AND DUCTILE DEFORMATION

It is hard to imagine how the solid, strong rock layers we see in cliffs today could have been deformed into folds and faults. Laboratory tests on cylinders of rock show that rocks deform in different ways as stresses increase. Figure 8.4 shows the typical stress-strain curve produced in one of these experiments. The rock first shows **elastic deformation** which means that it will return to its original shape and size when stress is removed. At the **elastic**

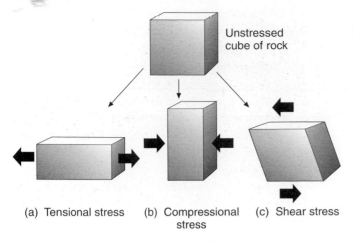

(a) Tensional stress   (b) Compressional   (c) Shear stress
                                    stress

Figure 8.3 *Effects of tensional, compressional and shear stress on a cube of rock*

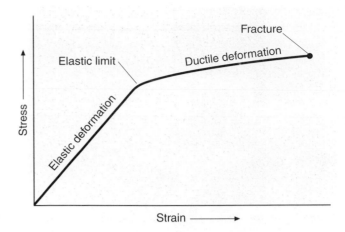

Figure 8.4 *A stress-strain curve for a cylinder of rock tested in the laboratory*

limit, the rock starts to show **ductile** or **plastic deformation** and begins to flow. At this stage, the changes in shape and size become permanent when the stress is removed so that bent materials stay bent. **Fracture** finally occurs when the stress is increased so much that the strength of the rock is exceeded and it breaks.

Try dropping pieces of plasticine and chalk on a hard surface from the same height to show ductile and **brittle deformation**. One material is brittle and will fracture on impact; the other is ductile and will bend but not break when it hits the surface.

When laboratory experiments were carried out on marble cylinders under similar compressional forces at different confining pressures, they gave one clue about

how rocks deform. In these short-term experiments, increasing confining pressure represents greater depth in the crust. The results of the experiment demonstrated that a rock can show brittle deformation (fracture) at shallow depths but can be ductile (bend and flow) at greater depths in the crust.

8.3.2   FACTORS CONTROLLING DEFORMATION

The conditions controlling deformation are complex. A wide range of factors affect rock and these factors interact with one another. The Table in Figure 8.5 describes the major factors.

Figure 8.5 *The factors controlling deformation*

Factor	Description	Effects
Temperature	temperatures generally increase with depth in the crust. The geothermal gradient varies from place to place from 5 °Ckm^{-1} to 75 °Ckm^{-1}.	At higher temperatures, rocks are more likely to show ductile deformation bending and flowing.
Confining stress (or pressure)	the uniform stress in rocks caused by the mass of the rocks lying above.	i) Rocks are easier to deform near the surface where confining stresses are lower than at greater depth in the crust. ii) Rocks tend to fracture under low confining stresses. iii) Rocks are more likely to be ductile at higher confining stress.
Time/strain rate	time refers to the length of time a stress is applied. The strain rate is the rate at which a material deforms.	i) Some rock materials show ductile deformation over longer periods of time but are brittle when the same stress is applied suddenly. ii) The lower the strain rate, the higher the chance of ductile deformation.
Composition of the rock	this refers to the mineral content and the water content of the rock.	i) Some rock-forming minerals like mica and calcite are usually ductile. Other rock forming minerals like quartz, olivine and garnet are more brittle. ii) Wet rocks are more likely to show ductile deformation than dry rocks. (One reason for this is that water may coat the mineral grains and so reduce the friction between grains.)

Figure 8.6 *a) Normal faults in Triassic sandstones at Bromborough (Wirral) b) Anticline fold at Saundersfoot (S. Wales)*

When sequences made up of different rock layers like sandstone and shale are compressed, these rocks deform in different ways. Sandstone is usually a stronger **competent** rock and is more likely to fracture during deformation, whereas shale is **incompetent**. This means the shale is usually more ductile than a competent rock and so flows more easily.

Faulted and folded layers are illustrated in Figures 8.6a and b. In Figure 8.6a the layers of rock show brittle deformation and faulting. Figure 8.6b illustrates how rocks are affected by ductile deformation resulting in folding.

8.4 What kinds of structures can be formed?

8.4.1 THE STRESS FIELDS PRODUCING DIFFERENT STRUCTURES

When a ball of plasticine is squeezed it forms an ellipsoidal (rugby ball) shape. The forces acting on this ball of plasticine can be resolved into three **principal**

stresses acting at right angles to one another. These are called P_{max}, P_{inter} and P_{min} (Figure 8.7). The stresses make up the **stress field**. P_{max} is the greatest stress, P_{min} is the minimum stress and P_{inter} is the intermediate stress. In the Earth the orientation of the stress field affects the type and patterns of structures produced. The load of the overlying rocks is always one of these principal stresses; it acts vertically downwards but it may not be the maximum stress.

8.4.2 WAYS OF MEASURING STRUCTURES

Dip is the angle in degrees by which the rocks have been tilted. It is measured between the horizontal and the maximum slope on the bedding plane (as shown on Figure 8.8), using a clinometer. You can make a simple clinometer by mounting a protractor on a piece of thick card and hanging a plumb line from the centre of the protractor.

Dip direction is the direction in which the rocks have been tilted. It can be measured using a compass and is usually given as a bearing from North, so East is 090°.

Strike is the compass direction of a horizontal line along the tilted layer of rock. Strike is a trend at right angles to the dip direction and so has two directions e.g. N–S is 000°–180°.

8.4.3 DUCTILE DEFORMATION: FOLDING

By bending strips of plasticine you can model the fold shapes produced by ductile deformation. Try deforming thick plasticine strips by pushing the ends towards one another to form simple fold shapes. Next, try bending thinner strips to see the types of fold produced.

Figure 8.9 shows the standard terms used for the parts of a fold. You will find it helpful to make a simple model using a piece of folded paper as you read through the

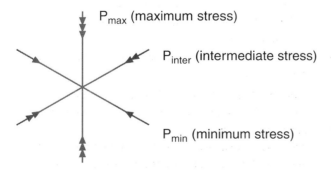

P_{max} (maximum stress)

P_{inter} (intermediate stress)

P_{min} (minimum stress)

Figure 8.7 *The three dimensional stress field that can cause rock deformation*

(a)

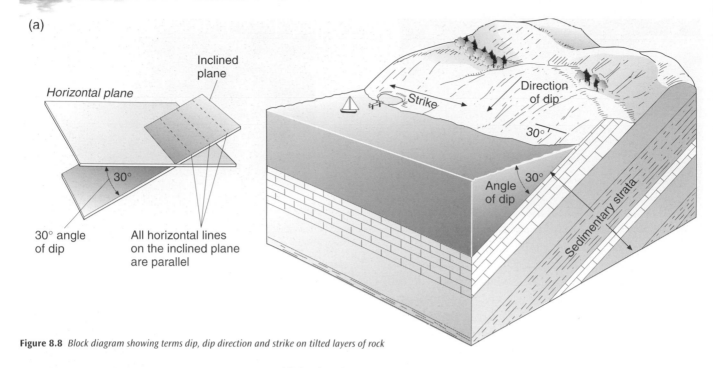

Figure 8.8 *Block diagram showing terms dip, dip direction and strike on tilted layers of rock*

Figure 8.9 *The parts of folds*

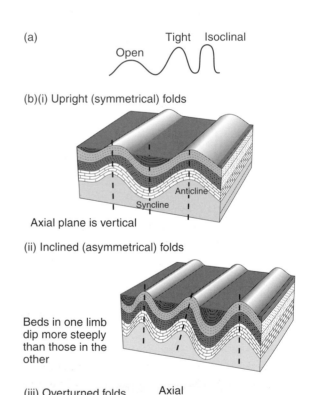

(a)

Open   Tight   Isoclinal

(b)(i) Upright (symmetrical) folds

Axial plane is vertical

(ii) Inclined (asymmetrical) folds

Beds in one limb dip more steeply than those in the other

(iii) Overturned folds   Axial plane

These folds develop into recumbent folds when the axis plane is tilted so it is horizontal

Upper limb of syncline and lower limb of anticline, tilted beyond vertical, dip in same direction

Figure 8.10 *a) Fold terms used to describe a fold according to the angle between its limbs b) Fold terms used to describe a fold according to the dip of its axial plane*

following description. You could try adding your own labels to the model to help you to remember the terms.

The place where the rocks are bent most is the **hinge** and the two sides of a fold are called **limbs**. The dip direction, dip and strike of each limb can be measured. The **axial plane** is the surface that divides a fold into two roughly equal parts and bisects the angle of the fold. The **axial plane trace** is where the axial plane intersects the Earth's surface. The **fold axis** is an imaginary straight line which is parallel to the hinge line. Two useful measurements of regular folds are **wavelength** and **amplitude**. Wavelength is the distance between two crests or troughs on a fold. The amplitude is half the vertical distance between the crest and trough of a fold.

Upfolds or arch-shaped folds are called **antiforms**. Downfolds or trough-shaped folds are **synforms**. The

Figure 8.11 *Landers Earthquake image, showing how a satellite captured an Earth movement over an area of 100 km²*

obvious difference between these fold types is that antiforms have limbs which dip away from each other whereas synforms have limbs dipping towards each other.

An **anticline** is an antiform in which the beds get younger away from the core of the fold; most antiforms are anticlines. A **dome** is like a very large over-turned bowl; it is an upfold with all the rock layers dipping outwards (see Figure 8.1a) away from the centre. Dome structures are of great importance as oil traps in the North Sea and elsewhere.

A **syncline** is a synform which has beds getting younger towards the core of the fold and most synforms are also synclines. A **basin** is a very large downfold where at the surface the rocks get younger towards the centre.

Anticlines and synclines have different shapes and some of the standard terms used to describe these shapes are shown in Figure 8.10.

For some folds, the fold axis is not horizontal but tilted. You can use a sheet of paper to model a fold like this by making an upfold and then tilting the top edge downwards. When a fold has a tilted fold axis it is described as a **plunging fold**. The **plunge** is the angle of dip of the **fold crest** or trough from the horizontal.

8.4.4 BRITTLE DEFORMATION: FAULTS AND JOINTS

If you try to bend a wooden ruler you will find that it snaps; it fractures easily because the material is prone to brittle deformation. On 28 June 1992 there was an earthquake with a magnitude of 7.3 on the Richter scale in Landers in Southern California. This was caused when the Earth's crust fractured in a sudden brittle deformation. The European remote sensing satellite ERS-1 obtained images of the area just before and just after this earth movement. As a result, the amounts of movement in the ground surface could be picked out. Figure 8.11 shows the black and white image of ground shifts produced by a computer from the satellite data. The lines are closer together where movement was greatest.

Faults like folds can also be described by standard terms. The **fault plane** is the fracture surface where movement took place. The fault plane can be measured by the dip angle, dip direction and strike. For some faults, it is vertical (has a dip of 90°) but for most faults the fault plane is merely tilted. The **throw** of a fault is the amount of vertical displacement (Figure 8.12). For some faults the movement is either horizontal or vertical but there are examples of faults where both horizontal and vertical movements have taken place.

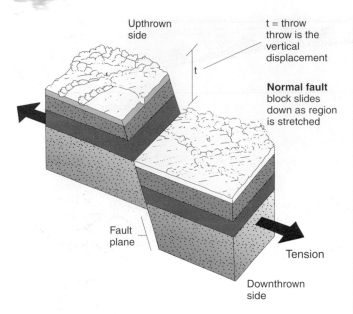

Upthrown side

t = throw
throw is the vertical displacement

Normal fault
block slides down as region is stretched

Fault plane

Tension

Downthrown side

Figure 8.12 *Block diagram showing a normal fault*

Whereas folds are usually produced by compressional forces, faults can be formed by compressional, tensional or shear forces. Shear forces result in **strike slip** (**transcurrent** or **wrench**) **faults** that show a horizontal movement parallel to the strike of the fault plane. Tensional stresses cause **normal faults** where, as the crust is pulled apart, one side slides down; these are the most common type of fault.

Compression produces **reverse faults** where one section of rocks is forced up over another. Reverse faults with a low angle of dip are called **thrust faults** and in large scale thrust faulting, blocks of rock can be forced several kilometres across other rocks. Normal, reverse and thrust faults are all **dip slip faults** which have moved parallel to the direction of dip of the fault plane. The different types of fault and the stresses that cause them are shown in Figure 8.13 and their main features are summarised in the Table in Figure 8.14.

If you look back at Figures 8.2 and 8.6a you will remember that faults may be recognised in two main ways. One is by the throw of the rock layers. The other way is by a scarp formed along the fault plane. There are also cases of large faults being marked by long straight valleys or straight river courses (Figure 8.24). These two features are best recognised on aerial photographs or maps of an area but they can also be identified in the field. Smaller scale features which can also be used to pick out a fault are **slickensides**. These are striations or small parallel scratches and grooves produced by fault movement. Faulting is also indicated by **fault breccias** (Figure 7.7); angular fragments formed by crushing and shattering of rocks along the fault plane as the fault moved. In some cases, finely ground or crushed material called **fault gouge** is produced; this material, similar to

clay, can become soft and sticky when it is wet. Mineral veins can also form along fault planes and are useful indicators because they are often of different colour or weather in a distinctive way.

Joints, like faults, are formed by brittle deformation. This means that joint patterns are usually regular and linked to other tectonic structures like folds and faults. When rocks are compressed they fracture at angles to the compressive stresses forming **shear joints**. **Tension joints** are formed at right angles to the main direction of extension when rocks are pulled apart. Joints can also be formed by other processes and may for example develop during cooling of a lava flow. Other types of joints, **unloading** (or **stress release**) joints, are formed when overlying material is removed from rocks.

Brittle deformation of some layers can take place as folding occurs. You can see this yourself when you bend an eraser between your fingers. At first it simply bends but as you squash the ends together very tightly, small cracks appear on the hinge of the fold. In rocks, the equivalent cracks are joints. Most often they form on the crests of anticlines or in the troughs of synclines.

8.4.5 CAUSING THE DEFORMATION

Deformation on a regional scale is caused by plate movement. Where plates are moving apart, the divergence causes tensional stress. Some ductile stretching of the crustal rocks can occur, but the main tectonic effect is faulting caused by brittle failure. The tension usually results in a series of normal faults causing the crust to move downwards in blocks rather like a staircase, so that this type of faulting is also known as **step faulting**. If this occurs on either side of the plate margin, step faulting causes the central block to subside in a **rift valley**. The East African Rift Valley, with its steep faulted sides and flat floor, flooded in places by long narrow lakes, is an excellent example of rift valley formation on land that has been produced by the development of a divergent plate margin in fairly recent geological times. Similar rift valleys form along the axes of ridges at divergent plate margins in ocean (axial rift Figure 4.10).

At convergent plate margins, compression produces a different set of tectonic features, often forming a mountain belt. Plate tectonic activity that produces such a mountain belt is called a **mountain building episode** or an **orogeny**. Large fold mountain belts are formed by continent–continent collision, where sedimentary rocks of the continental shelf are faulted, folded and uplifted. For example, when India collided with Asia, the Himalayan mountain chain was formed and shallow water limestones were elevated to altitudes of more than 8000 m.

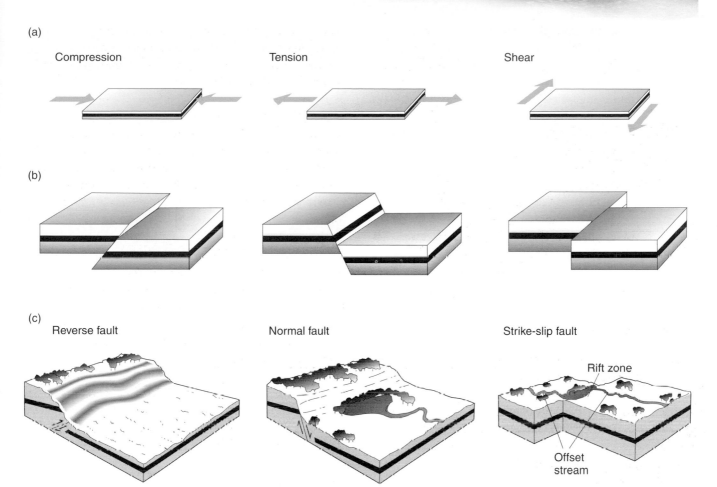

(a)

Compression   Tension   Shear

(b)

(c)

Reverse fault   Normal fault   Strike-slip fault

Rift zone

Offset
stream

Figure 8.13 *a) Compressional, tensional and shear forces deforming three layers of rock b) the results of brittle deformation under these forces c) common effects of these fault types on topography*

Figure 8.14 *Table summarising the features of the main types of faults*

Type of fault	Stress	Type of movement	Dip of fault plane
Normal	tensional	Dip slip movement. Vertical movement. The rocks *above* the fault plane appear to have moved down the fault plane in the direction of dip of the fault.	Fairly steep dip, usually 45° to 90°; often around 60° to 90°.
Reverse	compression	Dip slip movement. Vertical movement. The rocks *below* the fault plane appear to have moved down the fault plane in the direction of dip of the fault.	Shallower dip, usually 35° to 90°; often around 45°.
Thrust	strong compression	Dip slip movement. Vertical movement. The rocks below the fault plane appear to have moved down the fault plane in the direction of dip of the fault. One effect is that slabs of older rocks may have been moved tens of kilometres over younger slabs.	Gentle dip, less than 35°; often with angle of dip of 15° or less.
Strike-slip (also called wrench, tear or transcurrent fault)	shear	Strike-slip movement. Horizontal movement. Blocks on different sides of the fault plane have moved parallel to the strike of the fault in opposite directions past each other. N.B. For a person facing the fault: a) Right lateral or dextral strike slip faults have moved rocks to the right on the opposite side of the fault b) Left lateral or sinistral strike slip faults have moved rocks to the left on the opposite side of the fault.	Usually vertical.

During orogenics, the cooler rocks near the surface behave in a brittle fashion producing reverse faults and large-scale thrust faulting on occasion. Intense compression can cause thrust faulting on a scale of tens of kilometres and, sometimes, older rocks can be thrust over younger rocks for more than a hundred kilometres.

Meanwhile, in deeper warmer more ductile zones, intense folding can be taking place, producing tight and **isoclinal** folding, usually accompanied by metamorphism. Where two continents collide, the compression can be so intense that large scale folds are forced upwards within the rising mountain chain and then slide down the outer flanks of the chain as huge folds called **nappes**. Ancient nappes can be recognised because the lower sequences in these recumbent folds are upside down and the way up criteria described on page 192 show that these beds must have been inverted during the intense folding.

Tectonic features in Scotland, such as the Dalradian Tay Nappe and the Moine Thrust Zone accompanied in some areas by high grade metamorphism (see pages 124 and 220) show that the region must have been part of a collision zone in the past, probably on the scale of the collision that produced the Alpine and Himalayan mountain belts that we are familiar with today.

While divergent margins result in tension and convergent margins produce compression, the third type of plate margin, conservative margins, cause shear stresses. Lateral movement is produced at the transform faults characteristic of these margins, resulting in strike slip (or wrench) faults. The San Andreas fault through California (Figure 8.16) is an example of such a fault seen on land today, while the Great Glen Fault in the Scottish Highlands is a large-scale strike slip fault of the past (Figure 8.24).

8.5 Unconformities

An **unconformity** is a structure marking a time when there was a major break in the deposition of sediments in an area; during this time there was a period of uplift and erosion. The uplift was caused by earth movements which may have tilted, folded or faulted the rocks. After erosion, there is then a further stage of deposition when new sediments are deposited on top of the older rocks. The time gap, or **hiatus**, is where there is no record of the events which took place because they are not represented by layers of rock in the area.

Figure 8.15 shows the geological sequence seen at Horton-in-Ribblesdale, North Yorkshire. The rocks above and below the unconformity do not have the same dip, it

Figure 8.15 *Angular unconformity at Horton-in-Ribblesdale, where steeply dipping Silurian slates are overlain by horizontal Carboniferous limestone*

is marked by an **angular discordance** and so is called an **angular unconformity**. The older rocks are steeply dipping slates of Silurian age and the younger rocks are horizontal limestones of Carboniferous age.

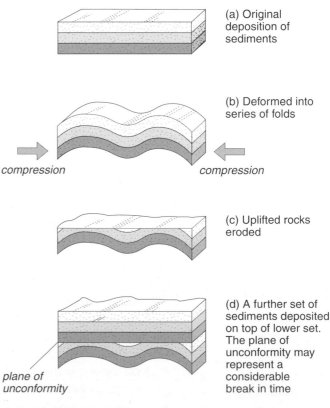

(a) Original deposition of sediments

(b) Deformed into series of folds

compression   *compression*

(c) Uplifted rocks eroded

(d) A further set of sediments deposited on top of lower set. The plane of unconformity may represent a considerable break in time

plane of unconformity

Figure 8.16 *The four main stages in the devolopment of an angular unconformity. a) deposition b) deformation (folding) c) uplift and erosion d) deposition*

Figure 8.17 *Indicators of unconformity*

Criteria	Indication of unconformity
Dip and strike of beds	Unconformities often have beds of different dip and strike above and below the unconformity.
Faults	Faults are often developed in older rock layers which are overlain by layers above the unconformity.
Igneous intrusions	Igneous intrusions may only cut older rock layers and be overlain by the layers above the unconformity.
Metamorphic rocks	Older metamorphic rocks may be in contact with unmetamorphosed layers above the unconformity.
Fossils	Fossils of different ages and possibly from different environments may indicate there has been a break in deposition.
Conglomerates/breccias (**Basal conglomerates**)	These sedimentary rocks often form on the unconformity surface at the base of the overlying sequence. The pebbles in these younger rocks are often fragments of the older rocks found below the unconformity (**included fragments**).
Irregular surfaces	These may form the unconformity surface. On a large scale they represent the irregular land surface produced by erosion. On a smaller scale they may be the surface left by boring organisms.

There are four stages in the development of such an unconformity. Initially, layers of sediment are deposited, become buried and lithified. Later the layers are deformed by folding or tilting. This is followed by a period of uplift and erosion, planing off the deformed layers. Finally, there is another period of deposition when new layers of sediment are deposited on top of the older rocks and eventually become rocks themselves. Figure 8.16 illustrates these main stages. Note that in (d) the younger beds above the unconformity **overstep** the rocks below; they lie on rocks of different age.

The Table in Figure 8.17 lists some of the criteria which can be used to identify unconformities in the field and also on geological maps. The most difficult type to recognise is where there is only an erosion surface between parallel sets of older and younger beds. This type of unconformity is called a **disconformity** and it is usually identified by the fossils of different age in the rock layers above and below the unconformity.

Unconformities are important because they provide evidence of changes in tectonic processes over time and so allow us to construct the geological history of an area, as shown in Chapter 11.

8.6 Geological maps

Although folds and faults can often be seen in quarry faces or even in hand specimens, many geological structures are of such a large size they are best picked out in aerial or satellite photographs, as shown in Figure 8.1.

The rock layers in Figure 8.1a have been folded into a plunging anticline. The aerial view shows the three-dimensional picture and helps us to understand what the structure will look like on a **geological map** which shows the surface distribution of rock types and ages.

Similarly rock sequences crossing the San Andreas Fault are displaced in the same way (Figure 8.1b), making the structure clearly visible on a geological map.

8.6.1 HOW ARE GEOLOGICAL MAPS MADE?

Geologists use their fieldwork skills to study surface **exposures** (places where rocks can be seen) in collecting data about rock types and structures in an area. The picture is complicated because softer rocks are often not exposed and structures like folds and faults may be obscured by soil and **drift**. Drift is sediment such as peat, till, sand and gravel laid down during and since the last ice age. In urban areas, the rocks are also obscured by buildings, roads, etc. and various types of **fill** or **made ground** formed by dumping material to level the ground surface or fill depressions.

The jigsaw puzzle of information is pieced together to show the total area over which a particular rock occurs or **outcrops** and how its outcrop pattern is related to the geological structure of the area. This allows geological maps to be produced; the two most common are **drift geological maps** and **solid geological maps**. Drift maps show the distribution of the superficial drift deposits under the soil; where there is no drift, they show the solid rocks beneath. Solid maps show the geology that would be seen if the buildings, soil and drift were removed. Nowadays, all information about the sub-surface that might be of value is recorded during mapping, including

Figure 8.18 *Table showing some of the sources of data and types of data used by the field geologist when compiling a geological map*

Field mapping of natural exposures	Field mapping of natural/built features	Recording information from excavations	Research into geological records	Remote sensing information
river or stream exposures	breaks in slope, vegetation/drainage changes	trenches cut for cables/ pipelines	well and borehole logs	satellite photography
coastal cliff sections	soil cover, rock foundation fragments in soils	road or rail cuttings	mine records (shaft and adit records, borehole logs)	aerial photography
inland exposures where there are steep slopes	areas of industrial/ mining activity	quarries, opencast mines and spoil heaps in mining areas	old geological maps and reports	geophysical data (gravity, magnetism)

details of the solid rocks, the drift, made ground and fill, the hydrogeological and engineering characteristics of the materials, landslide areas, distributions of past and present mining/quarrying activities and industrial uses. Any potential resources present and other factors relevant to land use planning are also recorded. All this information can be stored digitally on computer, allowing print outs to be made of different selections of information in which particular users are interested. The British Geological Survey have been developing this approach over recent years and they can print not only special maps for individual users, but also produce ranges of maps for certain areas, which they call **thematic maps**. An example is the recently produced report, 'A geological background for planning and development in Wigan', which includes these 10 thematic maps: distributions of boreholes, pits and site investigations; bedrock geology (solid geology); superficial geology (drift); hydrogeology; mineral resources; distribution of made and worked ground; previous and present industrial uses; engineering geology; shallow mining and geological factors relevant to land use planning. Parts of three of these maps are reproduced in Figure C8.1–C8.3.

The information for producing maps like these is taken from a wide range of sources, as shown in the Table in Figure 8.18.

Wherever rocks are exposed, the field geologist records rock type and description (colour, composition, texture, structure, thickness), fossil content and structural information including the dips of rocks, faults, joints and fold axes. Stratigraphic logs and palaeocurrent data may be recorded for sedimentary rocks (see page 91). The objective is to collect all possible evidence that can be used to produce a three-dimensional picture of the rocks and their origin, properties and resource potential.

8.6.2 TOPOGRAPHY, STRUCTURE AND OUTCROP PATTERNS

The pattern shown by a rock on a geological map is called the **outcrop pattern**. It is influenced by the **topography** or shape of the land surface and the geological structure. This means that where the rock layers are horizontal, the boundaries between the rock units are parallel to the ground contours (lines joining places of the same height). However, if the rock layers are dipping, then the patterns shown will be different and they will depend on the dip of the beds and the topography, illustrated in Figure 8.19.

8.6.3 USING GEOLOGICAL MAPS

Geological maps allow us to interpret the landscape and understand how the land shapes you see were formed. The area of Shropshire shown in Figure 8.20 is a view looking east across Wenlock Edge. It shows a gently rolling landscape where there are different layers of rock which have been eroded at different rates so a ridge with a steep scarp and a shallower dip slope is formed. The geological map and a section across it are shown in Figure 8.21.

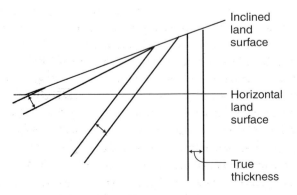

Figure 8.19 *Section showing the width of outcrop of dipping beds on an irregular topography*

Figure 8.20 *Oblique aerial photograph of Wenlock Edge, Shropshire showing the escarpment*

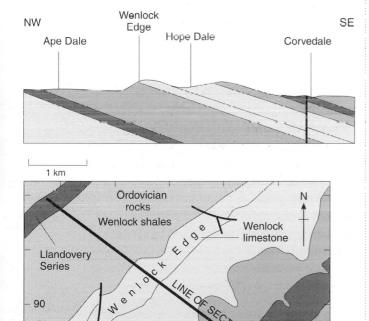

Figure 8.21 *Wenlock Edge: cross-section and simplified geological map*

Study of the map in Figure 8.21 tells you that the Wenlock Edge escarpment in the photograph is formed by the Wenlock limestone. This formation is dipping gently south east. The geological map also shows that the lower-lying ground is formed by softer rock layers such as the Wenlock Shales which have been eroded more. It shows the relationship between geology and topography in the Wenlock Edge area and so clearly illustrates the three-dimensional structure.

Geologists also study geological maps to work out the geological history of an area. They may use them to recognise where there are suitable structures for petroleum traps or underground water supplies (Chapter 9). Mining engineers use maps to identify faults which may show where mineral veins can be found (Chapter 10). In civil engineering projects, geological maps can be used to check the distribution of drift deposits which could be used as aggregates for construction. They also show where there are solid rocks which could form firm foundations. Waste disposal experts may find geological maps helpful to identify suitable landfill sites. Finally, in areas of recent volcanic or earthquake activity, geological maps are useful for people dealing with hazard assessment and planning for potential disasters.

8.7 Landscapes

Figure 8.22 *Photograph of Lulworth Cove, Dorset with Stair Hole in the foreground*

8.7.1 CONSERVING GEOLOGICAL FEATURES AND LANDFORMS

The conservation of species and habitats has become an important topic in the environment debate in recent years. Rocks, soils and landforms have been recognised as important in influencing how plants and animals live in communities and adapt to their environment. At a local level, county structure plans highlight the need to protect our heritage of geological features and landforms as well as conserve our wildlife.

Dorset County Council is an example of many local authorities which have already taken steps to produce a structure plan considering the importance of the county's geology and landscape. Figure 8.22 shows some of the outstanding coastal scenery which the planners are seeking to protect. The cove and cliff shapes in Lulworth Cove are the result of varied rock types occurring here. In recent times the rocks have eroded in different ways to create the landforms. The fold structures visible in the cliff sections were formed by deformation which took place about 15 million years ago, at the same time as the Alps were being formed.

8.7.2 LANDFORMS: RELATIONSHIPS TO DIP, FAULTS AND DRAINAGE

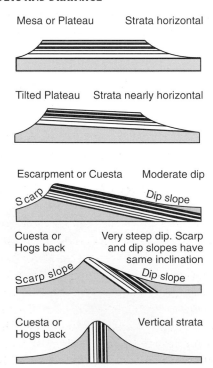

Figure 8.23 *The relation of landforms to dip*

Figure 8.24 *The Great Glen Fault*

Figure 8.23 shows how different landforms can be formed, depending on the angle of dip of the beds. A **plateau** is a large area of flat land in an area of high relief. It forms where the dip is horizontal.

An **escarpment** (**cuesta**) is a ridge with scarp and dip slopes formed where the rock layers are tilted, as was Wenlock Edge. The rock layers are of different resistance to erosion and there has been greater erosion of more easily eroded layers to produce the cuesta.

The **hogsback** is a narrow ridge formed where the dip is vertical (or nearly so). The erosion-resistant rock produces this prominent landform which has roughly equal slopes on each side. These landforms not only add interest to our landscape but also are used by geologists as important clues to the geological structure of an area.

Large faults can be marked by long straight valleys, a good example being the Great Glen Fault in Scotland. This is a major strike-slip fault which can be traced running in a north-east to south-west direction right across Scotland. There is a broad belt of shattered rocks along this fault and erosion has etched this out along the fault to form a trough. The trough is so large that it contains three major lochs: Loch Linnhe, Loch Lochy and Loch Ness. Besides producing a landform of aesthetic landscape value, the Great Glen Fault trough forms a vital transport link across the highlands. Figure 8.24 is an aerial view of this major landform.

Dendritic

Irregular (tree-like) branching of channels; characteristic of horizontally-bedded rocks or massive rocks with few weaknesses.

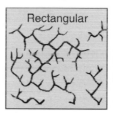

Rectangular

System of channels marked by right-angled bends; common on rocks with well developed joint patterns or on jointed foliated rocks.

Trellised

Rectangular channel arrangement with long parallel principle tributaries; characteristic of areas of escarpments and valleys ('scarp and vale topography') with long tributaries developing along the vales

Figure 8.25 *Distinctive drainage systems that are linked to rock types and structure*

In many parts of Britain, the drainage systems are related to the geological structure. The term **concordant** river systems is used where drainage patterns show a close relation to the geological structure. Figure 8.25 illustrates some of these.

8.8 Summary

1 Rocks are deformed by three different types of stress; compressional, tensional and shear stress. They respond through either elastic deformation, bouncing back when the stress is removed, through ductile deformation, by bending and flowing, or in a brittle fashion, by breaking.

2 The intensity of folding, the fold shape and other fold characteristics are controlled by a range of factors including the type, direction and amount of stress applied, the temperatures and time involved and the response of the rock material to these conditions.

3 Different types of brittle deformation are caused by different stress conditions. Tension produces normal faulting, compression causes reverse or thrust faulting and shear results in strike-slip (or transcurrent wrench) faults. Joints are commonly caused by tension.

4 The stress conditions that produce rock deformation are largely related to plate tectonic movement. Divergent plates produce tension, convergent plates cause compression and conservative margins are associated with shear.

5 Unconformities are the result of long time periods between episodes of sedimentation. They are seen most clearly when earlier rocks have been deformed and an erosion surface has been cut across them before the next series of sediments is deposited on top.

6 Geological mapping allows the tectonic structure of an area to be presented visually. The map can show up relationships between geology and topography more clearly.

8.9 Questions

1 The Table in Figure 8.5 shows some of the factors that affect whether a rock will fold or fault. How is it possible that some rocks are both folded and faulted?

2 Which of the following terms best fits the two different folds shown in the photographs in Figures 8.6b and 8.22? anticline/syncline; open/tight/isoclinal; upright/inclined/overturned/recumbent; plunging/horizontal axis; P_{max} vertical/P_{max} horizontal

3 Which types of fault are most likely to be associated with:
   a) a convergent/destructive plate margin?
   b) a divergent/constructive plate margin?
   c) a transform fault (conservative plate margin)?

4 Using Figure 8.16, Stage 4 as a model, draw:
   a) the unconformity you would expect to see if the older rocks had not only deformed by folding, but had also been faulted and intruded by a dyke before uplift and erosion;
   b) the unconformity you would expect if there had been no tilting, folding or faulting before erosion.

5 Which of the following, if found in the field:
   a) might help you to identify a fault?
   b) might help you to identify an unconformity?
      breccia, a spring, slickensides, gouge, overstep, change in slope, change in vegetation/soil

6 Use Figure 8.19 to explain how the width of outcrop of a bed changes:
   a) as its dip becomes steeper;
   b) as the slope of the land surface increases;

7 a) What is the strike of the rocks shown in Figure 8.21?
   b) Estimate their dip from the photograph in Figure 8.20.

8 a) Draw a block diagram to show how a pair of cuestas might develop using the photograph in Figure 8.20 and the map and cross section in Figure 8.21.
   b) Draw in streams to show how trellised drainage, as shown in Figure 8.25, might develop.

CHAPTER 9

Geoscience applied: resources, hazards, geotechnics

Introduction

A wide range of Earth resources is vital in constructing and maintaining our modern world and our individual lifestyles; these include constructional materials, industrial minerals, fossil fuels, water supplies and the 'hole in the ground' resource for the disposal of waste. Modern geoscience needs to be applied to find new resources, during extraction of the materials and in the rehabilitation of the landscape when extraction is complete. The destruction caused by natural hazards can be reduced by applying geoscience understanding. Geotechnical expertise is also vital to the success of many major engineering projects.

9.1 Case Study: how useful are the rocks? – the New Red Sandstone of the Cheshire Basin

When you are investigating how sediments in an area were deposited, by reviewing the published information available (as in the Case Study in Chapter 5, page 75), this can also tell you about the uses of these sediments. For the Cheshire Basin, this information shows that the rock sequences have had enormous value in the past and continue to be very important today. Examples include:

- the red sandstones that were widely used as *natural building stones* in the past.
- soft sandstones and gravel beds crushed to supply *aggregate* for construction.
- soft sandstones used as *moulding sands* to make moulds into which cast iron is poured to make castings.
- the *salt (halite)* that has been extracted from the area since Roman times. One working mine remains, providing salt for road gritting. Most salt is now recovered by controlled brine pumping (see page 154). The majority is used in the chemical industry and production in Cheshire is about five million tonnes per year.
- *gypsum* that is quarried to make cement, plaster of Paris, for filling paper and as a fertiliser; it may also be carved into alabaster ornaments.

- the *metal deposits* (e.g. copper, lead ores) that were deposited in permeable sandstones by warm saline fluids are no longer economic, but were once mined extensively.
- the *water supply* of the region, much of which is pumped out of the sandstones. Together the sandstone water reservoir rocks (aquifers) are more than one kilometre thick with porosites ranging from 20–30 per cent.
- *natural gas* in the Helsby Sandstone under the northern Irish Sea; it came from a Carboniferous coal source rock and is trapped under several different cap rocks.
- *crude oil* which is being exploited in the southern Irish Sea from New Red Sandstone rocks.
- a potential *geothermal energy resource* which, in the future, may be worth exploiting for domestic heating and similar purposes; where the sandstones are 4 km thick, the water trapped in them reaches temperatures of 80 °C.

This Case Study shows the wide range of important resources that has been, or can be supplied by the rocks from a fairly limited geological time (the Permo-Triassic see Appendix 7) and a small region (the Cheshire Basin) of the British Isles. The value and importance of the rocks and minerals from a much larger expanse of geological time across the whole of a region like the British Isles is very much greater.

Resources information from:

'Cheshire Minerals Local Plan, written statement', Collins, J.F.N., 1987. Pub. Cheshire County Council, Chester.
'Geothermal Energy – the potential in the United Kingdom', Ed. Downing, R.A. and Gray, D.A., 1986. Pub. HMSO.
'Hydrological Map of Clwyd and the Cheshire Basin, 1:100 000', 1989. Pub. British Geological Survey.

The Permo-Triassic aquifers of the Cheshire and West Lancashire basins', Gale, I.N., Evans, C.J., Smith, I.F., Houghton, M.T. and Burgess, W.G. 1984. Pub. The British Geological Survey.
'The petroleum geology of the Irish Sea and adjacent areas', Conference Abstracts, 1995. Pub. the Geological Society, London.

9.2 Applying geoscience

This Case Study of the Cheshire Basin shows the importance of resources from the ground in one area. The rock and mineral resources where you live may have an equal variety of uses and may be just as valuable. Geoscience investigations cover a range of other aspects as well. Your area will have been mapped geologically (as described on page 145) to show where the surface materials and the deeper solid rocks can be found. Thematic maps may also have been produced to show a range of other features of the area affected by the geology (see Figure C.8.1–C8.3). Maps showing areas suitable for water supply and of geothermal energy reserves may be available.

Potential flooding and landslide hazards in your region will have been studied by geoscientists and if necessary, a range of different solutions will have been put in place. Wherever large construction projects are underway, geoscience expertise is used to tackle the engineering problems involved. A range of geotechnical solutions are applied to problems associated with foundations for buildings, cuttings, slopes and tunnels, dams and engineered coastlines.

Nowadays, wherever large-scale resources are extracted, geoscientists are usually involved at all stages of the project. They are involved in the initial pre-prospecting work that may involve studying background data in maps, reports, old mining records, aerial and satellite photography, etc. They will carry out a geological reconnaissance that may involve mapping, geophysical surveying, drilling boreholes and excavating trenches and pits. They will collect samples and help to evaluate laboratory reports on them. During extraction of the resource, they will continue prospecting to give a detailed picture of the underground resource. They will advise on how the overlying material is to be stripped and, if necessary, stored and they will make recommendations on the day-to-day development of the mine or quarry. As the extraction nears its end, they will be involved in refurbishing the landscape and continued

monitoring of the site for several years after the project has been completed to ensure that all remains as it should be. The range of jobs will require different expertise at various stages, so that, over time, prospecting geologists, geophysicists, mine or quarry geoscience engineers, hydrogeologists and environmental geologists might be employed.

This illustrates how the geoscientists of today are involved in finding solutions to geoscience-related problems. Holes in the ground are excavated and then filled or preserved for their benefits; mine wastes are produced and disposed of; derelict land is reclaimed; slopes are stabilised; pollution is monitored and dealt with; problems of groundwater supply are tackled. Geoscientists are involved in the use and the conservation of the environment. The key word is sustainability; Earth resources must be exploited in such a way that environmental damage is minimised and the resources will continue to be available into the distant future.

Many resource and environmental issues will have been documented and discussed in the 'Minerals Plan' drawn up by local authorities in Britain to cover geoscience-related issues in their own areas. Geoscience studies will have been vital to the development of the area where you live, as the following pages show.

9.3 Rock resource

Globally, the production of rock materials for construction and industrial usage plays a key role in the economies of many nations. For example, in the USA the production of 'industrial minerals' (i.e. rocks and minerals) forms more than 50 per cent of the total production of materials from the ground (with fuels forming just over 40 per cent and metals around 3 per cent). This usage is also accelerating globally. Growth in the usage of industrial minerals over the last 50 years has been about 500 per cent, compared with that of fuels and metallic minerals at around 300 per cent.

Mining and quarrying makes a significant contribution

to the Gross Domestic Product (GDP), or total income of the UK every year. In the mid-1990s mining and quarrying, including the extraction of oil and gas, contributed more than £21 billion or nearly 3% of the GDP. Of this sum, oil and gas provided over 80%, coal around 8%, construction materials around 6% and other industrial minerals and metal minerals around 3%. These are the basic raw materials for the manufacturing, power supply and construction industries. The total value of these sectors to the UK economy, which are almost entirely based on these raw materials, contributed some £100 billion or 16% of GDP in the mid-1990s.

The construction materials include natural stone, roofing slates aggregates, cement, bricks, tiles and pipes. The industrial minerals are more specialist and include plaster, chemicals, ceramics, glass and foundry sands. If you look around the building where you are sitting you will see the widespread use of many of these materials.

9.3.1   CONSTRUCTIONAL MATERIALS

The largest single use of quarried materials in construction is for **aggregates**. The aggregates, largely crushed rocks or sand and gravel, are used:

- with cement to produce concrete;
- either uncoated, or with bitumen, as roadstone;
- as bulk fill, e.g. for building foundations.

The mortar used in brick and stone building (masonry) uses a mix of sand with cement – a further vital use of constructional materials.

In the UK, most sand and gravel workings come from the broad meltwater deposits of the Pleistocene ice ages. Many now form river terraces above existing rivers and are widely exploited particularly in the Thames and Trent valleys. Where sands and gravels are not so readily available, crushed rock may be a cheaper alternative (as in the Cheshire Basin Case Study above). Limestone is quarried commonly for this purpose and sometimes hard igneous rocks and sandstones may be used.

Since aggregate is a bulk resource, involving the movement of large volumes of material, transport costs are very high. This is why the construction industry needs aggregates close to cities. Unfortunately, many of the sand and gravel pits in those areas have been worked out and the remaining ones often occur in environmentally sensitive areas. The long-term solution to this problem may be superquarries, like the one recently established in Glensanda on the coast of western Scotland. Crushed rock aggregate can be discharged directly into bulk carrying ships and carried to coastal locations in Britain or overseas with costs that may be less than those for local road transport. All the aggregate used for the Channel Tunnel came from Glensanda superquarry and was made into concrete tunnel segments in the Thames Estuary before being taken south by ship to the tunnel itself.

Cement (usually called '**ordinary Portland cement**' or OPC) can be made by mixing pure limestone with shale or clay and heating it to around 1400 °C. Some impure limestones contain these materials in the correct amount and so can be used alone to make cement. The cement clinker produced at high temperature is cooled and ground to powder and then mixed with some gypsum to control the setting rate.

Bricks, tiles and pipes are made of **brick clay** excavated from brick pits. The clay is moulded to the correct shape and then fired to over 1000 °C in kilns – to produce a similar effect to high grade thermal metamorphism. The result is a tough weather-resistant 'rock' in the required shape. Some brick clays, such as the Oxford Clay of the Peterborough area contain quite high amounts of carbon; less fuel is needed to fire these clays which gives a significant cost advantage over low-carbon clays.

In the past, **natural stone** was widely used for the walls of buildings, especially in the 'limestone belt' (running from the south coast to the north east coast of England) and in the sandstone and igneous rock areas of the north and west of Britain. The use of this stone gave 'character' to picturesque villages and stately homes alike and some varieties, such as Portland Stone and Bath Stone, became nationally famous for their use in prestigious buildings such as cathedrals and town halls. Nowadays, the main use of natural stone is as thin cladding materials on the outsides of buildings made of steel and concrete. Many attractive igneous, sedimentary and metamorphic rocks are used for this purpose, some being transported from overseas. Despite a significant revival in the stone industry over the past 15 years, building stone only accounts for around 0.5 per cent of national stone production today.

9.3.2   INDUSTRIAL MINERALS

Gypsum ($CaSO_4.2H_2O$) is mined and then heated in a kiln to drive off some of the water and then ground down to the white powder, plaster of Paris ($CaSO_4.\frac{1}{2}H_2O$). When plaster of Paris is mixed with water, it expands a little and hardens to gypsum again. These properties make it ideal for smooth wall coverings, for plaster board and for a whole range of plaster casts, used for example by the ceramic industry and by dentists. Recently, natural gypsum has been coming under increasing competition from synthetic gypsum produced as a by-product of anti-pollution measures in coal-fired power stations. The sulphur dioxide (SO_2) produced by burning coal is not released into the atmosphere where it would make acid rain, but is reacted with limestone instead, to produce gypsum.

One of the major raw materials for the chemical industry is high-purity limestone, much of which is initially used to make soda ash (sodium carbonate, Na_2CO_3) as the basis of many other chemicals. It is also used as a flux to remove impurities in the iron and steel industry and to make heat resistant refractories for furnace linings.

Rock salt (formed of the mineral halite, NaCl) is also vital to the UK chemical industry, since the hydrochloric acid produced from it is widely used in the manufacture of other chemicals. It is largely obtained by brine pumping, primarily in the Cheshire Basin area (see Case Study, p 151) where hot water is pumped down to deep rock-salt deposits, the salt dissolves and the resultant brine is pumped up and evaporated to recover the salt. Salt mined in north west England and Northern Ireland is used largely for treating roads in winter.

Other important sources of chemicals are the potassium salts (potash) mined in north east England, fluorspar, barytes and coal and oil. Agricultural fertilisers are also produced from potash and limestone.

Earthenware pottery has been made from **pot clay** in many areas of Britain in the past, but the Potteries area in the English Midlands is best known today for producing ceramics. Today, most of the clay is brought into the area from the **china clay** (**kaolinite**) pits in south west England. There the clay was produced from feldspars in granite by hydrothermal alteration. Some of the clay was eroded and redeposited in lakes nearby as a fine-grained clay deposit called **ball clay**. Both are extracted for use in producing ceramics, ranging from coarse earthenware to the finest bone china. China clay is also extensively used as a filler in paper, to give the paper weight, a white colour and a smooth surface, and also as a filler in plastics, rubber and paints.

9.4 Fuel resource

Two of the pie diagrams (Figure 9.1a and b) give a guide to world and UK fuel production in the 1990s. Oil leads the way, both worldwide and in the UK. However, whilst world coal and natural gas production are about equal at around 25%, there is a different balance in the UK. The high UK natural gas production allows the export of natural gas, together with large quantities of oil. Meanwhile coal is imported to make up the shortfall in UK coal requirements. Nuclear and hydroelectric sources provide 10 per cent or less of UK and world fuel resources.

However, the picture for the future gives a different balance (Figure 9.1c). This shows only fossil fuels (coal, oil, gas, etc.). The diagram includes 'proved reserves' (those we know are in the ground and can be exploited), 17 per cent of the total, and 83 per cent of 'unproved reserves' (those we think might be in the ground).

Since it may be impossible eventually to get some of the unproved reserves out of the ground, or energy out of the unproved reserves in an economic way in the future, these estimates of fuel reserves may be high.

The overall balance shows that, while oil and gas are the most important fuels today, coal is the largest fuel reserve worldwide. Whether or not it becomes the fuel of the future depends on several factors, a major one being that the generation of electricity by coal causes more atmospheric pollution than the use of other fossil fuels.

Figure 9.1 *a) Recent world fuel consumption – 8380 million tonnes of oil equivalent per year b) Recent UK fuel consumption – 230 million tonnes of oil equivalent per year c) World reserves of fossil fuels – a total of 8200 billion tonnes of oil equivalent*

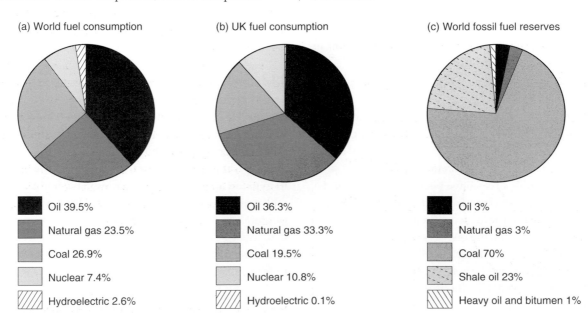

(a) World fuel consumption   (b) UK fuel consumption   (c) World fossil fuel reserves

(a)	(b)	(c)
Oil 39.5%	Oil 36.3%	Oil 3%
Natural gas 23.5%	Natural gas 33.3%	Natural gas 3%
Coal 26.9%	Coal 19.5%	Coal 70%
Nuclear 7.4%	Nuclear 10.8%	Shale oil 23%
Hydroelectric 2.6%	Hydroelectric 0.1%	Heavy oil and bitumen 1%

Reducing sulphur dioxide (SO_2) pollution through reaction with limestone (see page 153) increases costs and increases CO_2 pollution.

Fuel supplies are vital for industrial development. Currently in the UK, fuels supply 2.5 per cent of the Gross Domestic Product (the total UK annual income).

There can be no question that fossil fuels will continue to be the key to meeting the world's energy demands until well into the next century. Nuclear power is likely to have continued importance but there may be a move towards the use of more renewable energy sources, with solar power probably being the main hope for the future. Geoscience expertise has a key role to play in the development of all fuel sources. For example, if in future the use of solar power increased dramatically, the production of solar cells would require greater production of the specialist metals used in their manufacture.

9.4.1 CRUDE OIL AND NATURAL GAS

Crude oil is formed mainly of carbon (around 85 per cent) and hydrogen (12 per cent). **Natural gas** is mainly methane (CH_4) and together these are called **hydrocarbons**. They are trapped in oil or gas fields in the same way, as the result of six factors coming together. There must be:

- a source rock;
- the correct amount of heating of the source rock;
- a path for migration of the hydrocarbon;
- a reservoir rock;
- a cap rock;
- a trap.

Source rocks have a high carbon content, which can either be concentrated, as in coal or oil shale, or dispersed through mudstone or shale. The type of hydrocarbon produced depends on the source of carbon; accumulated marine plankton produces crude oil while plant remains are the main source of natural gas. When these source rocks are heated during diagenesis to the temperatures shown on Figure 9.2, the hydrocarbons are released from the carbon in the source rocks. The 'oil window' on this graph, the temperatures at which most oil is formed, is around 50–100 °C (depths of 2–3.5 km in areas of normal geothermal gradient). The main 'gas window' is at temperatures between 100 and 200 °C (depths of 3.5–7.5 km with normal geothermal gradient).

At higher temperatures, the organic material breaks down completely to leave a carbon residue. The depth at which this occurs is called the economic basement, since hydrocarbons cannot be produced below that depth.

Once released, hydrocarbons are driven out of the source rock by the compression of overlying rocks and can move upwards or downwards at this stage. However, once they have migrated away from the zone of highest pressure, they are naturally driven upwards, being less dense than the surrounding rocks and any water trapped in them. They migrate through the primary permeability of rocks (spaces between the grains) and the secondary permeability (cracks and fractures) to rocks with enough pore space for them to accumulate. The route through which the fluids move is their migratory path. The porous and permeable rocks in which hydrocarbons can accumulate are called **reservoir rocks**, and the most common are poorly cemented sandstones and conglomerates and reef limestones.

Hydrocarbons migrate through reservoir rock and will eventually reach the surface of the Earth or the sea floor unless they meet an impermeable rock. Such rocks act as seals and are called **cap rocks** – clays, shales and evaporites form the most common cap rocks.

The hydrocarbons can leak around cap rocks unless the caps are shaped in a way that can trap the hydrocarbons within the reservoir rocks. These shapes can be formed in a number of ways, as shown in Figure 9.3 and are called **traps**. Traps are either stratigraphic – formed by the depositional shapes of the rocks, or structural – formed by folding and faulting. In all traps, the hydrocarbon 'bubble', which may be gas, oil or gas above oil, is trapped within the reservoir rock as a layer floating on the groundwater trapped in the rock.

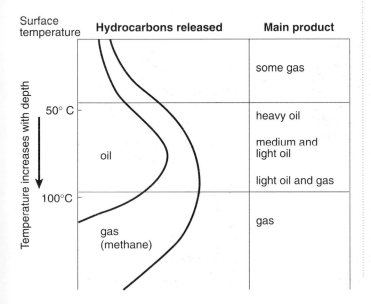

Figure 9.2 *The release of hydrocarbons by burial and increased temperature*

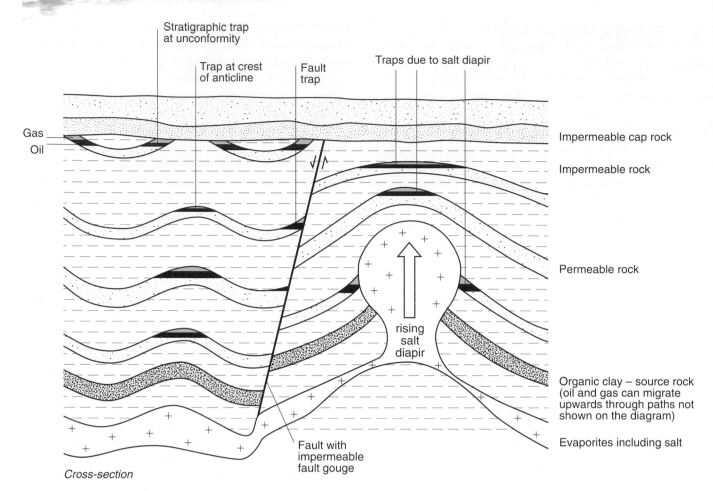

Figure 9.3 *The different types of oil and gas traps*

9.4.2 GAS HYDRATES

Gas hydrate is a frozen form of methane that is stable at low temperatures (near 0 °C) and pressures produced by a few hundred metres depth. Such conditions are found beneath ice sheets and in sediments on the margins of oceans where some of the pressure is due to the depth of ocean water. The methane originated either by the natural gas generation of the Earth or from gas source rocks as described above.

Large deposits have been detected by seismic-reflection surveying in onshore glaciated areas and in ocean sediments close to continental margins. Indeed, it is estimated that the amount of carbon contained by these gas hydrates is equivalent to the total carbon content of all other fossil fuels across the globe added together. In the USA alone, estimates of the amounts of gas hydrates are in thousands of trillions of cubic metres, a large percentage of all potential US fuel reserves. At present, the technology has not been developed to allow commercial exploitation of these reserves but methods being explored involve either heating or depressurisation of the frozen gas.

A current major concern is the effect that global warming may have on these deposits. Methane is a more potent 'greenhouse gas' than carbon dioxide, with more than 10 times the potential for trapping heat than CO_2. Significant warming of the Earth could cause huge volumes of the frozen methane to be released. This may well result in an enhanced greenhouse effect and accelerated global warming.

9.4.3 COAL

Coal is formed of thick sequences of vegetation which have undergone diagenesis. For such vegetation to become buried, four factors are necessary:

- there must be an environment in which land plants grow fast and luxuriantly;
- when they die, they must fall into an area where there is little oxygen (an anaerobic environment) which will prevent their decay, such as a bog or swamp;
- there must be rapid subsidence of the area so that thick sequences can build up;
- finally, much sediment must be brought in to bury the vegetation deeply so that diagenesis takes place.

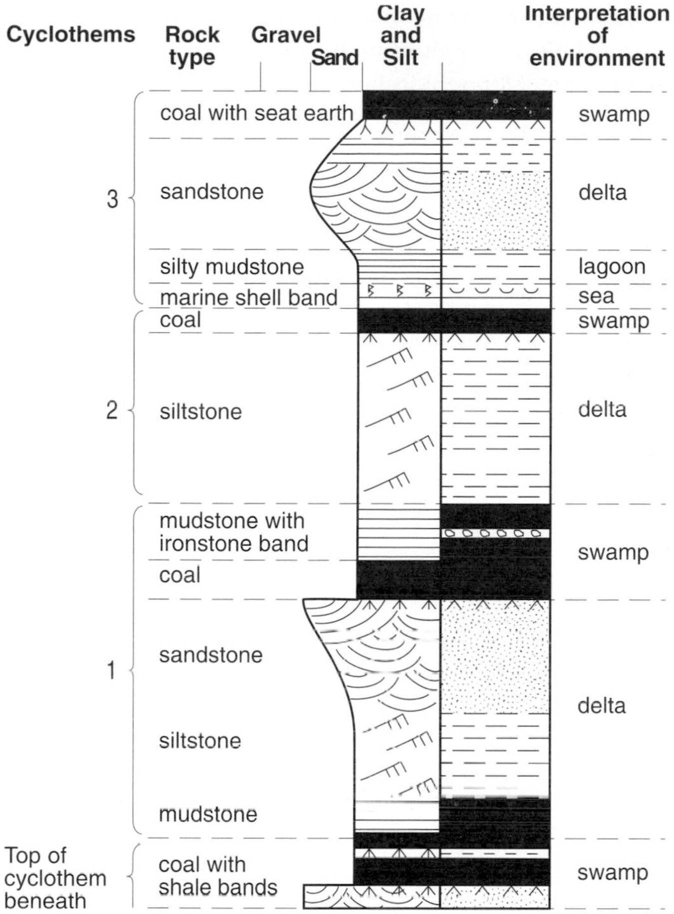

Cyclothems	Rock type	Gravel Sand	Clay and Silt	Interpretation of environment

Figure 9.4 *Coal Measure cyclothems*

Conditions like these occur in the swamps that have developed on top of large deltas in tropical areas today. High temperatures cause the vegetation to grow rapidly and when the plants die they fall into the swamp. Deltas are areas of rapid subsidence since delta sediments compact readily and the huge mass of sediment causes an isostatic effect, depressing the Earth's crust in that area. Similar but more intense conditions were widespread during Carboniferous times and many of the world's coal reserves were deposited at this time, including those in the UK. Sea level change during Carboniferous times in the northern hemisphere is associated with the glaciation that was affecting the southern hemisphere at the same time. The relative sea level changes were usually sudden, producing cyclic sequences of sedimentation called **cyclothems**. The stratigraphic log of three typical Coal Measure cyclothems is shown in Figure 9.4.

Complete cyclothems began when the delta swamp became flooded by the sea and a new small-scale delta started building out into the area. The delta first built out over the marine sediments by depositing pro-delta muds. On top of these, delta-front sands accumulated until the delta rose to sea level, when delta platform sand and muds with some channel gravels were deposited. This new delta top became colonised again with vegetation, forming a soil beneath. When the area was flooded again, the whole, or part of the sequence, was repeated. Eventually the vegetation became a coal seam with a soil (called a **seat earth**) beneath.

Because such subsidence and delta-building events occurred over a wide area, individual coal seams usually also occur with even thicknesses over wide regions. Seams tend to thicken towards the centre of depositional areas and thick seams may split into two thinner seams. In the original delta platform environment, channels may have cut through the vegetation deposits to produce 'washouts' in coal seams. Such variations all cause mining problems, which can be greatly increased by folding or faulting in coalfield rocks.

Permian coals in Australia and China were formed in temperate rather than tropical swamp conditions and have also produced some very extensive deposits. Worldwide, coal-forming conditions did occur at other geological times as well, such as in the Jurassic and Tertiary, but their deposits are small in comparison with the Carboniferous and Permian deposits.

A diagenetic sequence in the formation of coal of different qualities can be recognised, as shown in Figure 9.5. This sequence is called '**the coal series**' and the deposits are divided into different 'ranks'.

While burial is important, it is temperature which is the main control on the rank of coal, and temperature is usually linked with depth, due to the geothermal gradient. Organic deposits formed at the Earth's surface are called peat, but most peats will not become coals because the rate of subsidence and burial is not great enough. Where peats are buried and the temperature increases above 40 °C, 'volatiles' or hydrocarbon gases are lost causing an increase in carbon and **lignite**, a 'brown coal', is formed. Above 70 °C, lignite becomes **bituminous coal** – the black coal which formed the basis of much of Britain's mining and industrial industry in the past. Low-grade metamorphism, above 170 °C, can transform bituminous coal into the hard, high-quality coal called **anthracite**. As Figure 9.5 shows, the increase in coal rank reflects a decrease in volatiles, an increase in carbon content and an increase in the fuel value (calorific value) of the coal.

9.4.4 EXPLORING FOR HYDROCARBONS

Exploration for coal, oil or gas in a new region is likely to begin with geophysical techniques. When these have identified promising areas, if rocks are not exposed, the only sure way of discovering the detailed characteristics of the rock sequence is to dig a pit or drill a borehole.

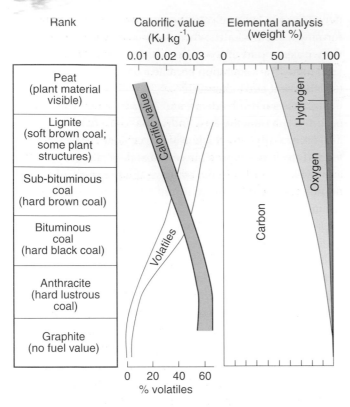

Figure 9.5 *The coal series from peat, through coal, to graphite*

Borehole drilling methods produce samples from a narrow hole, centimetres in diameter but hundreds of metres long. Different techniques include:

- auger drilling: to sample soft deposits like unconsolidated sediments;
- rotary drilling of sedimentary rocks, producing a stream of rock chips;
- percussion drilling with a hammer drill on harder rocks, producing a stream of rock chips;
- reverse circulation drilling, using water and mud as lubricants and to bring rock chips to the surface; more expensive but sampling is far more precise;
- diamond core drilling by a diamond tipped bit lubricated by water and muds, giving cores (lengths of continuous rock cylinder) which are lifted to the surface at intervals; more expensive, but gives a complete sample even at great depths.

Information about the chips and cores is recorded according to depth by borehole logging. Chips are inspected to determine the rock type and microfossils may be extracted to date the rock. Cores are thoroughly described in terms of rock types, and structures and then stored for future reference. While coring techniques are much more expensive than other drilling methods, cores

Figure 9.6 *Methods used in downhole logging*

Downhole logging method	How it works	Response to different rock types					
		clay/ shale	porous sandstone (+water)	porous sandstone (+hydro carbon)	impermeable sandstone	oil shale	coal
Calliper	measures width of hole; the softer the rock, the greater the diameter	wide	normal	normal	normal	wide	normal
Gamma ray	measures natural emission of gamma rays emitted by radioactive decay; clays and shales are rich in potassium which emits gamma rays; hydrocarbon source rocks can be rich in gamma-emitting uranium	high	low	low	low	high	low
Resistivity	measures how well rocks conduct electricity; water in pore spaces is the main conductor; low porosity = low water content = low conductivity = high resistivity; high porosity = high water content = high conductivity = low resistivity	very low	low	high	high	low	high
Rock density	radiation is fired at the rock and the amount reflected is measured; dense rocks reflect more radiation, low density rocks reflect less	high	low	low	high	low	very low

provide much more detail. For example, the dip of bedding can be determined, sedimentary structures and other rock characteristics can be described and measurements on permeability, etc. can be carried out.

Since the drilling of boreholes of whatever type is costly, geologists are keen to get as much information from the hole as they possibly can. To do this, **downhole logging** techniques are used and these have become highly sophisticated in recent years. A capsule of instruments, called a **sonde**, is lowered down the hole on a wireline (thus the alternative name of **wireline logging**). This is drawn up the hole slowly from the bottom while the instruments record data as the depth is logged. The information is sent up the cable and recorded at the surface. Some of the measurements that can now be made by these methods is listed in the Table in Figure 9.6. A plot of the type of data that might be recorded by downhole logging is shown in Figure 9.7.

Downhole-logging technology is developing all the time and the latest techniques include measuring sound-wave velocity in the rocks and detecting the effects of neutron bombardment. It is also possible to lower tiny TV cameras downhole to 'see' the characteristics of the rock and even to 'fire' short cylinders into the side of a hole to extract small cores.

Downhole logging is a widely used technique on opencast coal sites. Several hundred shallow boreholes are drilled rapidly without coring, and are then logged by downhole methods. The results usually clearly show the coal seams and allow their depths to be accurately established, as shown in Figure 9.8.

Following such logging, some further boreholes are drilled, with coring only around the predicted depth of each seam, to enable sampling of the coal to be made. Then, the seams can be identified in relation to the known seams in the area, and contour maps drawn, showing the subsurface distribution of all the seams, before actual mining takes place.

9.5 Water resource

Water is a vital resource for life. In arid countries in particular, the existence of all settlements and farming areas is dependent on water supplies. Lack of clean water is a particular problem in developing countries, where some 25 million people die each year from water-borne diseases. The supply of water is a constraint in developed countries as well and has an important bearing on agricultural, industrial and urban development. In populated areas, much water is recycled by the use of sewage treatment plants but even so, a reliable initial supply remains essential.

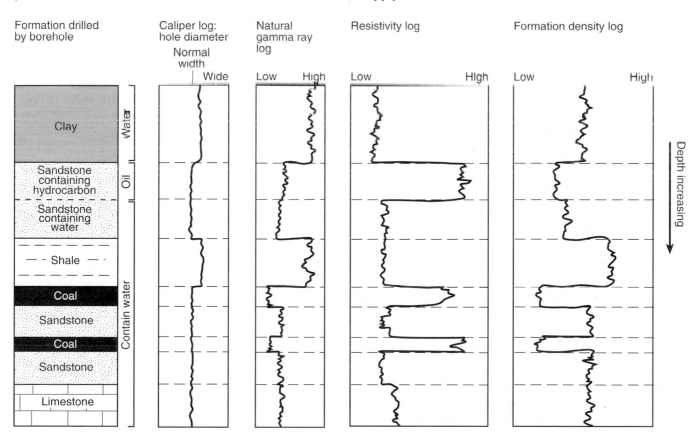

Figure 9.7 *Generalised plots from downhole logging*

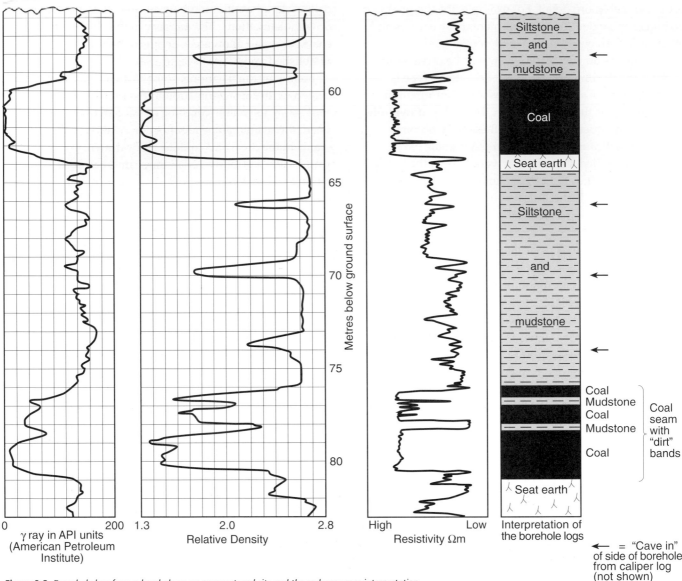

Figure 9.8 *Downhole logs from a borehole on an opencast coal site and the rock sequence interpretation*

The two major sources of water are surface water supplies, from rivers, lakes and reservoirs, and groundwater supplies, pumped from the rocks beneath. Where surface water is abundant, as in countries like Iceland, the more expensive groundwater is rarely used. In arid coastal regions water may be available from the desalination of sea water, but in most arid areas, such as central Australia, groundwater is the only source of water available. In Britain, some 20 per cent of water usage is from groundwater, with 80 per cent coming from surface water supplies.

There is a large variation in the balance between surface and groundwater usage across Britain. Western parts are generally wetter, have more locations suitable for reservoirs and population is generally low so most water is supplied by surface water. In the drier, more populated

eastern part of the country, less water is available and up to 50 per cent may be supplied by groundwater.

The study of surface water supplies is largely the province of the hydrologist, who examines rainfall, catchment areas, water discharges, etc. It is the hydrogeologist who investigates groundwater supplies, as well as being concerned with selection of sites for reservoirs and the choice and monitoring of sites for waste disposal.

Water which falls to the surface of the Earth as rain, snow, etc. either flows into rivers and lakes as runoff, flows into and through the soil as throughflow, or percolates down into the rocks beneath to form **groundwater**. This downward percolation through soil and rocks is called **infiltration** and continues until the water reaches the zone where all the pores and spaces in

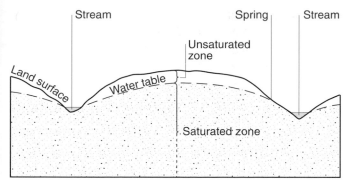

Figure 9.9 *The water table*

the rock are filled with water. This is the **saturated zone**, and the top of this zone is called the **water table**.

The water table rises or falls according to the season, being higher in wetter seasons. Its shape also follows the shape of the land surface, so it is at higher levels under hills and lower beneath valleys. Where the water table reaches the surface, the saturated zone has also reached the surface, and so water 'leaks' out to form a spring, a marsh or bog (or it may flow directly into a river or lake). These features are shown in Figure 9.9.

Beneath the water table, water flows through the spaces between the grains (primary permeability, see page 88) and through fractures in the rock (secondary permeability) 'downhill' from where the water table is high to where it is lower, the steeper the slope of the water table (the **hydraulic gradient**) the greater the rate of flow.

Hydrogeologists 'prospecting' for underground water supplies need to find permeable rocks with a large volume that are recharged by rainwater at a faster rate than water can be extracted. Such rocks, that can supply water in economic quantities, are called **aquifers**. Most aquifers are sandstones (that have high primary permeability) or limestones (with high secondary permeability due to jointing). Different types of aquifer are shown in Figure 9.10.

An aquifer that is not capped by an impermeable rock is an **unconfined aquifer** and boreholes drilled through the water table should produce economic supplies of water. Such water-supplying boreholes are called wells. Some aquifers are 'held up' above the normal water table by an impermeable layer and are called perched aquifers.

If an aquifer is capped by an impermeable layer, it is a **confined aquifer** and it can only be recharged by rainwater where it is unconfined, i.e. where there is no cap. If the unconfined part is higher, then the water is under pressure. This water will rise up a borehole drilled into the confined aquifer and may reach the surface and flow out. This flowing borehole water is called an **artesian water supply**.

Many aquifers in central Australia are artesian, but since the water has travelled long distances through the rock over many thousands of years, it has usually become very saline and is not suitable for drinking. Showering in such saline aquifer water is not a pleasant experience, it is impossible to get your shampoo to lather properly!

In coastal areas, freshwater aquifers can become polluted by sea water, which is denser and flows into the aquifer beneath the fresh water. If too much fresh water is pumped out, the sea water is drawn up to the surface. Once the whole aquifer becomes polluted by salt, it can never be removed by fresh water and so the aquifer is ruined. This is a particular problem on some Mediterranean islands where there is a natural shortage of fresh water.

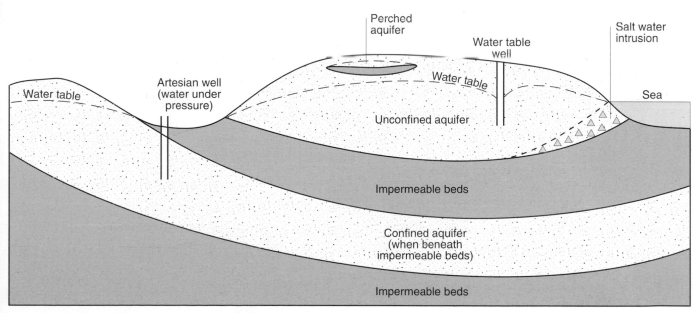

Figure 9.10 *Aquifers and wells*

Groundwater from aquifers is usually clean water, because any pollution is removed during the movement of water through tiny pore spaces. Although groundwater is initially more expensive than surface water supplies because it has to be pumped from the ground, this cost is offset by the reduced treatment costs, since surface water often requires expensive purification.

Aquifer water often has a high concentration of ions, dissolved from the rock as the water passed through. It is this that can give the pleasant taste to spring water exploited by suppliers of bottled water. However, aquifers can become polluted, for example, by leaking sewage or by the liquids washed out (leached) from waste disposal areas and, once polluted, they never recover.

Predictions for the future show that water shortage and water cleanliness are likely to be key global issues for the 21st century. Geoscientists will have a vital role in dealing with this problem. One method currently being considered in countries that have marked wet seasons is to pump some of the wet season water into aquifers. In this way, the wet season surplus will be stored for later use and water loss by evaporation from reservoirs during the dry season is reduced. This artificial aquifer recharge method may eventually become more important than the building of new reservoirs.

9.6   The hole in the ground resource

Holes in the ground are vital resources in developed countries like Britain which produces huge volumes of waste every year. These wastes range from the relatively 'safe' wastes of debris from demolished buildings, through domestic waste and sewage, to the highly toxic chemical, oil-based and radioactive wastes produced by some industries. Each of these has to be disposed of in a way that does not cause dangerous pollution. Over half of these waste materials are disposed as landfill in abandoned quarries and other low-lying areas. Unless the areas are capped, rainwater infiltrates and flows through the waste, dissolving out toxic and other materials to produce a **leachate**. If the rocks below are permeable, the leachate flows down into the water table.

Many years ago, there were no policies covering the disposal of waste materials and so some highly toxic materials were disposed of in areas where the underlying rock was permeable. Some of these are beginning to cause pollution problems to the aquifers in nearby areas, as shown in Figure 9.11.

More recently, potentially hazardous wastes were disposed on the 'dilute and disperse' principle. They were dumped in areas that had some permeability, so that the wastes were gradually carried into the water table. There, they were continually diluted by additional groundwater so that, by the time they reached the surface, the pollution had become so dilute as to be 'safe'. Some geologists argue that this is an effective method still, while others consider that pollution, however much diluted, cannot be made 'safe' in this way.

The present policy is to 'concentrate and contain', where potentially hazardous wastes are placed in impermeable areas and the leakage of toxic material to aquifers is kept to a minimum. Impermeable sites must be chosen, or permeable sites must be lined with impermeable clay liners or sheets of plastic called membranes, or both. The wastes disposed in these areas are carefully monitored and may be 'diluted' by less toxic waste. Leachate is still produced and must be collected and removed for treatment.

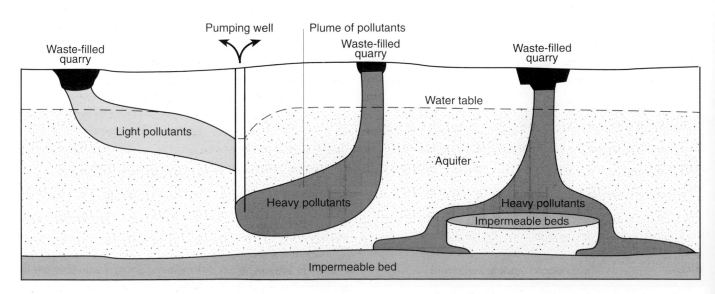

Figure 9.11 *Aquifer pollution*

Less hazardous wastes like domestic wastes can cause problems as well. These produce not only leachate but the decay of organic materials within them generates methane gas and this percolates sideways and upwards. Methane is highly explosive if it collects in nearby buildings, and houses have been blown apart by methane from waste tips. Most of today's domestic waste disposal sites collect the methane and pipe it to a place where it can be burnt safely. Alternatively, the methane can be used for fuel, for example, in nearby brick production or for generating electricity on a small scale.

Abandoned brick pits are widely used for waste disposal because of the natural low permeability of the clay and wastes may be transported from many miles away to fill them. Old sandstone, limestone and igneous quarries are usually suitable only for the disposal of low risk wastes due to their high permeabilities, unless they are specially lined, which is a costly business.

It is essential to monitor the hydrogeology in all these cases. Abandoned quarry sites have first to be checked for the permeability of their rocks and for the amount of groundwater flow through the area (which depends not only on rock permeability, but also on the hydraulic gradient). The sites then have to be designated according to their suitability for different types of wastes. These may be as low toxicity constructional/quarrying waste, moderate toxicity domestic waste, highly toxic industrial waste, etc. The best methods of confining the waste and minimising the leakage have then to be determined. During use, the hydrogeology of the area must be monitored to detect any unexpected leakage and this monitoring will continue for many years after the site has been filled, capped, landscaped and left.

Similar restrictions apply to the disposal of radioactive waste, except for intermediate- and high-level wastes. These contain radioactive pollutants with half lives of many thousands of years that will remain highly dangerous for long into the future. Disposal regulations for this type of waste are much more stringent – so much so, that a 'safe' place for the disposal of this waste has yet to be found in Britain.

Waste disposal in the UK has recently been affected by the imposition of a landfill tax. This has had the effect of more than doubling the cost of hiring a skip for waste disposal but it is releasing funds for local projects to improve the environment.

9.7 Natural hazards

Some surface processes are catastrophically fast. An event that could kill thousands of people and wipe out millions of pounds' worth of property might eventually be preserved in the geological record only as a thin layer of sand or mud. However, these layers may contain enough evidence for us to establish what happened and make predictions that could help to save lives in the future.

Worldwide, about one person in 10 000 is killed by a natural disaster annually, but the risk is much lower in the geologically and climatically stable British Isles. Most deaths due to natural hazards worldwide are the result of windstorms followed by earthquakes, then floods, then volcanoes, landslides and tsunamis. Windstorm hazards are beyond the scope of this book, but earthquake and tsunami hazards, volcanic hazards and flood and landslide hazards are discussed below.

9.7.1 FLOOD HAZARD

There are three main classes of flood hazard: flash floods, river floods and coastal floods. Flash floods are the result of 'short sharp storms' over small river basins that devastate small areas. A flash flood destroyed part of Lynmouth in north Devon in 1952 killing 16 people. Such storms are very difficult to predict and therefore to protect against. Evidence of flash flooding could be preserved in the geological record as poorly sorted layers of conglomerate.

River floods result from heavy rainfall over much larger areas and the flood plains of whole river systems are at risk. When the River Elbe flooded in 1997, vast areas of central Europe became inundated. Easter 1998 brought extensive flooding and deaths in the Midlands of Britain. The flood risk is worse if the area is underlain by impermeable rocks or where the roads and buildings of urban development have sealed the ground surface. The techniques for dealing with river flood risk involve preparing flood hazard maps and graphs that predict the likely intervals of damaging floods of various magnitudes. This information is used to plan flood prevention techniques such as raising banks, dredging and widening channels, building diversion channels and constructing dams and reservoirs to hold floodwater. Wide sweeps of gravel, sand and mud in the rock record are evidence of such floods.

Local flooding can be caused by the breaching of dams or by landslides sliding into reservoirs causing the water to flow over the dam and flood the valley below (as in the Vaiont Dam disaster, page 169).

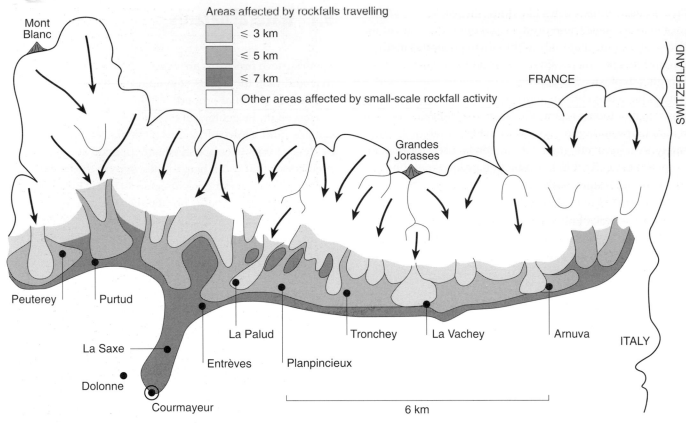

Areas affected by rockfalls travelling

≤ 3 km
≤ 5 km
≤ 7 km
Other areas affected by small-scale rockfall activity

Mont Blanc

Grandes Jorasses

FRANCE

SWITZERLAND

Peuterey · Purtud

La Saxe

Dolonne

Courmayeur

Entrèves

La Palud

Planpincieux

Tronchey · La Vachey

Arnuva

ITALY

6 km

Figure 9.12 *A mass wasting hazard map showing rockfall risks of part of the Mt Blanc area near the border between France and Italy*

Coastal flooding is often the result of a storm surge, when winds drive sea water up the shoreline, combined with high spring tides that occur twice monthly. When these coincide, a flood on the scale of that which affected the east coast of Britain in 1953 can occur. In this flood, many coastal areas between the River Humber and Kent were inundated and more than 300 people died. The Netherlands also suffered badly in this storm. The response has been to reinforce the coastline by building sea walls and other flood barriers. One of the largest-scale flood prevention measures ever carried out in Europe was the construction of the Thames Barrier. This series of barriers can be raised across the Thames if a storm surge brings water up-river. It should save large areas of urban London from flooding, but will increase the flood dangers downstream of the barrage. Hurricanes and typhoons cause coastal flooding risks in tropical areas and tsunamis can flood coasts in areas prone to earthquakes (Papua New Guinea, July 1998) and volcanic eruptions.

Rising sea levels associated with global warming may increase the likelihood of coastal flooding worldwide in the future.

9.7.2 LANDSLIDE HAZARD

Mass wasting processes range from very slow creep to catastrophically fast slumps, debris flows and debris avalanches (page 82). While creep and other slow-moving processes can damage property, it is the fast ones that endanger life. These are usually grouped together as landslides.

Landslides are sudden movements of masses of rock and soil like the event which affected the Holbeck Hall Hotel in Scarborough in 1993. They may affect areas covering many square kilometres and can be triggered by the build up of groundwater pressures or by earthquakes. They tend to occur where there are steep slopes, weak underlying rocks or weak structural planes like joints or fault planes. Human activities such as removing tree cover and constructing buildings often contribute to slope failures in developed areas. These hazards are difficult and expensive to prevent and it is often impossible to repair the damage caused.

The 1993 Holbeck Hall landslide was triggered by heavy rainfall seeping into deep shrinkage cracks. The cracks had developed in the underlying glacial till over several summers that were drier-than-average.

The increased pore water pressure (pressure exerted by water in the pores of the till) triggered a failure along an arc-shaped rotational slip plane (page 82) and eventually one million tonnes of material flowed on to the beach as the 30 m high slope collapsed.

In areas prone to frequent landslides, risk assessments are usually carried out and maps of potentially dangerous areas are prepared. A good example is the rockfall hazard map that has been drawn for part of the Mont Blanc massif (Figure 9.12). It is based on geological mapping of the materials deposited by debris avalanches over the past 3000 years. The map shows that a number of small settlements are at risk from small- to medium-sized falls while some large settlements of thousands of people could be affected by major debris avalanches. Debris avalanche deposits are frequently found in the geological record of unstable areas.

A similar approach can be used for mudflow hazards, as shown for the Mt Rainier area in Figure 9.13. This is based on mapping of the mudflows that have affected the area over the past 10 000 years. It shows that the mudflow risk in valleys within 25 km of the volcano is high and it still significant in the densely populated valleys up to 100 km away. A similar map prepared for the Mt St Helens area before the 1980 eruption successfully predicted the main hazard areas and saved many lives.

Methods that have been found to be most effective in reducing dangers in landslide-prone areas where life and buildings are endangered include:

- using planning regulations to control the siting of buildings;
- using building codes to ensure that slopes are stabilised during new building projects;
- controlling drainage of vulnerable areas by using lined ditches, shallow wells, etc.;
- reducing the load of overlying materials at the head of unstable slopes;
- reducing gradients of slopes prone to slipping;
- building buttresses at the toes of unstable slopes;
- planting vegetation with extensive root systems to stabilise slopes and reduce the water content of the material through high rates of evapotranspiration;
- treating surface materials with chemicals which promote reactions that stabilise the minerals in the slopes;
- filling permeable rock formations with cement to reduce pore water and pore-water circulation and increase strength;
- increasing insurance premiums on property to discourage people from building homes in high risk areas.

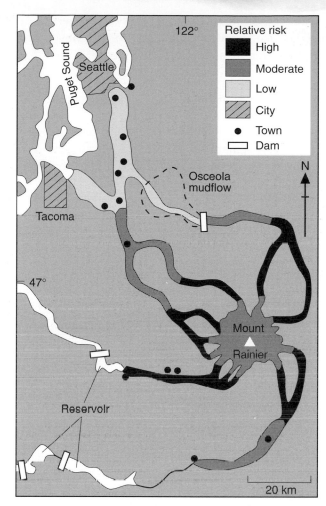

Figure 9.13 *A mass wasting hazard map of mudflow risks of the Mt Rainier area in the north western USA*

The amount of money saved through this range of methods is calculated to be up to a hundred times the amount spent. Calculations also show that damage can be reduced by around 90 per cent, by using these preventative measures.

9.8 Rock engineering

It is a startling fact that each year, humans move more rock, soil, sand and gravel than all the rivers on the planet. Indeed, predictions are that by the middle of the next century, humans may be moving more than twice as much earth materials as all Earth's surface processes combined. The movement of much of this material is linked to engineering projects, in quarrying the raw materials for construction, in excavations for cuttings, foundations, etc., in the building of embankments, dams and other constructions or in general landscaping and reclamation.

The engineering properties of rocks and superficial materials like glacial sands and clays or soils, involve a range of factors, as shown in Figure 9.14.

In particular we need to consider:

- strength in foundations – the resistance of the material to compression;
- strength on slopes and in tunnels – the resistance of unsupported materials to failure;
- resistance to abrasion – resistance to the erosive effects of water currents in rivers and on coasts;
- the likelihood of events such as earthquakes.

Strength is determined largely by the internal strength of the material and the effects of water. Internal rock strength can be assessed in hand specimens through a range of laboratory tests; commonly performed tests measure:

- strength under compression – the compressional stress on a specimen is steadily increased until it fails;
- strength under shear stresses – this is measured in a shear box, in which one part of the box is moved sideways relative to the other;
- strength under tension – the simplest form of tension testing applies stretching stresses to the rock until it breaks (fractures).

These tests give a reasonable guide to the strength of the rock *in situ*, but cannot take into account larger scale factors such as weaknesses caused by some of the factors shown in Figure 9.14, including rock variability, fracturing or pore water pressure.

Under high **pore-water pressure**, the grains are forced apart, cohesion between them is reduced and they are more likely to fail. Water can be concentrated along impermeable beds, causing them to lose cohesion, or along fracture surfaces, causing them to slip, as with the Holbeck Hotel. For this reason, many failures are associated with rainstorms; indeed, in storms even the mass of the additional rainwater may have an effect.

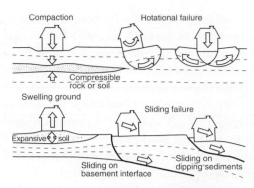

Figure 9.15 *Foundation failure problems*

A particular problem linked with earthquake-triggered landslides is that liquefaction of soils or other unconsolidated sediments can occur. The increase in pore-water pressure is so great that grains are forced apart and the solid material acts like a liquid for a few moments. In this time it can flow down very shallow slopes and large buildings can move, sink or fall over. Liquefaction was a major cause of structural damage in the Mexico City and Kobe (Japan) earthquakes (pages 21–22).

9.8.1 FOUNDATIONS

Geotechnical investigation is carried out on all major construction sites, in particular to establish whether the foundation material is likely to be prone to compaction, swelling, rotational slip or sliding (see Figure 9.15). Clays are particularly affected by compaction. Expansion of clays and other materials that swell when they absorb water can also cause problems if the water table rises into them during construction. Rocks prone to shear failure may fail through rotational slipping or by sliding on slopes.

Where there are problems like these, the solutions can include spreading the load of the construction using rafts of concrete or the sinking of concrete piles to firmer foundation rocks beneath. Drainage systems can be installed to reduce pore-water problems.

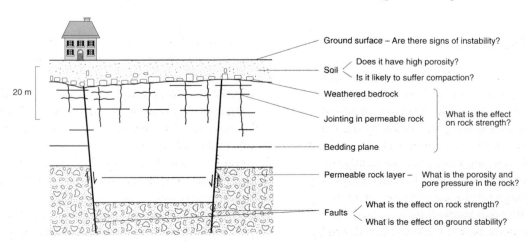

Figure 9.14 *Geological factors needing consideration in engineering projects*

(a)

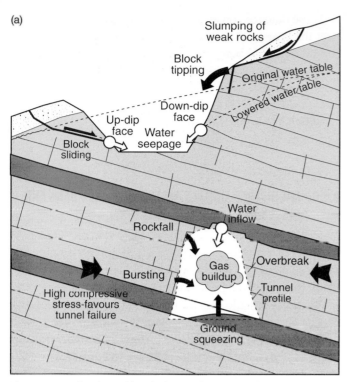

(b)

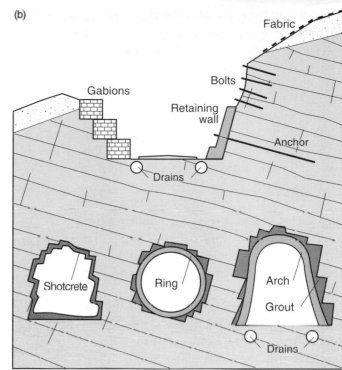

Figure 9.16 *Engineering problems in slopes and tunnels – and some remedies*

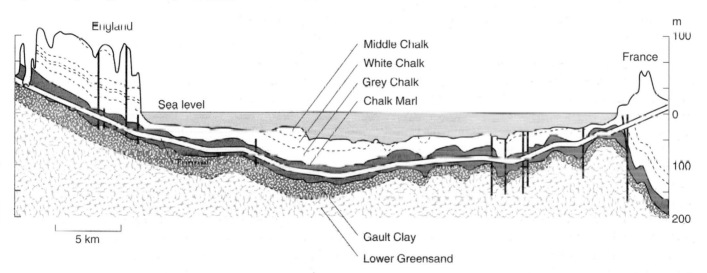

Figure 9.17 *A geological cross section of the Channel Tunnel*

9.8.2 SLOPES AND TUNNELS

All slopes can be subject to failure, whether natural hillsides or cliffs, excavated cuttings or tunnels, or constructed embankments. The processes involved are largely those of mass wasting, increased by human activity. More resistant rocks are subjected to rock fall or rock slide, while less resistant rocks fail mainly by rotational slip or sliding. Some of the most frequently found engineering problems, and some potential solutions, are shown in Figure 9.16.

Nearly all slope-stability problems are reduced by efficient drainage. Thus, the minimising of pore-water pressure in this way is a major priority. Loose materials can be dealt with by forming them into very shallow slopes, by planting vegetation to bind them together and to remove water through the transpiration of the plants, or by covering them in netting or fabric. Rock slides can be prevented by the building of retaining walls of materials such as concrete or of **gabions** (rectangular wire mesh boxes filled with boulders). Rock falls can be prevented using **rock bolts** to tie loose blocks into the firmer wall rocks.

Tunnels have special problems due to the confining pressure of the overlying rocks. **Confining pressure** is caused by the mass of overlying material but acts in all directions, in the same way that water presses all around a submarine and not just on the top surface. The curved shape of the hull of a submarine is designed to withstand these pressures and arch or cylinder shapes can withstand confining pressures in rocks in the same way. In tunnels without reinforcements, the ground can swell up from below; some old mine tunnels have completely closed up in this way. If tunnel sides are unsupported, they can fail dramatically in rock bursts. Tunnels are also more greatly affected by pore-water pressures than other excavations, so good drainage systems are vital.

The Channel Tunnel is a good example of an engineering project carried out in difficult conditions (Figure 9.17). First, detailed geotechnical investigations were carried out including borehole and seismic surveys. These showed an open synclinal structure complicated by faults in just a few places. This allowed the 50 km long tunnel to be cut for most of its length within the 25 m thick Chalk Marl layer, a rock much less permeable than the Chalk above. The **rockhead** (thickness of rock above) was more than the minimum of 20 m required between the top of the tunnel and the sea bed and the overall lack of faulting meant that the problems of increased water flow along fault planes could largely be avoided.

9.8.3   RESISTANCE TO ABRASION – RIVERS AND COASTS

River banks and coastal areas are particularly prone to erosion where there are cliffs of clays or of other poorly-cemented sediments like silts or sands. On coastlines in particular, huge sums of money have been spent building coastal defences to prevent buildings falling into the sea. Where waves hit beaches at an angle, each wave carries sediment up the beach at an angle and then it flows straight back down the beach slope. As a result, sediment is moved steadily along the beach in a 'sawtooth' motion known as **longshore drift**. Many different types of defences have been built to prevent sediment being removed by longshore drift, so exposing cliffs to greater erosion. These range from **groynes** built at right angles to beaches to trap sediment moving along the shore, to sea walls, harbour walls and breakwaters. Barriers built along beaches to protect cliffs may be made of gabions, concrete blocks, or of large boulders brought in by ship from distant super quarries. **Revetments** can be built below the high tide mark as barriers to trap sediment. In some areas, the only effective method of dealing with beach erosion is by **sand feeding**, where sand is transported from elsewhere by trucks and dumped on the beach.

In low-lying areas, banks like the famous dykes of the Netherlands, are frequently constructed to prevent flooding during storm high tides.

These defence constructions cost great sums of money over the years and an alternative method of 'managed coastal retreat' is being applied in some areas. Here, it is cheaper to dismantle buildings and move them inland to safer sites, allowing the cliffs to be eroded naturally. The eroded cliff material may then be transported down the coast by longshore drift, adding material to erosion-prone sites elsewhere.

9.8.4   ENGINEERED SURFACE-WATER SUPPLIES – DAMS AND RESERVOIRS

The sites of dams and reservoirs are chosen for a range of political, economic and geographical reasons, with the result that the geology is rarely 'ideal'. Nevertheless, within these outside constraints, the best site must be chosen and the geological problems minimised. Thus a range of thorough geological investigations is necessary in planning a dam and the reservoir that will result. These fall into six main areas:

- hydrological factors;
- sedimentation problems;
- stability of the sides;
- groundwater movement/leakage;
- dam foundations;
- construction materials.

Hydrologists investigate the amount of rainfall, catchment area characteristics and runoff under various conditions. Hydrological factors related directly to the geology include the topography, vegetation and soil characteristics of the catchment area (the area from which water drains into the reservoir). Where slopes are steep and poorly vegetated with thin soils, runoff is fast and most precipitation flows into the reservoir rather than infiltrating the ground.

In catchment areas prone to heavy erosion, much of the sediment will be carried into the reservoir and this can severely reduce its volume over time. Some reservoirs near the Himalaya have a working life of less than 100 years for this reason.

The water-tightness of a reservoir depends on the head of water (which controls its pressure) and the permeability of the rock; it is the head of water which is often more important. This is because if the water table in the surrounding hills remains higher than the reservoir, there will be net groundwater flow into the reservoir and leakage from the sides will not occur, no matter how permeable the surrounding rock may be. If the water table is lower in the surrounding areas, water will flow as groundwater out of the reservoir but providing the

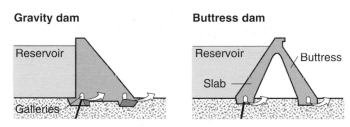

Embankment dam

Rock facing, Rock or earth fill, Core, Filter, Toe drain, Cut-off

Arch dam

Reservoir, Drain

Gravity dam

Reservoir, Galleries

Buttress dam

Reservoir, Buttress, Slab

Figure 9.18 *The main types of dam*

surrounding rock is impermeable, water loss will be negligible. If the rock is permeable and likely to lose water, primary permeabilities (due to flow through pore spaces) can be reduced by using expensive clay or plastic linings; secondary permeabilities (due to cracks and fissures) can be reduced by grouting which involves pumping a slurry of cement into the holes to seal them.

There are particular problems when dams are sited on permeable rocks because the height of the water behind the dam greatly increases groundwater pressures. Thus the potential for leakage is much greater and sometimes, water paths through permeable rocks can be so widened that the dam is weakened and collapses. Where rocks are permeable, a trench is normally excavated in the rock beneath the dam site and filled with impermeable

material – this underground barrier to groundwater flow is called a cut-off 'curtain'.

The type of dam chosen depends largely on the quality of the foundations and the shape of the valley but the type of construction materials available may play some part. The four main types of dam are shown in Figure 9.18. Some dams are composites of these with, for example, an arch dam between two gravity dams.

Embankment dams are used where the foundation rock is weak but there are large volumes of construction material available. The impermeable core is kept in place by permeable shoulders of rock or soil. Their sheer size and mass resists the pressure of the reservoir water. Gravity dams also depend on their shape and size to resist the water pressure; they are formed of one huge concrete block. Buttress dams are a form of gravity dam where less concrete is needed because large concrete slabs are supported by the buttresses leaving a space in the centre. Arch dams may be constructed in narrow valleys, where the bedrock on either side is strong; the curved shape of the concrete dam holds it in position against the valley walls.

All dams leak to some degree, because of the huge water pressures involved, but dams are successful where loss by leakage and evaporation is much less than the water gain from the catchment area.

Careful geotechnical investigation is crucial before the building of any major dam, as some catastrophic disasters have shown. Some 2600 lives were lost in the Vaiont Dam disaster in northern Italy in 1963. The project involved constructing a 266 m high dam across the Vaiont River to create a reservoir for hydroelectric power. The site and

Figure 9.19 *Map and cross section of the Vaiont Dam and reservoir*

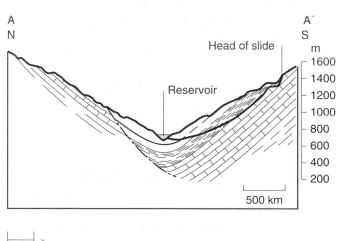

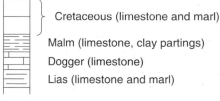

Line of section, A, Scar of former landslide, Dam, Reservoir, Plave R., A′, N, 2 km

A N, A′ S, Head of slide, Reservoir, m, 1600, 1400, 1200, 1000, 800, 600, 400, 200, 500 km

Limit of 1963 landslide

Extent of flooding after landslide

Dip of strata

Cretaceous (limestone and marl)

Malm (limestone, clay partings)

Dogger (limestone)

Lias (limestone and marl)

geological structure is shown in Figure 9.19. The valley was chosen because it was deep and narrow and so could store large volumes of water. The project was completed in 1960 but on 9th October 1963, some 270 million cubic metres of rock slid into the reservoir at a speed of around 25 metres per second. The effect was like dropping a large bag of potatoes into a bath full of water. The landslide created a 100 metre high wave which flowed over the dam and destroyed a number of villages in the valley below.

The main trigger was very high rainfall preceding the failure and errors made in calculating the volume of water which could be stored in the reservoir. The failure occurred when increased pore water pressure along a bedding plane between clay and limestone caused the overlying limestone beds to break away and slide downhill, creating seismic tremors as far away as Brussels. Minor sliding had been observed (and ignored) during the construction of the dam and after the dam was completed, with a slip of up to 35 mm per day being recorded at one stage. This story is a chapter of mistakes. Mistakes like these have not been made in the many thousands of successful large-scale engineering projects across the world in which geotechnical engineers have played a part.

9.9 Summary

1 A wide range of valuable resources can sometimes be obtained from quite small areas of country; these include constructional materials, industrial minerals and fossil fuels.

2 Underground water supplies are vital resources in Britain and in many other parts of the world.

3 Safe waste disposal is an industry of increasing importance as the amount of waste increases and the sites where it can be safely disposed of become fewer.

4 Death and destruction from natural hazards can be reduced by careful study of the hazards and the geological evidence they leave and by applying a wide range of solutions.

5 All major construction projects involve geotechnical surveying and the solving of geotechnical engineering problems; such projects include foundation building, slope stabilisation, tunnel, river and coastal defence construction and the building of dams to produce reservoirs.

9.10 Questions

1 Which resources are being extracted from the area where you live and which were important in the recent past?

2 What is the range of Earth resources most widely used in your home area and how are they transported there?

3 In which areas of your local region is the work of the environmental geologist likely to be needed to return them to a near natural state when mining, quarrying or other industrial activity have been completed?

4 Which natural hazards are most likely to affect areas where you live or where you go on holiday? What steps are being taken to minimise these hazards?

5 Which of the following sedimentary sequences could include an aquifer or an economic hydrocarbon reservoir rock? In each case, consider sediment texture (size, sorting, shape, orientation, packing) and likely sediment sequences (overall volume, likely presence of impermeable beds, presence of permeable flow channels, etc.).
   a fluvio-glacial sequence; a desert dune complex; a deep sea turbidite sequence; a reef/lagoon sequence; a delta.

6 Use Figure 9.8, which shows the results of downhole logging of a Coal Measure sequence, to answer these questions:
   a) how can coal seams be distinguished from other rock types using the downhole logging records?
   b) The sudden drop in the apparent density at depths of 58 m, 66 m, 70 m and 74 m might be mistaken for a coal seam, but the column shows that this is not the case. What might have caused these 'false' readings?
   c) Why is more than one method of borehole logging necessary?

7 For a major engineering project of your choice, consider what geoscience expertise might be necessary at each stage of the project and what geoscience problems might be encountered and solved.

CHAPTER 10

Mineralisation: mineral deposits to metals

Introduction

This chapter considers the location and exploitation of metallic minerals. A Case Study of Mount Isa mine introduces the mineral industry and orebodies. The formation of ore deposits is considered in the context of the chemistry of the minerals. The discovery and exploitation of a new orebody leads on to mineral processing, and the extraction and refining of metals. Finally the chapter reviews the mineral industry in relation to world economic development.

10.1 Case Study: Mount Isa Mine, Queensland, Australia

Figure 10.1 *The location of Mount Isa*

Mount Isa in Queensland (Figure 10.1) is one of the largest underground mines in the world, with an annual output in recent years of 10 million tonnes of ore. The controlling company invests heavily in research and development, which has made Mount Isa one of the most advanced and mechanised mines on Earth. The ores of four metals are extracted; copper, silver, lead and zinc.

The production and value of each metal from Mount Isa mine for the year July 1995–June 1996 are shown in Figure 10.2.

Figure 10.2 *Production and approximate value, from Mount Isa, 1995–6*

Metal	Production (tonnes)	Value (£ million)
silver	510	44
lead	156 000	70
zinc (in concentrate)	203 000	140
copper	178 000	350
Total metal production	*537 510*	*604*

10.1.1 FORMATION OF THE SILVER-LEAD-ZINC OREBODIES

The silver-lead-zinc orebodies were formed in 1700 Ma old shales through several stages as illustrated in Figure 10.3.

(a) As sediments were deposited on the sea floor, hot aqueous solutions rose up through fractures in the crust carrying metal ions which were precipitated as metal sulphides in thin layers on top of the sediments. These layers were buried by more sediments.

(b) The strata, including the orebodies, were tilted and faulted.

(c) Erosion brought the orebodies near the surface again where they are found as distinct bands within shales, extending over hundreds of metres. They contain silver lead and zinc as bands of galena, sphalerite, pyrite and other sulphide minerals. When the bands are close enough together and of high enough grade (percentage metal content), they are worth mining.

(d) Rainwater carrying dissolved oxygen and carbon dioxide percolated to a depth of 60 metres. As a result the primary orebodies (first formed) have been partly chemically altered by tropical weathering, changing the sulphide minerals to secondary carbonate minerals.

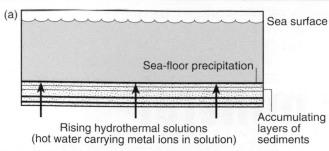

Figure 10.3(a) *Deposition of sediments and their mineralisation by hot circulating fluids*

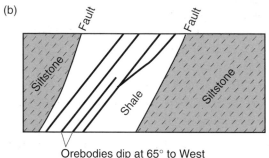

Orebodies dip at 65° to West
Figure 10.3(b) *Tilting and faulting of the orebodies*

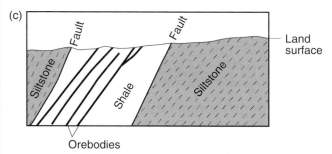

Figure 10.3(c) *Erosion and subsequent exposure of the orebody at the surface*

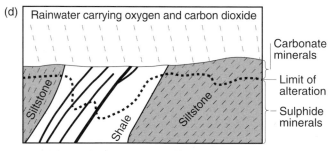

Figure 10.3(d) *Chemical alteration by circulating rainwater*

10.1.2 FORMATION OF THE COPPER OREBODIES

The copper probably originated in nearby basalts. After major faulting the copper was dissolved by hot aqueous solutions during regional metamorphism and was carried into the shales by the percolating fluids. The copper ore mineral chalcopyrite crystallised in veins and as **disseminated deposits** in which the ore mineral is dispersed as fine particles. These deposits are the copper orebodies of Mount Isa (Figure 10.4).

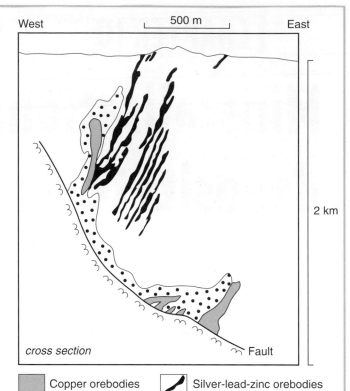

West | 500 m | East | 2 km

cross section Fault

Copper orebodies | Silver-lead-zinc orebodies
'Silica and dolomite' | Metamorphosed basalts

Figure 10.4 *Vertical section through the Mt Isa orebodies*

10.1.3 DEVELOPMENT OF THE RESOURCE

The successful development of any mineral resource depends on many factors. In the following story, phrases in *italics* emphasise events relating to one or more of the nine factors listed below. As you read the story, consider how these factors have affected the success of Mount Isa:

- single-minded individual/entrepreneur
- financial capital
- competition from other mining operations
- richness of ore
- world markets
- demand for metal
- production costs of mining and refining
- infrastructure costs of services and facilities
- government policy about investment

1 In 1923 *gold prospectors* in Queensland found *pieces of rich silver-lead ore*. *They could afford* to peg out only 10 hectares of mining leases. *Other prospectors* rushed to buy neighbouring leases. Surface mining began with picks and shovels.

2 Later in 1923, an *engineer*, William Corbould, assessed the area. He *floated a company* in Sydney while his local agent bought up leases from the miners. In 1924, the capital of

Mount Isa Mines Limited was used to buy leases and put down shafts. The ore raised was *poor quality*.

3 Optimists claimed that this could be another 'Broken Hill' (a famous and successful Australian mine); pessimists said it was *twice the distance* to a sea port, and the ore only *half as rich*, as at Broken Hill. In addition, a *town with amenities* was needed and *ore processing was difficult*.

4 Corbould went abroad to raise *more money*. In 1927, he persuaded a London *mining financier* to invest all his assets in the mine. The town expanded, and a mill, smelter and powerhouse were added. A railway was completed to the coast and a dam built to ensure a water supply. All these depleted the *capital* but added to the *assets* of the company. By 1930, the ore processing plant was still incomplete, more capital was needed and the world was now in *The Depression* (major recession).

5 In 1930, the American Smelting and Refining Company (ASARCO) lent the company money and took over management. Rich copper ore had been discovered but the emphasis remained on lead production. Continuing problems of flooding, ore smelting, and fresh food supplies required yet *more capital*.

6 In 1931, initial lead production soon reached 3350 tonnes per month. The *world lead price* was A$36 per tonne (Australian dollars) but fell in 1932 to A$19 per tonne. Interest payments could not be made and debts rose. Yet government encouragement of overseas investment kept 1000 men employed during The Depression. In 1934, the lead price rose and debts reduced. In 1937, the company made its first profit of A$140 000, but profits fell as *wages*

rose and the shipping monopoly charged *high rates* to export the metals.

7 World War II created a *demand* for copper for armaments. In 1942, production of lead stopped and copper began. Production peaked in 1945. Military conscription depleted the labour force, but improved efficiency and the discovery of *higher grade ore* maintained production.

8 In 1946, copper production stopped and lead re-started to meet *soaring demand* at a much higher price. In 1947, the ever-patient shareholders received their first dividend. Parallel production of both ores to provide four metals, begun in 1953, continues today.

9 Modern surveying techniques and borehole samples have provided three-dimensional detail of the geology, with better understanding of the ore-forming processes. Computer models aid the planning of mining operations.

10 After 65 years, Mount Isa remains a major producer – an unusually long life for a large mining operation.

As you can see, Mount Isa has developed to a successful position from a slow beginning!

10.1.4 FROM CASE STUDY TO GENERAL PRINCIPLES

We look at the geological principles of mineralisation in the rest of this chapter, using several individual mineral deposits as examples. As you will see, the same principles operate in all economic mineral deposits, yet every deposit is unique. The full economic potential of each deposit can only be assessed, and realised through mining, by understanding its geological history.

10.2 Minerals and Ores

Most of our mineral resources come from the Earth's crust. Figure 3.3 in Chapter 3 gives some estimated average abundances of elements in crustal rock. However, many of the minerals that form economic deposits do not appear in this list for reasons that will become clear.

10.2.1 MINERALS IN THE EARTH'S CRUST

The Earth's crust is a complex mixture of chemical compounds – and the occasional uncombined element (for example, gold). These naturally occurring elements and compounds are called minerals. The exact number of different minerals is not known, but, excluding the organic compounds in coal and oil, more than 4000 have

been identified. Of these, some 300 are common enough, or of sufficient economic value, to be considered as important.

Almost all minerals have ionic structures. As Chapter 3 explained, most minerals are silicates, compounds of common metals with silicon and oxygen, and these form over 90 per cent of the Earth's crust; some, like china clay, are economically important. The remaining 10 per cent of the crust consists of less common minerals, together with a range of molecular compounds trapped or held in solution under pressure, such as water, carbon dioxide, hydrogen sulphide and hydrocarbons.

There are two distinct groups of elements in the crust:

- eight abundant elements which form the common rock-forming minerals.
- the rest, among them most metals of particular interest to industry.

If the crust were a homogeneous mixture, with the elements evenly distributed, we could not have a minerals industry! Only because some compounds have been naturally concentrated can they be mined economically. The minerals industry extracts these mixtures of minerals and separates them into individual chemical compounds.

10.2.2 ORE MINERALS AND ORES

Ore minerals are those which can be used as an economic source of metals. An **ore** is a rock containing an ore mineral in relatively high concentrations, from which a metal can be extracted economically. **Gangue** minerals are the non-economic minerals in an ore and they form the waste during mining and mineral processing.

Figure 10.5 *Data for the ore reserves, grade and cut-off grade for Mount Isa mine in 1966*

Metal	Ore reserves, million tonnes	Grade	Average cut-off grade
copper	66	3.3%	0.5%
zinc		6.8%	3%
lead	11.7	5.6%	5%
silver		134 g t^{-1}	100 g t^{-1}

The **grade** of a metal ore is the proportion by mass of the metal in the ore, usually expressed as a percentage (for common metals) or in grams per tonne (for rare metals). The **cut-off grade** is the lowest percentage that can be mined profitably at current prices, and the **reserve** is the mass of ore above the cut-off grade. Data for the ore reserves, grade and cut-off grade for Mount Isa mine in 1996 are given in Figure 10.5.

10.2.3 CHEMISTRY OF ORE MINERALS

Most ore minerals are simple chemical compounds. This is because more complicated compounds, such as most metal silicates, are generally too expensive to process economically. The simple compounds are ionic in structure, with the metal forming the cation (positive ion). The common anions (negative ions) in ore minerals are oxide, sulphide and carbonate. Appendix 6 shows the names of some ore minerals and their chemical formulae.

10.2.4 THE METAL CONTENT OF AN OREBODY

Since ores are mixtures of ore and gangue minerals, the actual percentage of a metal in an ore is very variable. It is important to be able to calculate the metal content of a potential ore body in order to evaluate it, as shown in this example from Ecton in Britain.

In the late eighteenth century, Ecton Copper Mine in Staffordshire worked a rich copper orebody. The main ore mineral was chalcopyrite, and the main gangue mineral was calcite. The orebody contained reserves of 200 000 tonnes of ore, with about 33 per cent chalcopyrite. From this we can calculate:

- the grade of the orebody;
- the total mass of copper in the orebody;
- the mass of gangue minerals thrown away.

The calculation runs as follows:
Chalcopyrite has the formula $CuFeS_2$. This allows us to calculate the relative molar mass of chalcopyrite, $CuFeS_2$, since the relative atomic masses are: Cu = 64, Fe = 56, S = 32.
Thus the molar mass of $CuFeS_2$ = 64 + 56 + 32 × 2 = 184. Therefore in every 184 g of chalcopyrite there are 64 g of copper so the percentage of copper in chalcopyrite
= 64/184 × 100 = **34.8** per cent.
The percentage of copper in the orebody
= per cent chalcopyrite in orebody × per cent copper in chalcopyrite
= 33 × 34.8/100 = 11.5 per cent. Thus the grade of the orebody was 11.5 per cent.
This figure allows us to calculate the mass of copper (and also gangue) in the orebody.
The mass of copper in the orebody
= 200 000 tonnes × 11.5/100
= **23 000 tonnes**.
The mass of gangue mineral (calcite)
= 200 000 tonnes × 67/100
= **134 000 tonnes**.
This shows how, even for a high grade ore, metal mining inevitably produces enormous quantities of waste rock. Even more waste comes from making shafts and tunnels, and from extracting the metal from the ore mineral.

10.3 Mineral deposits formed by igneous processes

Most mineral deposits formed by igneous processes develop by crystallisation in magma chambers, and are therefore found in intrusive igneous rocks. The composition of the magma determines the type of ore body that may form. **Magmatic segregation deposits** occur in mafic (basic) igneous rocks, while **pegmatite ore deposits** are usually associated with granites.

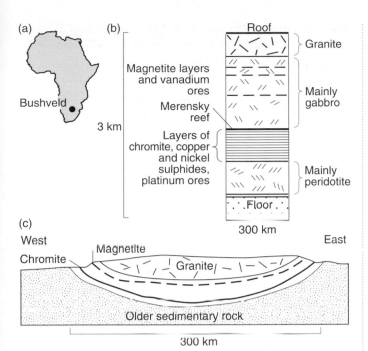

Figure 10.6 *a) Location of the Bushveld Complex, South Africa b) A rock sequence typical of the Bushveld Complex c) A cross section through the Bushveld Complex*

10.3.1 MAGMATIC SEGREGATION DEPOSITS FROM MAFIC MAGMA

The fractional crystallisation of a cooling body of mafic magma (p 60) forms cumulates of silicate minerals, rich in iron and magnesium. However metals are so difficult to extract from complex silicate structures that they are rarely used as ore minerals. Fortunately, in some mafic and ultra-mafic magmas, oxide minerals also form, from which metals are easier to extract. Examples are shown in Appendix 6.

These oxides are usually found in very small amounts, so when a rich layer is found it can be an important orebody, such as in the Bushveld Complex in South Africa. The Bushveld is a large saucer-shaped intrusion, now partly exposed on the Earth's surface, as shown in Figure 10.6. Ore minerals include chromite, magnetite and ilmenite with smaller amounts of vanadium, platinum and associated platinum group elements. Copper and nickel sulphide minerals are also important.

The chromite deposit consists of numerous thin layers from a few centimetres to two metres thick. Crystals of oxide minerals settled out on the bottom of the magma chamber with thin layers of silicate minerals between them. Later, conditions changed and the sulphides settled out with the platinum ores in a distinct layer called the Merensky Reef.

Most mining so far has been on the edges of the intrusion. If future mining progresses into the middle, the accessible reserves will be vast. In terms of the potential value of the metals, the Bushveld Complex is probably one of the Earth's most valuable orebodies.

10.3.2 MAGMATIC SEGREGATION DEPOSITS FROM SULPHUR-RICH MAFIC MAGMAS

Some mafic magmas are so rich in sulphur that the crystallising magma can become saturated with sulphur. A dense layer of molten metal sulphides, immiscible with the silicate magma (like oil and water, they do not mix), separates out and sinks, collecting less reactive metals such as platinum from the silicate magma on the way. Metal sulphides crystallise on cooling, particularly those of iron, copper and nickel. It was this process that formed the Merensky Reef in the Bushveld Complex (Figure 10.6), where the grade of platinum is up to 11 g t^{-1} (cut-off grade is 5 g t^{-1}).

10.3.3 SUDBURY BASIN, CANADA

'Houston . . ., we seem to have found shocked rock formations here on the Moon that are very similar to those we examined during our training in Sudbury.' This cryptic statement from the astronauts on the first Moon-walk in 1969 gave evidence to support the new theory (now widely accepted) that the Sudbury Basin was formed by a meteorite impact. This is an unusual example of evidence from the Moon being used to convince us about an event on the Earth.

Figure 10.7b shows the structure of the Sudbury Basin in ancient metamorphic rocks, about 3000 Ma old.

The evidence for the meteorite impact includes:

Figure 10.7 *a) Location of the Sudbury Basin b) A cross section through the Sudbury Basin*

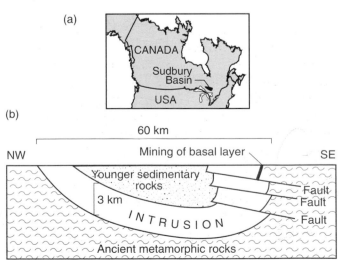

- shatter cones (distinct conical fractures in the rock).
- breccias (crushed rocks) caused by the impact.
- an oval basin, thought to be an impact structure.

The impact intensely fractured and heated the rocks, causing magmas to come up from deep underground, some even from partial melting of the mantle. This is very unusual because most magmas in continents are derived from crustal rocks.

The magmas crystallised into a layered intrusion formed mainly of gabbro. Radioactive dating indicates that the meteorite struck some 1850 Ma ago. The ore minerals are found at the base of the gabbro intrusion, where many layers of sulphide minerals crystallised and settled on the floor of the magma chamber. This has become one of the world's most important sources of nickel ore. At one time the nickel from the Sudbury Basin formed 70 per cent of annual world production, and this basin is said to contain 23 per cent of the world's nickel reserves. The copper reserve is far less important in world terms because copper is found in many more deposits elsewhere.

10.3.4 PEGMATITE ORE DEPOSITS

Rocks are classified as pegmatites on the basis of the size of individual crystals which can be gigantic, up to many metres in size. Experiments suggest that pegmatites are formed from magmas that have high concentrations of volatiles (substances with low boiling points), like water, fluorine and boron. The volatiles lower the viscosity of the magma allowing it to migrate away from the pluton. It then crystallises in fractures as veins, dykes and lenses.

In a pegmatite, crystals of quartz, potassium feldspar and mica may be so large that they can be mined separately. Valuable metals may also be present; in some pegmatites grades of these may be sufficient to form an ore.

In Namibia in south western Africa, a large pegmatite ore deposit is worked at Rössing as the world's largest open-cast uranium mine. The grade is 0.031 per cent U_3O_8, close to cut-off grade, but the huge volume of ore and ease of mining make it an economic operation; the reserves form 5 per cent of the world's total uranium reserves. Annual production reduced dramatically in the early 1990s as demand fell following nuclear accidents like Chernobyl and the survival of the mine depends on the world nuclear power industry.

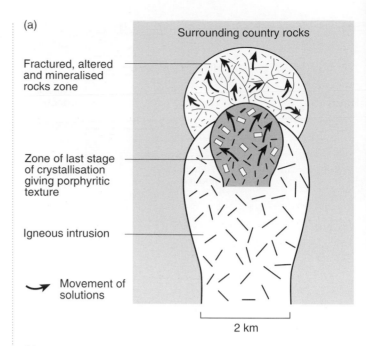

(a)

Surrounding country rocks

Fractured, altered and mineralised rocks zone

Zone of last stage of crystallisation giving porphyritic texture

Igneous intrusion

Movement of solutions

2 km

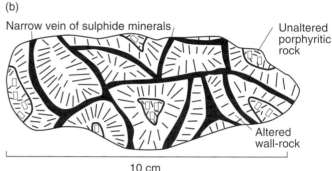

(b)

Narrow vein of sulphide minerals

Unaltered porphyritic rock

Altered wall-rock

10 cm

Figure 10.8 *a) A cross section through a porphyry ore deposit b) A porphyry ore sample*

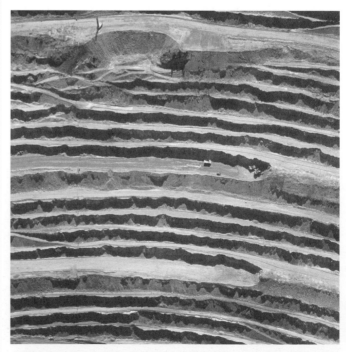

Figure 10.9 *Copper mining at Bingham, Utah, USA. The tiny vehicles are in fact multi-tonne wagons*

10.3.5 PORPHYRY ORE DEPOSITS

Igneous rocks with a **porphyritic** texture (p 58) can have associated **porphyry ore** deposits (Figure 10.8a). These are often formed in island-arc plate-tectonic environments.

As magma cools at depth, large crystals can grow, held in a little residual melt that is rich in aqueous solutions containing metal ions. If this magma escapes suddenly through fractures in the crust, much reduced pressures can lead to a rapid 'boiling' of the water, when the steam pressure can produce more fractures in the rocks above. Magma, aqueous solutions and steam rush up into the new fractures and rapidly cool and crystallise, giving a matrix of many small crystals around the larger crystals.

This process may be repeated several times as further explosions of steam cause more fractures and more crystallisation. The final result is an ore deposit of sulphide minerals dispersed throughout the rock as a network of numerous tiny veins (Figure 10.8b). The hot **hydrothermal solutions** may also react chemically with the rock, producing new minerals along the edges of the fractures; this is called **wall-rock alteration**.

Porphyry ore deposits are large and low grade (e.g. 0.4–1.5 per cent metal) and have only been mined since 1900. Such deposits contain 50 per cent of the world's copper and 70 per cent of the world's molybdenum reserves. Important by products are gold, silver and tungsten ores.

Bingham Canyon Mine in Utah, USA, was the first to be developed in a porphyry orebody: chalcopyrite ($CuFeS_2$) and bornite (Cu_5FeS_4) are the dominant ore minerals. With half of the deposit now mined, it still has ore reserves of a thousand million tonnes (Figure 10.9).

10.4 Ore deposits formed by sedimentary processes

Ore mineral deposits can be formed by three different groups of sedimentary processes; these produce:

- residual and weathered ores;
- placers;
- precipitated chemical deposits.

10.4.1 RESIDUAL AND WEATHERED ORE DEPOSITS

Strong chemical weathering of rocks under hot and seasonally wet climates can form deeply rotted layers of rock called laterite. The weathering removes soluble materials, leaving an insoluble **residual deposit** in which aluminium may be concentrated. This is the only process which concentrates aluminium (the third commonest element at 8.1 per cent of the crust) to economic levels.

During chemical weathering in both warm and hot climates, feldspars in granites are decomposed by slightly acidic rainwater to form kaolinite (as deposits of china clay) as shown in Equation 1 at the foot of the page

Since feldspars contain 18–28 per cent alumina (Al_2O_3) and kaolinite contains 40 per cent alumina, the aluminium is concentrated by this reaction.

In hot climates this extreme weathering can continue, breaking down the silicate minerals completely and altering the alumina to insoluble hydrated aluminium oxides, as shown in Equation 2. A laterite rich in aluminium oxide is called **bauxite**.

A bauxite deposit for use as an aluminium ore should contain low levels of impurities such as iron and titanium oxides. Bauxite is earthy and uncemented, so it can easily be eroded by running water; hence most ore deposits are found in low-lying areas where erosion rates are very slow.

Bauxite reserves occur in the wet tropics; the top four countries are Australia (24.5% of world reserves), Guinea, West Africa (24.4%), Brazil (12.2%) and Jamaica (8.7%).

Equation 1
$$2KAlSi_3O_8(s) + 2H^+(aq) + H_2O(l) \rightarrow Al_2Si_2O_5(OH)_4(s) + 2K^+(aq) + 4SiO_2(aq)$$

potassium feldspar	acid	rainwater	kaolinite	ions	silica in solution

Equation 2
$$Al_2Si_2O_5(OH)_4(s) + H_2O(l) \rightarrow Al_2O_3.3H_2O(s) + 2SiO_2(aq)$$

kaolinite		water	bauxite (insoluble hydrated silica aluminium oxide)		in solution

10.4.2 PLACER DEPOSITS

Gold panners seek gold by working in rivers with pans and sieves. They know from past experience that certain rivers carry flakes and nuggets of gold, depositing them in the bed and banks of the river to form a **placer deposit**. Gold is an ideal placer mineral, being very dense and chemically unaltered by water. Most placers occur in river sediment (alluvium), or on a beach if the ore has reached the sea.

In flowing water, sorting of the sediment is controlled by the size, density and hardness of the grains, and by the energy available. Relatively dense grains of ore minerals carried by a river will be deposited if the flow decreases. The key physical properties of good placer minerals are density and hardness as shown in Appendix 6.

Cassiterite, SnO_2, the ore of tin, is a good placer mineral because it is chemically resistant, with a relative density of 7.0, and a hardness in Mohs' scale of 6.7. For several centuries, cassiterite has been mined from alluvial gravels in Malaysia and Brazil. In small deposits, high pressure water jets are used to wash the gravel and tin ore into a slurry which is then pumped to the concentrator. More commonly, dredgers scoop up the gravel in shallow water and pass it through a concentrator. The high density minerals are separated by gravity methods, relying on the high density of the ore and dense impurities are removed by magnetic or electrostatic separation. The concentrate, now 70 per cent tin, is ready for the furnace.

Australia is the leading producer of mineral sands from beach placer deposits. Wave action in the intertidal zone or wind action on the beach has separated sands into black deposits of mainly ore grains and white sands of quartz grains. The original source of the ore grains was trace quantities of minerals in granites that were eroded and transported from inland mountains.

10.4.3 FOSSIL PLACER DEPOSITS

'Fossil placers' are placer deposits formed millions of years ago, which became buried and formed sedimentary rocks (usually conglomerates). Such ores are harder and thus more costly to extract than loose sediments, but can be mined economically if the ore is valuable. In the Witswatersrand Goldfield in South Africa, a Precambrian quartz pebble conglomerate containing flakes of gold, along with silver and uranium has been mined for a hundred years and accounts for 50% of world gold production.

The world's largest uranium ore deposit in the Elliott Lake area of Ontario, Canada, is similar. Densely packed quartz pebbles, perhaps from a river delta, are set in a matrix containing pyrite, brannerite, UTi_2O_6, and uraninite, U_3O_8, which may have settled out with the pebbles. This deposit predates significant oxygen in the atmosphere, which accounts for the deposition of these easily oxidised minerals.

10.4.4 PRECIPITATED CHEMICAL DEPOSITS

The silver-lead-zinc orebodies of Mount Isa (Case Study, page 171) are examples of **precipitated chemical deposits**, where minerals formed by chemical reactions in solution settle out as layers of insoluble compounds on the sea floor.

This type of mineralisation has also formed the important **banded iron formations** (BIF). Several major BIF deposits are known worldwide, including those of the Hamersley Ranges in Western Australia (Figure 10.10).

BIF deposits are made of fine grains of silica and iron oxides which precipitated in large basins during the Precambrian, before oxygen was freely available in the atmosphere. Ripple-marks and mudcracks suggest precipitation in shallow water and a low-energy environment. The presence of cyanobacteria ('blue-green bacteria') is thought to have been another important factor in precipitating silica and iron oxides. Thus BIF deposits seem to have formed in a very specific combination of atmospheric composition, marine environment and a particular type of organism, a combination only present for a specific period of the Earth's history around 2500 Ma ago. The magnetic iron oxide, Fe_3O_4, was precipitated reflecting a limited oxygen content in the atmosphere at that time – lower levels of oxygen would have caused precipitation of iron(II) carbonate, $FeCO_3$, whereas higher levels of oxygen would have formed iron(III) oxide, Fe_2O_3, deposits.

During diagenesis, a distinctive fine banding into alternating pale chert (silica-rich) layers and dark magnetite and hematite layers developed. Later concentration by **secondary enrichment** enhanced the grade from 30 per cent to 65 per cent iron. In this case, silica was leached away and more iron oxide was precipitated, this time as Fe_2O_3, from percolating groundwaters. Just as important as the high grade of iron

Figure 10.10 *Location of the Hamersley Ranges, Western Australia*

are the low levels of impurities such as phosphorus which cause problems during steel-making.

The scale of these Hamersley deposits is remarkable; they extend unchanged over wide areas (more than 200 kilometres) reaching thicknesses over 300 metres. One estimate is that, at current levels of production, there is enough high-grade ore in the region to last several hundred years, and enough lower grade resource for tens of thousands of years!

10.5 Ore minerals formed by hydrothermal processes

Warm or hot aqueous solutions moving through rocks can result in various types of **hydrothermal ore deposit**. Easily visible hydrothermal deposits in the form of veins have been exploited for minerals in the British Isles for thousands of years. The commonest minerals mined were sulphides, particularly galena, sphalerite and chalcopyrite.

10.5.1 ORIGIN OF HYDROTHERMAL SOLUTIONS

The origin of the solutions is groundwater held in pores and cracks in the rocks. That water may originally have come from:

- **meteoric water:** rainwater infiltrating from the surface;
- **sea water** percolating from the sea floor;
- **formation water:** sea water trapped in sediments;
- **magmatic water:** water expelled from igneous intrusions.

The deeper in the crust the water is found, the higher its temperature and pressure, reaching more than 300 °C in rocks at depth. The water may already contain dissolved ions from its source, and may also be acidic. As it moves through pathways in the rocks it can pick up further metal cations by simple dissolving, by forming soluble complex ions (particularly if chloride or sulphide anions are present), or by reacting with anions in the rock (so dissolving metal cations such as calcium, lead or zinc). The result is a hot brine solution containing large quantities of metal cations in surprisingly high concentrations.

As these hydrothermal solutions move, usually upwards through the rocks, conditions may change (lower temperatures, lower pressures, change in pH) and metal cations may precipitate rapidly, or crystallise more slowly, to form a mineral deposit.

These hydrothermal processes can occur in many very different environments, but three situations where they commonly form are:

- at or near the surface of the crust (for example, as shown in Figure 10.11);
- deep below the surface in sedimentary basins;
- deep below the surface, associated with igneous heat.

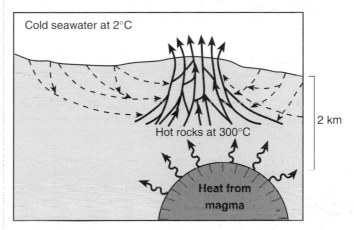

Figure 10.11 *Hydrothermal circulation below the sea floor; hydrothermal solutions are produced by heated sea water dissolving metal ions from rocks below the sea floor*

10.5.2 HYDROTHERMAL SOLUTIONS AT OR NEAR THE EARTH'S SURFACE

Chapter 4 discussed the formation of 'black smokers' near ocean ridges (page 61) and the metasomatic processes involved were described in Chapter 7 (pages 132–3). Particles from the black 'smoke' accumulate around the vent, building a chimney of anhydrite ($CaSO_4$), barite ($BaSO_4$) and metal sulphides, as shown in Figure 10.12.

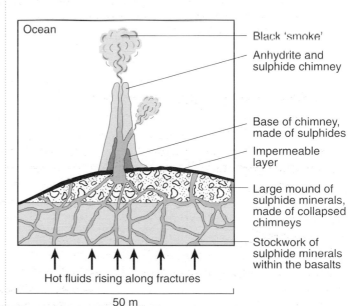

Figure 10.12 *A diagram of a sulphide chimney*

Some hot water also escapes through cracks in the ocean floor basalts, and minerals are precipitated there to leave a network of veins of metal sulphides as shown in Figure 10.12. Over time, large deposits from collapsed chimneys can accumulate to give a sulphide mound. Active black smokers are not yet commercially exploited, but could in future provide valuable resources.

However, **massive sulphide deposits** from ancient hydrothermal vent systems have been extensively mined in many places. There are essentially two types: Cyprus-type and Kuroko-type deposits.

In the Troodos Mountains in Cyprus, 20 sulphide mounds, from ancient chimneys formed on pillow lavas, contain networks of mineralised veins, which show the routes taken by the solutions. The ore contained about 10 per cent chalcopyrite and sphalerite, a little gold and silver, the rest pyrite. Although only a small deposit of 50 million tonnes of ore, 3000 years ago it was a vital source of metals for the ancient civilisations of the Mediterranean region.

In Japan, the Kuroko deposits are associated with silicic volcanic rocks, such as rhyolite. The setting of an island arc environment means that the massive sulphide mounds and fragmented network below contain a wider range of minerals than the Cyprus-type deposits – typically

chalcopyrite, sphalerite, galena, silver minerals, native gold, barite, gypsum and pyrite are present.

Perhaps the most important deposit of this type being mined at present is the Precambrian Kidd Creek deposit in Ontario, Canada (Figure 10.13). Worked for over 30 years, this is still one of the largest zinc mines in the world, and an important source of copper and lead. The deposits, originally horizontal, have been upended by Earth movements to give a vertical ore body.

10.5.3 HYDROTHERMAL SOLUTIONS FROM SEDIMENTARY BASINS

In the Mississippi valley, USA, large deposits of lead and zinc ores occur in limestones. Such deposits, resulting from hydrothermal circulation through permeable rocks, are now called **Mississippi Valley Type** (MVT) deposits. Long after the limestones formed, solutions at temperatures between 50 °C and 150 °C flowed from the centre of a sedimentary basin up the dip into the limestones on the margins, shown in Figure 10.14. The solutions carried metal cations and a variety of anions, including sulphide and sulphate ions, picking up further ions as they travelled. Hydrocarbons from organic matter in the basin also flowed up the dip, causing reducing conditions. Such solutions usually originate from thick sequences of shales becoming compacted in a sedimentary basin and losing their formation water. Evaporite layers may also provide strong saline solutions, in some places capable of dissolving metal ions, such as copper ions from red beds. These solutions may later crystallise in joints, fractures and even large voids to give ore deposits in veins or large pipes.

(a)
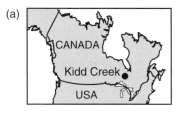

(b)
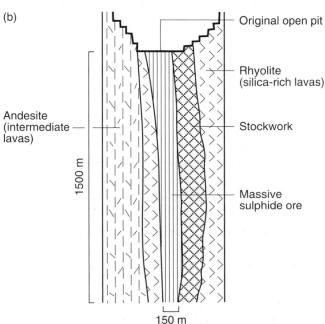

Figure 10.13 *a) Location map of the Kidd Creek ore body b) A cross section of the massive sulphide ore body at Kidd Creek*

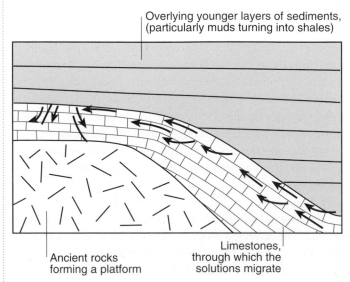

Figure 10.14 *The migration of solutions from a sedimentary basin*

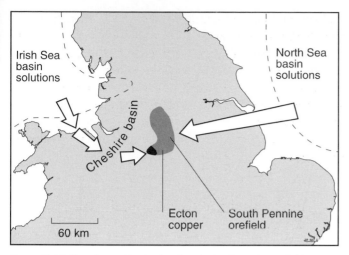

Figure 10.15 *Map of central England to show the South Pennine Orefield*

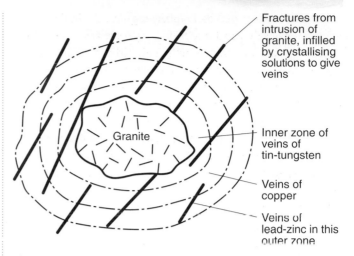

Figure 10.16 *A cross section of the zoning of minerals around granite intrusions in Devon and Cornwall*

Figure 10.17 *The sequence of minerals deposited by hydrothermal solutions from the Cornwall and Devon granite intrusions, showing the temperature/distance relationship*

Distance to granite	Main metals	Minerals		Temperature
closest	tin and tungsten	cassiterite and tungsten ore	SnO_2 $FeWO_4$	450 °C
	copper	chalcopyrite and copper iron tin ore	$CuFeS_2$ Cu_2FeSnS_4	
furthest	lead and zinc	galena and sphalerite	PbS ZnS	below 200 °C

The South Pennine Orefield in Britain is located within the Peak National Park (see Figure 10.15). The ore minerals, including galena, sphalerite, barite, calcite and fluorite, are found in veins in the Lower Carboniferous Limestone. When these ore deposits formed, the limestone was close to a deep basin containing Lower Carboniferous mudstones and Middle Carboniferous shales from which came the hydrothermal solutions. As millions of tonnes of ore exist, and each litre of solution only gave a few milligrams of mineral, the volumes of migrating solutions must have been enormous – one estimate is 2000 km³.

On the western edge of this orefield is an unusual copper mineralisation which may also be an MVT orebody. The chalcopyrite is found in a number of vertical pipes, running along the ridge of an anticline, the most important of which was the Ecton Pipe, mentioned earlier (page 174). The dominant mineral is calcite, and inside many calcite crystals are tiny 'bubbles' of liquid called **fluid inclusions**, thought to be samples of the original hydrothermal solution trapped when the crystals formed. Physical and chemical analyses have yielded information about the composition of the hydrothermal solution (very high salinity), and the conditions under which the ore deposit formed (about 80 °C).

10.5.4 HYDROTHERMAL SOLUTIONS ASSOCIATED WITH IGNEOUS INTRUSIONS

Sedimentary rocks close to large igneous intrusions may contain many hydrothermal veins with a wide variety of minerals. During the late stages of crystallisation of granite, magmatic water, bearing ions such as tin, tungsten and lithium, migrates as hydrothermal solutions through the surrounding country rocks.

The country rocks have usually been deformed by the intrusion from below, opening up faults and joints, and have also been heated by the cooling magma. The hydrothermal solutions mix with the much greater volumes of water contained in the sedimentary rocks, and this water already contains silica and ions such as lead, zinc, copper, arsenic, silver, and sulphate. Eventually, the migrating solutions crystallise in veins, often mainly quartz with small amounts of ore minerals.

Classic examples of this type of mineralisation surround the granite intrusions of Devon and Cornwall, shown in Figure 10.16. Different minerals are found in zones around the granite, and research using fluid inclusions has shown the temperature-distance relationship in Figure 10.17.

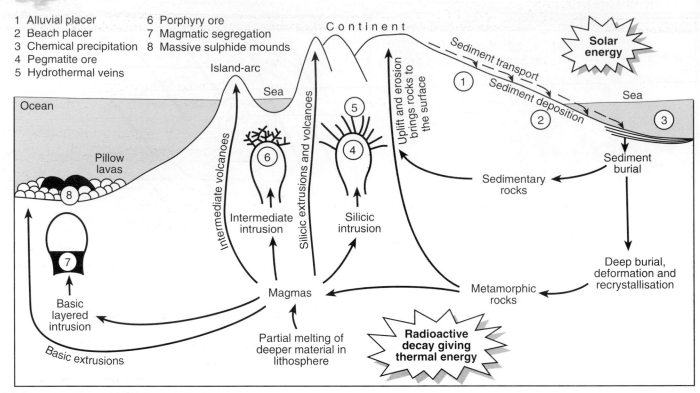

1 Alluvial placer
2 Beach placer
3 Chemical precipitation
4 Pegmatite ore
5 Hydrothermal veins
6 Porphyry ore
7 Magmatic segregation
8 Massive sulphide mounds

Figure 10.18 *The rock cycle and some ore-forming processes*

10.5.5 MINERALISATION AND THE ROCK CYCLE

One way of summarising the numerous ore-forming processes we have examined is to consider their positions in the rock cycle, as shown in Figure 10.18.

10.6 Commercial development of an orebody

10.6.1 STAGES IN OREBODY DEVELOPMENT

How are ore deposits found, developed and processed into metals? The stages are outlined below.

1 Exploration using a range of techniques.
2 Evaluation to assess the grade, size and economics of the orebody in relation to supply and demand for the metal, to prove the economic viability of the new mine. The type of mining necessary may be a major factor.
3 Development of the infrastructure; buildings, mine shafts, roads, housing, services (e.g. water and electricity), machinery and vehicles.
4 Mining to extract the ore from the ground.
   There are three designs of open-cast mine:
   • open pit: a deep hole in the ground, often with a spiral road system.

   • strip-mining for shallow, wide deposits such as coal and clay.
   • dredging of underwater ore-bearing gravels or sands.
   Every underground mine (deep mine) has a unique design based on the properties of the ore and surrounding rocks, the most efficient way to mine and safety factors.
5 Mineral processing (ore dressing) to separate and concentrate the ore, using its physical and chemical properties. Usually the ore is crushed to liberate grains of ore minerals so they can be separated from the gangue minerals.
6 Metal extraction:
   • by smelting; the concentrate is roasted with carbon to reduce it to the metal.
   • by electrolysis; electrical energy is used to extract the metal from a melt or aqueous solution containing the metal ions.
7 Refining: purifying the metal by further smelting or electrolysis.
8 Marketing: the economics of selling and shipping the metal (or the ore concentrate) to a buyer, which are affected by such factors as the discovery of new deposits, supply and demand, commodity prices, the state of local and world economy, changes in taxation, existing stockpiles, technological advances, political and social changes – and wars!

We shall look at the geological aspects of mineral exploration and orebody development in some detail.

1. Decision to undertake initial research of region:
   This is begun by studying all documents of past work in region.

Is the broad geology of the region likely to have the right kind of mineralisation?	OR Is there any known past mining and what was the grade of ore?	OR Has aerial photography, remote sensing or fieldwork shown visible signs of ores in the area?
↓	↓	↓
Yes	Yes	Yes
↓	↓	↓

2. Decision to carry out prospecting of a region using one or more of the following regional reconnaissance techniques:
   – airborne geophysical survey (e.g. magnetic, gravity)
   – geochemical survey (stream-sediment sampling)
   – remote sensing by aerial photography and satellite imagery
   – broad geological mapping
   If successful identification of possible orebody, then:
   ↓

3. Decisions to carry out detailed surveys and possibly stake mining claim
   using one or more of the following detailed reconnaissance techniques:
   – thorough geological mapping on the ground
      ground geophysical surveys (e.g. using gravimeter, magnetometer, resistivity, seismic)
   – geochemical surveys (stream-sediment sampling, soil sampling, biogeochemical)
   – trenching or trial boreholes sunk to collect samples and assess grade of ore
   If successful identification of orebody, then:
   ↓

4. Decisions to stake mining claims and assess size and value of orebody.
   Usually all the following techniques are used:
   – detailed topographic survey
   – detailed geological survey
      further boreholes sunk and logging of cores
   – petrographical and chemical analysis of cores
   – assaying of ore samples to assess grade of ore

↓	↓	↓
If successful, then:	It could be successful in future:	If unsuccessful:
↓	↓	↓
develop the orebody	hold claim and wait	give up claim and go away

Figure 10.19 *Flow chart of decisions and actions during mineral exploration*

10.6.2 MINERAL EXPLORATION DECISIONS

The decision to start mining a new orebody is the final action in a long line of events. The flow-chart in Figure 10.19 is a simplified order of events during exploration, and relies on a successful outcome at each stage. Each stage is extremely costly, with total costs up to £50 million. This final decision may take many years to reach.

10.6.3 MINERAL EXPLORATION TECHNIQUES

The four principal techniques in mineral exploration are:

- remote sensing;
- geophysical surveys;
- geochemical surveys;
- boreholes and logging.

Remote sensing is the collection of information about an area without being in physical contact with it, using aircraft, satellites, and even spacecraft. It is particularly valuable for building up knowledge about large, inhospitable, inaccessible regions. The Global Positioning System (GPS) enables accurate location during surveying. From the data, topographical and geological maps can be constructed, and natural resources, including orebodies, detected.

There are two distinct data-gathering systems:

1 Photographs from cameras, including black-and-white, colour and infra-red (to detect heat sources), and multispectral (for selected detail).
2 Electronic scanners or sensors record data digitally, from which maps are drawn by computers. Applications include geophysical techniques and satellite imagery, often used by Earth scientists.

Satellites are solar-powered with data-collecting systems which transmit information to Earth. The sensors collect reflected sunlight or thermal radiation from the ground, scanning a 185 kilometre square at any one time, and covering the whole world every 16 days. At present there are two kinds of scanner; Landsat Multispectral Scanners, and the Landsat Thematic Mapper using seven extra wavelengths, (two particularly good for geology) and with 10 times better resolution. This imagery is used by developing countries to provide base geology maps, and in mineral exploration to detect hydrothermal alteration, patterns of fractures and faults, and changes in rock colour due to weathering of ores.

Geophysical techniques are used to determine the physical properties and structures of rocks below the surface.

- Seismic surveys: earthquakes or explosions send shock waves through rocks. Geophones detect the reflected waves, from which a profile of the rocks and their structures can be built up.
- Gravity surveys: gravity at the Earth's surface depends on many factors including the densities of the underlying rocks. A gravimeter is used to survey a wide area for significant variations from normal. A high-density rock will give a positive anomaly ('high'), a low-density rock will give a negative anomaly ('low'). As most ore minerals are relatively dense, searching for positive gravity anomalies can be very effective.
- Magnetic surveys: small changes in the Earth's magnetic field due to magnetic minerals, particularly in igneous and metamorphic rocks, can be measured by towing a magnetometer behind an aircraft. These airborne surveys are popular, using relatively cheap equipment. Ground surveys may be carried out using hand-held magnetometers.
- In a resistivity survey, a current is passed between two electrodes in the soil, and the voltage drop is measured.

Many sulphide minerals have low resistivity (high conductivity) compared with silicate minerals.
- Electromagnetic waves produced by a transmitter induce currents in conducting minerals, especially sulphides, which can be detected (rather like an airborne metal detector).
- Radiometric surveys detect the radioactive decay of some elements in rocks, particularly uranium. Portable Geiger-counters have now been replaced by more sophisticated instruments. Aerial surveys have found uranium sources in the inhospitable Canadian Shield region.

Figure 10.20 shows anomalies detected by three of these geophysical techniques during mineral exploration.

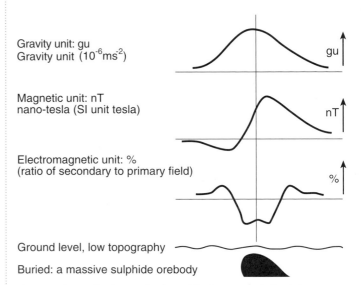

Gravity unit: gu
Gravity unit (10^{-6}ms^{-2})   gu

Magnetic unit: nT
nano-tesla (SI unit tesla)   nT

Electromagnetic unit: %
(ratio of secondary to primary field)   %

Ground level, low topography

Buried: a massive sulphide orebody

Figure 10.20 *Graphs of anomalies detected by three geophysical techniques during mineral exploration*

Geochemical surveys involve sampling sediment from streams and lakes to find ores in the rocks upstream. Even in deserts, rare storm floods carry material downstream into depressions. Later, detailed geochemical soil sampling can be used to pinpoint the source. Soft sediments are collected for later analysis, and some samples may be treated using the familiar gold-pan swirling method. Dense minerals stay in the pan as **heavy mineral concentrates** and can be analysed.

The analysis of water samples can also detect valuable elements. The acidity of the water will partly determine the concentration of the ions in solution. Sometimes vegetation samples may be analysed as certain plants take up metals preferentially.

Samples are usually analysed in the laboratory, using various chemical methods to determine the concentrations of elements. From these data, computers map the distributions, showing up any anomalies and allowing the geochemist to hunt down the source orebody.

The combination of modern automated analytical techniques with powerful computers has revolutionised both geochemical and geophysical exploration and interpretation.

The same geochemical techniques can be used for environmental monitoring of, for example, water supplies and waste disposal sites.

Borehole and logging methods used to gain rock samples and other data are described on pages 158–9. Rock chippings are inspected to identify minerals, and panned for heavy mineral concentrates. Cores are described in terms of rock types, structures and minerals, and parts may be sent for analysis; the rest is stored for future reference. More information can be obtained by the downhole logging techniques described in Chapter 9.

10.6.4 MINING THE DEPOSIT

Open-pit mining (Figure 10.21) is far cheaper than underground mining. Many mines begin as open-pits until the depth becomes uneconomic, then change to an underground operation below the hole. Deep ore deposits use underground mining from the beginning.

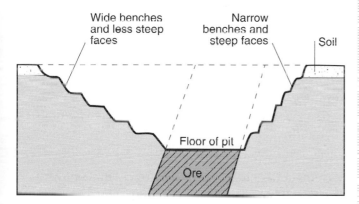

Figure 10.21 *Open pit mining*

The relation between depth and the volume of overlying material (**overburden**) is very important in determining whether open-pit mining will be economic, although grade, depth and size of the ore body are also major factors. A typical stripping ratio of overburden to ore for open-pit operations is about 2:1 to 3:1.

Open-pit mining needs careful management of the inevitable environmental problems from vehicles and blasting. Precision timing of the explosions can give better fragmentation and less dust. Dust levels can also be reduced by spraying water onto the ore, roads and vehicles. Once mining has ended, the pit may be reclaimed by infilling the hole, or by blasting down the steep edges to reduce hazards, and then improving the appearance by re-vegetation.

Underground mining is far more complicated, hazardous and expensive, requiring even more careful planning and costing. Modern mines have large shafts (vertical tunnels), levels (horizontal tunnels), raises (inclined shafts) and ramps (low-gradient roads). Machines and vehicles are large, rugged and are used 24 hours per day.

Gently dipping orebodies are usually mined by room-and-pillar methods, leaving pillars of rock to hold the roof up (see Figure 10.22). Under certain weak rock conditions, longwall mining may be used, where the roof is allowed to collapse after mining. This is also a common coal mining technique.

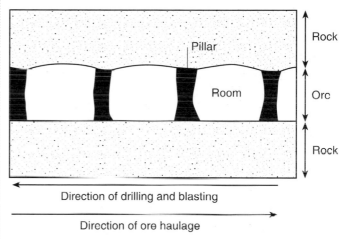

Figure 10.22 *Underground mining by the room-and-pillar method*

Steeply dipping orebodies are mined by blasting ore from the roof, a method called stoping; later on the **stope** (the empty space left) may be backfilled with waste rock.

Mines are usually designed so that all ore goes to the crusher at the bottom before haulage to the surface. It reaches the bottom either by truck or by tipping down a shaft called an ore-pass. Underground crushing is environmentally preferable in terms of dust and noise. But the main economic gain lies in the more efficient haulage of smaller ore to the surface processing plants. These methods are used at Kidd Creek, Ontario (Figure 10.23).

In many ways, underground mining may be less damaging to the environment than an open pit because it is almost invisible, except around the shafts where the ore arrives on the surface. In old mining areas where the roof rocks have collapsed, there may be considerable problems with ground subsidence, and long-forgotten shafts may suddenly reappear at the surface.

Mine drainage water is often acidic (low pH), especially in sulphide-rich ores or where wet soils overlie certain rocks. Such acid mine-drainage into rivers can carry high levels of metal ions in solution which may be toxic to plants and animals, including humans who drink

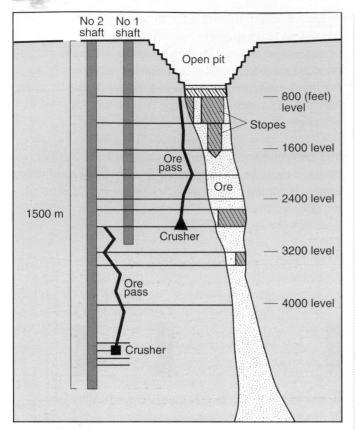

Figure 10.23 *Cross section of the underground mine at Kidd Creek, Ontario*

the water. Attempts are often made to reduce water flow from the mine or raise the pH (often by treatment with limestone), but these may be unsuccessful at times of flood.

10.6.5 ORE TO METAL

Modern production plants are closely controlled by computer systems, with few employees and much technology. Large volumes of water and heavy electricity demand are normal. Constant quality control and recycling of materials at all stages improve efficiency and reduce waste.

The simplified flow-diagram, Figure 10.25 on page 187, shows the production of copper at Mount Isa through the mineral processing and smelting stages.

Mineral processing involves first crushing the ore to **liberation size**, where each grain is made of only one mineral, through a number of mills. Between each crushing process the material is screened (through a large scale sieve) to remove material already fine enough. The normal crushing sequence is first the primary (jaw) crusher (at the mine) then the secondary (cone) crusher (at the plant), then a rod mill (rotating drum with steel rods) and finally a ball mill (with steel balls).

Ore minerals are then separated from the gangue to make an ore concentrate by a variety of methods. Dense ores use gravity separation, for example by using shaking tables or spiral separators. X-rays are used in the separation of diamonds; magnetism for iron and chromium; and electrical conductivity for iron-titanium ores.

Froth flotation methods are often used for high value low-grade ores such as sulphides. A complex organic reagent is used to coat the ore grains making them water repellent. Then air is blown into the base of the tank. The grains stick to the air bubbles which rise up to the surface where the froth overflows and is collected Different reagents can be used to separate different ore minerals.

The wastes are dumped in tips which are eventually landscaped and revegetated. Fertilisers are added, often with lime to reduce acidity, and grasses resistant to toxic metals are sown. Such vegetation-covered tips hold fine particles on windy days and are more pleasing to the eye. The finest particles leave the plant suspended in 'muddy' water which is pumped into large ponds where the particles settle out as 'slimes'. When dry, they are like quicksand and very dangerous to walk upon.

Metal ore concentrates are then **smelted**, in this example for extracting copper, by:

- roasting to remove sulphur;
- heating to over 1000 °C to form a melt with two layers; the ore melt and the slag which is discarded in waste tips;
- mixing of the ore melt with silica to remove iron; the resultant melt is then cast into metal blocks for further refining.

The metal blocks are 99.7% copper, but the electrical industry needs 99.98% purity so further **refining by electrolysis** is needed (Figure 10.24). The impure copper blocks form the anodes and during electrolysis, copper ions move through the electrolyte to pure copper cathodes leaving behind impurities either in a sludge at the base of the tank or in the electrolyte. The purified copper from the anodes forms the final product.

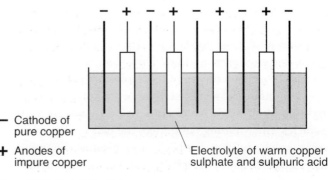

− Cathode of pure copper

+ Anodes of impure copper

Electrolyte of warm copper sulphate and sulphuric acid

Figure 10.24 *Electrolytic refining*

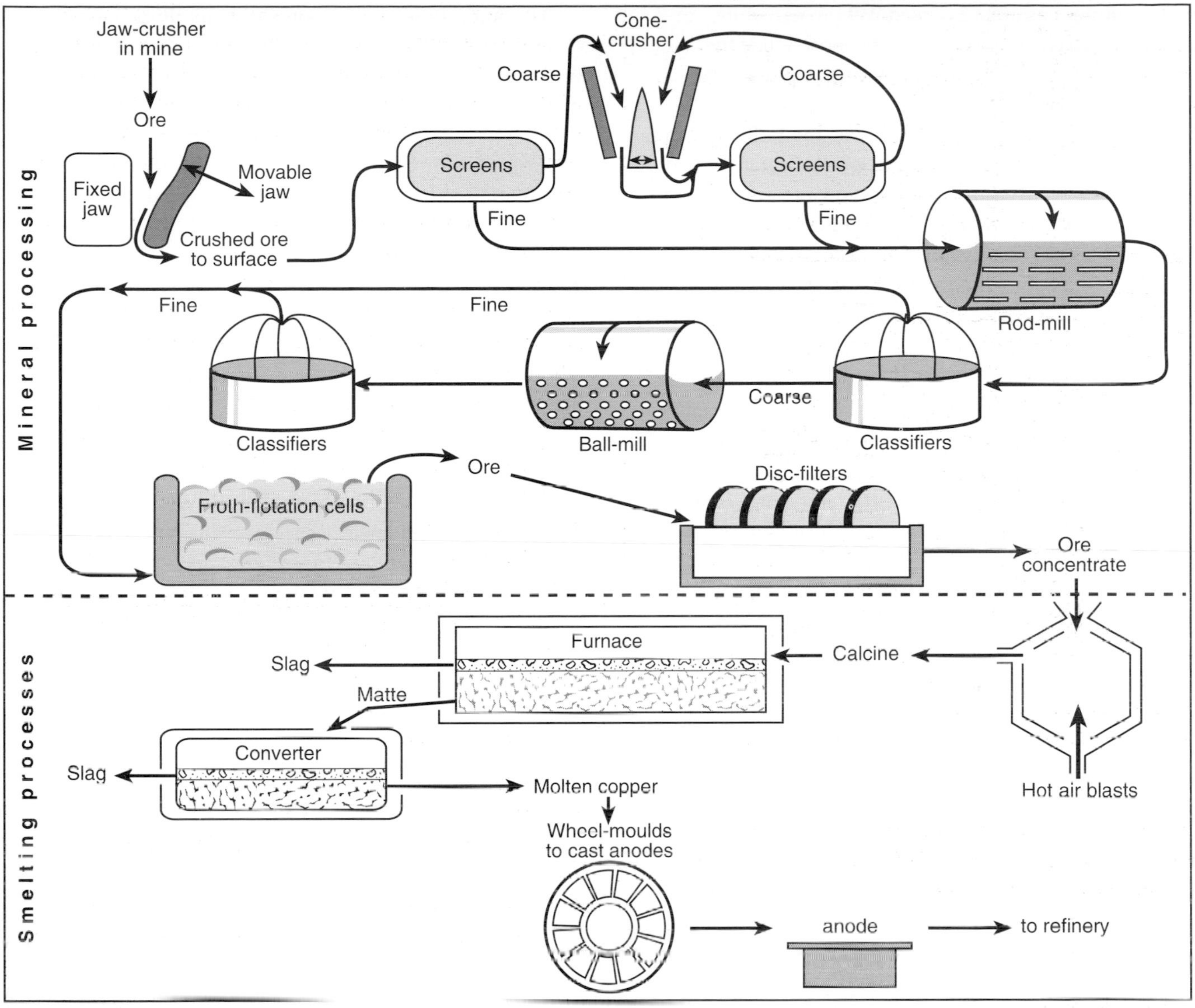

Figure 10.25 *Flow diagram of production at Mount Isa*

10.7 The mineral industry: past, present and future

Historically, the discovery and exploitation of minerals has been a vital activity in the development of human cultures. The barter of gold and gems is known from Stone Age archaeological evidence; and the Bronze Age and Iron Age are names given to the periods in history when these metals were used extensively.

Early trading of metal ores around the Mediterranean, and even of tin from Cornwall, by the Phoenicians was followed by the Roman invasion of Britain in search of lead. Centuries later came the famous voyages of discovery to Africa, the Americas and Australia with explorers seeking valuable minerals to carry home to Europe.

The invention of the steam engine led to the mechanisation of mining which began the Industrial Revolution in the late 18th century. Suddenly, the demand for minerals increased rapidly and has continued relentlessly ever since.

Today the mineral industry continues to provide the raw materials for most manufactured goods and it is still the basis of the economy for many countries. Even an industrialised country like Britain relies on its own rock and mineral wealth to boost its total income or Gross Domestic Product, providing about 2.8% of the GDP in the mid-1990s. There is a worldwide trend towards increasing consumption of hydrocarbons, coal and bulk industrial minerals, with metals forming a relatively less important part of the mineral industry.

British ore deposits crucial to the Industrial Revolution have been heavily exploited in the past but there are now cheaper sources of most metal ores overseas, so British metal mining has all but ceased. Where new mines or extensions to existing mines are proposed, it is the responsibility of the mining company to pay for the reclamation of the land surface, the cleaning up of contaminated areas and the effects of any pollution. In the past, mining companies did little to rehabilitate mined-out areas. Nowadays, with strict planning agreements and mining companies having much greater responsibility for the environment, the situation has greatly improved.

Although there are still some potentially rich ores in Britain, these are generally small deposits requiring underground mining. They usually cannot compete with the large scale opencast mining of low grade ores overseas. This, together with the pressure to conserve the environment and the potential high costs of extraction and reclamation in Britain, means that they are unlikely to be mined in the foreseeable future.

10.8 Summary

1 Elements are not distributed evenly in the Earth's crust. Exploitation of minerals depends on their natural concentration.

2 Mineral deposits can be formed by igneous processes:
   a) by fractional crystallisation in mafic magma chambers.
   b) through magmatic differentiation of sulphur-rich mafic magmas.
   c) associated with the crustal and mantle melting caused by meteorite impacts.
   d) in pegmatite formation during later-stage crystallisation of granitic magmas.
   e) during porphyry formation involving hydrothermal solutions.

3 Sedimentary processes can produce economic mineral accumulations:
   a) when rock weathering leaves residual deposits.
   b) in placer and fossil placer deposits.
   c) where minerals are deposited on the sea floor by chemical reactions.

4 Hydrothermal processes can produce mineralisation at economic levels:
   a) when hot mineralised fluids pass through rocks, resulting in massive sulphide deposits close to ocean ridges and sulphide deposits in limestones (MVT).
   b) where rocks are affected by hydrothermal solutions close to igneous intrusions.

5 Ore minerals are concentrated in rocks by natural processes which separate compounds from each other. There are many such processes, and they can be used as a basis for classifying ore minerals.

6 Exploitation and development of an orebody may involve:
   a) geophysical techniques: seismic, gravity, magnetic, resistivity, electromagnetic, radiometric.
   b) geochemical techniques: stream and soil sampling.
   c) boreholes and logging.
   d) mining techniques that depend on the local conditions and nature of the deposit.

10.9 Questions

1 What factors affect the decision to operate a mine by open-pit or underground methods?

2 A large orebody to be mined in open country has the following characteristics:
   - estimated overburden removal for open pit operation = 245 000 tonnes per day.
   - estimated ore production = 77 000 tonnes per day.
   - estimated metal content in this daily production of ore: copper = 200 tonnes; nickel = 25 tonnes.
   a) Calculate the grade of the copper ore.
   b) Which type of mining operation would you recommend for this ore body?
   c) What environmental impacts may result from your choice of mining operation for this ore body?
   d) How would you recommend that these effects on the environment should be minimised?

3 From the Case Study of the Mount Isa mine at the start of Chapter 10:
   a) Construct a three-column table selecting information from the history of the Mount Isa Mine:
      Column 1: the nine factors listed on page 172.
      Column 2: examples of each factor with the dates.
      Column 3: a brief explanation of how the factor affected the event.
   b) Suggest which three factors were the most crucial in determining the outcome.

CHAPTER 11

Rock dating: relative and radiometric methods

Introduction

To understand the geological history of an area you need to be able to work out the sequence of events. This can be done using a wide range of methods, some of which have been used since the early days of geology and some that have been developed only recently. The most important of these are the application of stratigraphic principles and laws to field situations, the relative dating and correlation of rocks using key fossils and the use of radiometric dating to give the ages of rocks in years or in millions of years.

11.1 Case Study: the rocks beneath my feet

Do you remember when you first became aware of the geology of the countryside around you, or even the town where you may live? When a friend of mine was young, he was taken to the top of a mountain, near his home on the coast of Wales, and told how the fossils showed that the mountain had once been under the sea. He had nightmares after that, dreaming that the sea level rose suddenly and flooded his home!

For me, the local heathland of Surrey formed the battleground for many Scout night games. The underlying geology consisted of loosely consolidated pebbles, which had been carved into ridges and gullies by the rain. One careless movement sent a shower of pebbles rattling down into the gully, instantly betraying your presence to the 'enemy'.

Seen in the cold light of day, the Blackheath Pebble Beds consist of beautifully rounded flint pebbles, with occasional layers of 'soft' sand. The local DIY enthusiasts dug this (illegally) for mixing with cement to make mortar, although the sand grains were too well rounded to make strong concrete. Rainfall easily soak through the beds, carrying the nutrients away from the surface layers so that a poor soil developed. This could support only a sparse vegetation of birch, pine and heather; ideal for a public open space, but useless for farming.

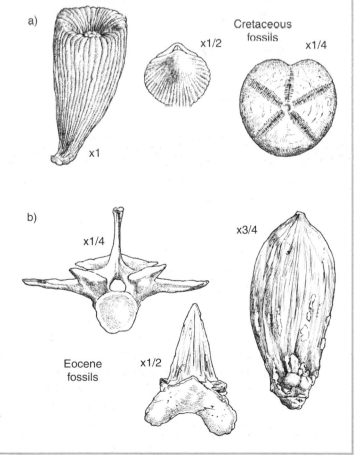

Figure 11.1 *a) Fossils from the Chalk found in the Blackheath Beds; a coral, a brachiopod, an echinoid b) Fossils from the London Clay; a crocodile vertebra, the fruit of a palm tree, a shark's tooth.*

From time to time, fossils turned up in the pebble beds. These were mostly echinoids, which were preserved in flint, and usually as worn as the pebbles themselves. Modern echinoids (i.e. sea urchins) live only in the sea and are too fragile to survive the battering from waves that produce banks of pebbles like those found in the Blackheath Beds. Where had they come from? Where had the flint pebbles themselves originated? How did the whole deposit find itself some 120 metres above sea level, overlooking London? How old were the beds themselves? These were some of the questions I asked myself.

The Chalk of the North Downs lay only a short cycle ride away to the south, and, by pedalling steadily uphill for several kilometres, you could find abandoned chalk pits. Within the Chalk, many nodules and layers of flint could be found and some of these contained echinoids, corals, brachiopods and other fossils of marine creatures (Figure 11.1a) just like those in the Blackheath Beds. The Chalk must have been eroded and the flints from the Chalk transported and then deposited as rounded pebbles to form the Blackheath Beds.

So, one question was answered, but another one had appeared. Surely younger rocks like those of the Blackheath Beds would have been deposited on top of older rocks like the Chalk, so how could they now be found at a lower level? The

clue to help solve this problem came from the cycle ride home. It was almost possible to do the journey without pedalling, because the land surface was of similar gradient to the angle of dip (or tilt) of the beds beneath. This formed a perfect introduction to a dip slope, and hence my first introduction to landscape features. The Pebble Beds had been deposited on top, but since the whole sequence had been tilted and eroded, the Pebble Beds could only be found at lower levels, as you can see in the cross section in Figure 11.2. This shows that, because of the dip of the beds, the further downhill you go, the younger the beds become.

A few hundred metres downhill from my home were some allotments. Unlike the heathland higher up, the soil here was extremely heavy clay, the London Clay. In later visits to brickpits in the London Clay I found pieces of fossil wood, riddled with animal borings and seeds of palm trees. I also discovered marine bivalve fossils and occasional sharks' teeth; bones of crocodiles and land mammals were also reported (Figure 11.1b). The London Clay formed the youngest rocks in the area.

The map and cross section in Figure 11.2 show how I was eventually able to fit all these geological features around my home town together. If you look for similar clues in your home area, you may be able to understand your local geology in the same way.

Figure 11.2 *a) Geological cross section along the line AB on the map in Figure 11.2 b); b) The geology of the North Downs and part of the London Basin*

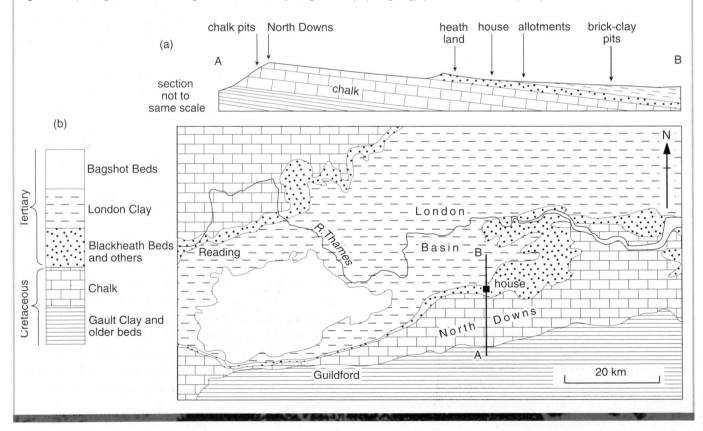

11.2 Sorting out the sequence of events

Through earlier chapters you will have seen how we now understand rocks like those in my home area as the deposits of different sedimentary environments laid down in different conditions. The climatic conditions changed through the northward movement of the area we now call Britain due to plate tectonics. Chapter 8 showed how plate collisions have been powerful enough in the past to cause large-scale folding in rocks. It was folding that produced the tilting of the rocks found in the south London area today. But how can we find out what the order of events was? How is it possible to date events in the geological past?

During their work, all geologists have to establish the sequence of events represented by the rocks they are examining. First we will look at 'geological' ways of placing rocks in relative order. This is known as **relative dating**; it puts each episode in time sequence but can not tell us how long ago, in years (or millions of years) the event occurred. To tell us this we have to use other methods based on geochemical and geophysical measurements; these are called **absolute dating** methods.

11.2.1 THE PRINCIPLE OF SUPERPOSITION

The geology of an area is often summarised in a geological column, like the one shown in Appendix 7. You may have studied the geological column for your own area and will have noticed that the oldest sedimentary strata are always shown lying beneath the younger ones. This may sound obvious, but when geology was a young science this was a vital discovery, and is known as the **Principle of Superposition**.

In most parts of the world, younger strata do indeed lie on top of older ones, but exceptions occur when Earth movements have been so violent as to completely overturn a sequence of beds. This means that we need to prove which way up a sequence is, and we refer to the Principle of Superposition, rather than the Law of Superposition, a law being something which is always true.

The geological column showing rocks in sequence is also known as a stratigraphic column because it summarises the **stratigraphy** of the area. Studying stratigraphy involves examining sequences of sedimentary strata and linking them to sequences of the same age to show how the region changed over space and time.

Figure 11.3 *Unconformity between Precambrian metamorphic rocks and Old Red Sandstone conglomerates on the Isle of Kerrera*

11.2.2 BREAKS IN THE SEQUENCE

In the Case Study (page 189), you may have realised that there must have been a break in the processes of deposition between the Chalk and the Blackheath Pebble Beds. In the field you can see an uneven, eroded surface where the younger beds rest on the Chalk. Also, the pebble beds show that much Chalk must have been eroded away, to release so many flint fragments. These had plenty of time in which to be rolled around on the sea floor and thoroughly rounded.

Such a break of deposition produces a junction between the rocks above and below known as an unconformity (see Chapter 8 page 144). Because rocks are missing from the sequence, it is usually difficult to say how much time is represented by the break, or exactly what the conditions were like in the area during the time when no sediments were being deposited.

In the London area, the Earth movements which led to the unconformity were relatively gentle, being a distant effect of the Alpine mountain building episode. In other examples of unconformities the effects were much greater; there are large differences between the angle of dip of the beds above and below the unconformity and millions of years may have passed between the formation of the two groups of rocks. An example is shown in Figure 11.3.

In Figure 11.3, further evidence for unconformity comes from the fact that **sedimentary** rocks overlie **metamorphic** ones. This shows that there must have been such a long time between the laying down of the upper and lower sequences that the older rocks could be buried, metamorphosed, uplifted and the beds above eroded before the younger sediments were deposited.

11.2.3 'WAY-UP' STRUCTURES

What kind of evidence might help us to determine whether a series of beds is the right way up, or has been turned upside down? Look back to the Case Study on page 189 and decide how many different clues show that the Blackheath Pebble Beds are younger than the Chalk.

In practice, many rocks contain **'way-up' structures**. These are structures like those shown in Figure 11.4. Because of their shapes, it is clear if they have been turned upside down. Thus if the 'way-up' structures are the

wrong way up, the whole sequence of strata must have been inverted by large-scale folding.

Figure 11.4 *Some structures which may be used to determine 'way-up'; a) mudcracks, dried with sand in the cracks b) load and flame structures where a sand bed has collapsed down into mud c) cross bedding in sandstone d) burrows e) pillow lavas where pillows sag down between other pillows f) a channel in mudstone filled with sand g) a rootlet bed beneath a coal seam h) ripple marks in sandstone*

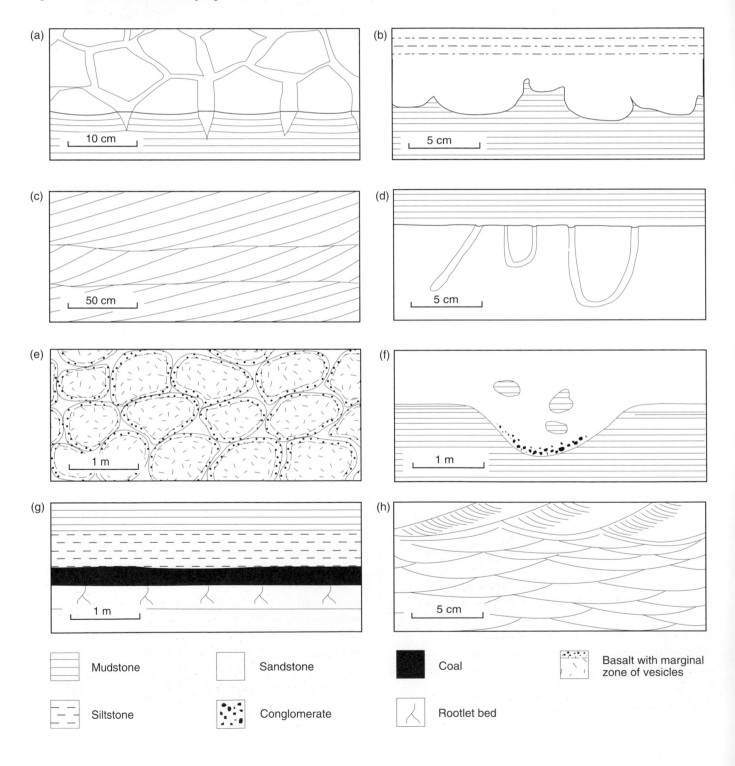

11.2.4 INCLUDED FRAGMENTS

Just as the Blackheath Pebble Beds were largely derived from material eroded from the Chalk, most beds above an unconformity contain included fragments of older rocks. The fragments are always older than the rocks in which they occur, so they may be used to show the relative ages of the two rocks – this is the **Law of Included Fragments**. If they can be dated by radiometric means (see page 196), a limiting date can be given to the age of the younger sediments. This has been useful in determining the age and origin of the Triassic pebble beds of the English Midlands and Cheshire Basin (Case Study in Chapter 5). Palaeocurrent studies show that the rivers which deposited the sediments flowed from the area which is now south west England. Some of the pebbles are granites and dates of around 280 Ma have been obtained from the micas they contain by radiometric methods. This means that the pebbles are the same age as the granites of Devon and Cornwall, or perhaps of Brittany. Thus the pebbles could not have come from the more abundant, but older granites of the Lake District or Scotland.

11.2.5 CROSS-CUTTING RELATIONSHIPS

Virtually all rocks are cut by later features, such as joints, and there is a wide range of such cross-cutting structures, including dykes and sills, faults and mineral veins. These must have formed later than the rocks that they cut, i.e. they must be younger. Since this is always the case, we can speak about the **Law of Cross-cutting Relationships**.

In Figure 11.5a the quartz porphyry (dyke 1) cuts the sandstone and so is younger, the dolerite (dyke 2) cuts the quartz porphyry and is then cut by the unconformity below the limestone. So the rock formation sequence is first sandstone, then dyke 1, then dyke 2 and finally, the limestone. Work out for yourself the sequence of events in Figure 11.5b.

Figure 11.5 a) Cross-cutting relationships seen in a cliff cross section b) Map of part of the foreshore on the Isle of Kerrera

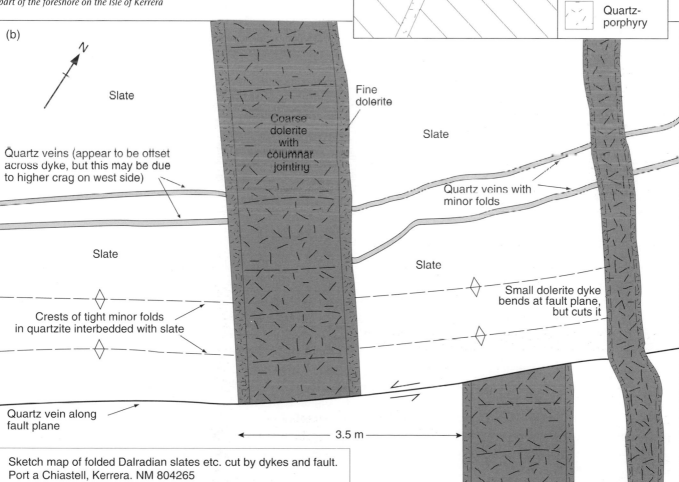

11.2.6 THE USE OF FOSSILS

The Law of Cross-cutting Relationships is particularly useful for establishing relative dates in rocks of igneous or metamorphic origin, which seldom contain recognisable fossils. In sedimentary rocks however, fossils can often be used to establish age relationships. The first person to attempt to use fossils to date rocks was **William Smith**, in the late 18th century. Smith was a canal engineer who taught himself to recognise the fossils found in different strata in canal cuttings. He realised that strata which appeared to have been formed at the same time contained the same groups of fossils. Once these had been identified, they could be used to relate the ages of other rock sequences to the first ones investigated. Smith became known as 'Strata Smith', and is generally credited with being the 'Father of English Geology'. Smith's mapping work enabled him to predict the geological conditions which the canal 'navvies' would encounter, and thus to deal with problems in advance. This, in turn, enabled the companies to complete their canals in a shorter time and to solve their engineering problems more efficiently.

William Smith appreciated that once a species of fossil had disappeared, no identical form occurred again, thus making it unique to a particular period of time. He also noticed that the changes between the consecutive species were often very slight, but he did not attempt to explain *why* this happened. Although Smith may well have been aware of the developing theory of evolution, he died at the time when Charles Darwin was still gathering his thoughts, after the voyage of the *Beagle*, and thus avoided the controversy which broke soon after Darwin published his *Origin of Species*, 20 years later.

Since the 19th century, geologists have been refining the methods that Smith pioneered, of using fossils to establish relative dates of strata. Of course, not all fossils are suitable for establishing dates. Some are too rare; thus *Archaeopteryx* a bird-like fossil, is exciting in that it shows possible links between reptiles and birds, but only eight specimens have ever been found, so it would be a useless fossil to depend upon for dating rocks, since the chances of finding one are so slight. Other fossils show very little evolutionary change over long periods of time: for example, the brachiopod *Lingula* ranges from the Ordovician Period to the present day, with very few recognisable changes in its structure; these types cannot be used for dating either. Some organisms are benthic, i.e. they spend most of their life cycle on or in the sea bed, so they tend to occur only in association with particular rock types and are not widely distributed.

These examples show that some groups of fossils are much better than others for dating rocks. The best groups have the following characteristics:

- they were common (large numbers originally existed);
- they had good preservation potential (so many were fossilised);
- they evolved quickly (so higher beds in a sequence contain different types);
- they are widely distributed (thus pelagic 'floating' groups are better than benthic groups confined to the sea floor);
- they are found in a variety of rock types;
- they are easily identified (if we can not tell different types apart easily, they are not much use).

Many microfossils have these key characteristics but are also so small that they can be found in abundance in chips or cores of rock from boreholes. Thus they have an extra key characteristic:

- small size (abundant in small specimens of rock).

Appendix 5 lists the most commonly found groups of fossils, together with their characteristics. By applying the list of characteristics above to the different fossil groups in this Appendix, you should be able to work out which ones are most useful in dating rocks and which ones are least useful.

Some of the best groups of fossils for dating include graptolites and cephalopods. The following example shows how ammonites (which are cephalopods) have been used to set up a relative dating system that can be used very widely.

Figure 11.6 shows the distribution of several species of ammonite collected from cliff sections in rocks of Jurassic age, mostly on the coast of Dorset. If the collecting and identification has been very thorough, these vertical distribution lines may be broadly equated to the **range** of each species, i.e. the span of geological time between the first appearance of the species and its extinction. If these time ranges are unique to each species, we can use some of them as **index** fossils; these are key fossils for dating certain sequences over a wide area. The time sequences they identify are called **zones**. The Jurassic ammonites in this example allow the sequence to be divided up in such detail that the zones can be divided into sub-zones. You will see that there are several ammonite species with identical ranges, but only one is picked as a zonal, or subzonal index fossil. This may be because it is of more widespread distribution, or is more common than the others. This would allow more reliable comparisons to be made with other regions; a technique known as **correlation**.

The first zone, named after *Amaltheus margaritatus*, has been subdivided using the occurrence of similar species of the genus *Amaltheus*. These zones work neatly because their ammonite zone fossil only lived at that time.

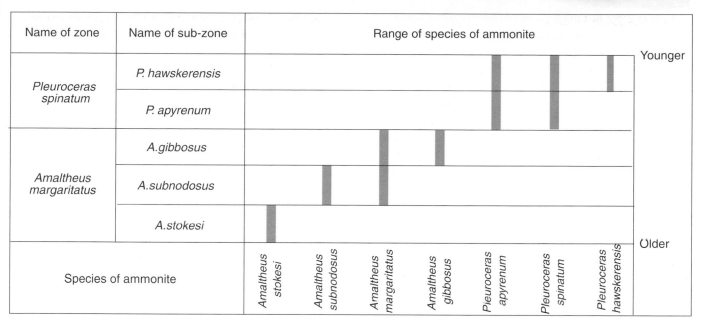

Figure 11.6 *Time ranges of ammonites and their use as zone fossils in correlating Jurassic strata*

Figure 11.7 *Changes in fossil groups at the Palaeozoic/Mesozoic boundary*

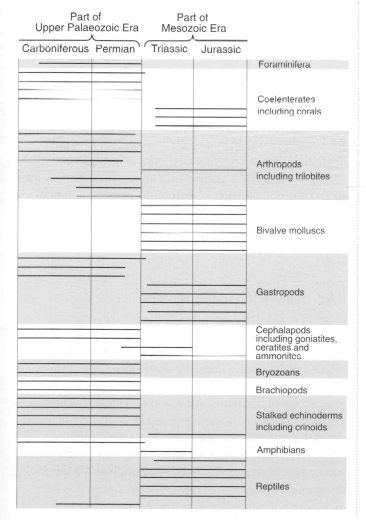

The situation for the *Pleuroceras spinatum* zone is more complex because no fossil came into being and then became extinct over a time short enough to form a zone. Here the *Pleuroceras apyrenum* subzone is identified by beginning where *Pleuroceras apyrenum* first appears and ending when the next zone fossil, *Pleuroceras hawskerensis* first appears. Wherever possible, we try to use the first appearance of a new species to mark the base of a time unit, rather than the disappearance of an older species.

11.3 Geological time and its subdivisions

11.3.1 AN INTERNATIONAL FRAMEWORK

The international framework used for the subdivision of geological time is called the standard geological column (Appendix 7). This was originally constructed using the relative dating methods described above. As the Appendix shows, geological time was subdivided into **eons**, then into **eras** and then into **periods**; smaller subdivisions were also added later. Dates in millions of years (Ma) have been added fairly recently using the radiometric methods described later.

How were the divisions of the geological column originally drawn up? At the boundaries, there were major changes in the life forms, with many different groups of organisms becoming extinct within a relatively short space of time in mass extinctions, to be replaced by others. In addition to this, in Britain where much of the work of constructing the column was originally done, unconformities often form the boundaries. As a result the subdivisions of the column generally work particularly well in Britain, but not so well in other regions where more complete sequences are found.

The Mesozoic/Cenozoic boundary has been of great public interest, since that is the time when the dinosaurs finally became extinct. The Palaeozoic/Mesozoic boundary is, however, equally significant, with even more organisms becoming extinct at that time (see Figure 11.7), although few of them have the romantic appeal of the dinosaurs.

The base of the Palaeozoic Era, which coincides with the base of the Cambrian Period, was identified by the first appearance of fossils with hard parts. At the time when the column was being drawn up, no fossils of any sort had been found below the base of the Cambrian, so any rocks occurring beneath this level were called simply **Precambrian**. Radiometric dating methods have since shown that the length of Precambrian time is many times greater than that of the whole of the rest of the column put together. Even though fossils have now been found in Precambrian rocks they cannot be used in dating and correlation because they show little evolutionary change.

The geological periods are subdivided into smaller spans of time called **epochs**. Further subdivisions are made, down to the level of a zone, using the method shown for ammonites above. Some of the best zone fossils, like the ammonites, allow a discrimination of as little as 0.5 Ma or so. This sounds a relatively crude measurement, until we remember that for a rock of 365 Ma, it is equivalent, in human terms, to recalling the events of one morning, a year ago.

Different names are used for spans of geological time and the sequences of rocks formed during those times. For example, the Carboniferous Period is the time between the Devonian and Permian Periods; the rocks formed during that time period are the Carboniferous **system** of rocks.

11.4 Absolute dating

11.4.1 EARLY ATTEMPTS AT ABSOLUTE DATING

So far, we have examined some of the ways in which sequences of rocks may be placed in relative order, but we have not attempted to give the succession absolute dates in years. In the past, geologists have tried to work out the absolute ages of rocks and the age of the Earth itself, but until relatively recently, these have been impossible to determine accurately.

However, geologists have continued to try to calculate actual ages, and several different methods have been used. These have ranged from calculating how long it

might have taken for the sea to reach its present salinity, to measuring sedimentation rates and determining how long it would have taken for an estimated thickness of sediments to have accumulated. Most of these estimates were made in the 19th century, and they produced some widely different results. For example, the rate of sedimentation method produced dates for the base of the Cambrian ranging from 3 Ma to 1584 Ma, depending on the researcher.

Some 19th century geologists became convinced that the Earth was much older than the 6000 years that most people believed at the time. One of these was **Charles Lyell**, who carried out detailed work on Mount Etna in Sicily. He measured the approximate average annual output of lava from the volcano. He then calculated how long it would have taken for the whole volcanic structure to be constructed, and obtained a figure of at least 50 000 years. However, Lyell went further, by showing that the oldest lavas rested on sediments containing fossils. These were no different from the organisms living in the area in his day, so clearly belonged to the youngest part of the geological column, the Quaternary. This implied that the Earth itself must be many *millions* of years old. Lyell's instincts told him this must be the case, if there was to be enough time for all the processes which we can observe going on around us to shape the Earth as we know it.

In some sedimentary environments, counting the layers has proved to be successful. In a classic piece of work, the Swedish Baron G. de Geer was able to date significant events in the Pleistocene 'Ice Age' by counting varves in meltwater lakes (see page 94). Each varve comprised a thicker pale layer deposited in the summer grading up into a thin dark winter layer, so one varve in general meant one year. By laboriously counting these varves, and comparing one location with another, de Geer was able to build up the detailed story of the retreat of the ice sheets from Scandinavia, and to work out absolute dates for the events.

11.4.2 RADIOMETRIC DATING METHODS

The various methods discussed in the previous section are usually referred to as geological methods of dating rock sequences. In other words, they can be applied by any observant geologist, with access to field sites, or a good library of geological literature, and of course, a pocket calculator. However, another range of methods has been developed, which requires the use of a well-equipped laboratory with facilities for processing rock samples and a mass spectrometer. The mass spectrometer is used to measure the quantities of isotopes of key elements present in a sample, as shown below. The dating methods depend

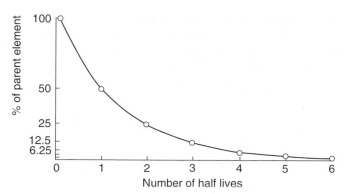

Figure 11.8 *The half-life curve*

on being able to measure the minute amount of radioactivity trapped in some rocks.

Rocks are composed of minerals, which in turn are composed of elements. Each element is defined by its **mass number** and its **atomic number**. For example, potassium may be shown as $^{39}_{19}K$, where 39 is the mass number and 19 is the atomic number. It is the atomic number which defines the position of the element in the Periodic Table and which determines the chemical properties of the element. The mass number indicates the total number of protons and neutrons in the nucleus. However, there is another variety of potassium, with the same atomic number, but a different mass number, i.e. $^{40}_{19}K$. This $^{40}_{19}K$ is unstable, i.e. radioactive. It is known as an **isotope** of potassium, from the Greek, isos – equal, topos – place, i.e. occupying the same place in the Periodic Table. In practice, elements are normally shown by their symbol and mass number only, e.g. ^{40}K, described as 'potassium 40'.

Radioactive decay takes place when the unstable **parent isotope** breaks down to form a new **daughter product**. For example, ^{40}K breaks down by different forms of radioactive decay to produce two different elements with different atomic numbers, namely the metal calcium (^{40}Ca) and the inert gas argon, (^{40}Ar). It is the decay of potassium to argon that we can use for dating purposes.

When these principles are applied to dating a rock, the method is termed **radiometric dating**, or **radioisotopic dating**. It is best understood if we consider an igneous rock, such as dolerite in a dyke. The magma rises in the crust until it reaches a cooler zone and then begins to crystallise. While the magma remains liquid, elements including radioactive isotopes, can move freely and can be lost or gained by the magma. Eventually however, the rock crystallises completely and cools down to a temperature below which it becomes a closed system – so nothing can be added or taken away. From then on, the radioactive parent element continues to decay, but the daughter element cannot escape from the rock. Using a mass spectrometer, it is possible to determine the relative numbers of parent and daughter atoms in the rock and to calculate the ratio between them. The older the rock is, the more daughter atoms there will be relative to the number of parent atoms.

The steady rate at which a radioactive element decays can be measured in the laboratory. This rate of decay is the **decay constant**. Rates of decay are also given as half-lives. The **half life** is the time taken for half of the original radioactive atoms to decay. Figure 11.8 shows a typical half-life curve. You can see that one half-life has elapsed when 50 per cent of the parent atoms are left. Two half-lives have passed when 25 per cent of the parent atoms are left, and so on.

One of the earliest attempts to date rocks was based on the decay of the radioactive element uranium, which decays, via radium, to form lead. Later, other radioactive decay series were employed as radiometric 'clocks', and the main ones are shown in the Table in Figure 11.9.

The Table in Figure 11.9 shows that there is a big difference between the half-life of ^{40}K (1277 Ma) and that of ^{14}C (5570 years). Because of their long half-lives ^{40}K and similar methods can only be used for dating appropriate rocks of more than a few hundred thousand years in age, whilst the ^{14}C method can only be used on materials up to

Figure 11.9 *The main methods of radiometric dating*

Method (half life in years)	Strontium–Rubidium dating $^{87}Rb – ^{87}Sr$ (47 000 × 10^6)	Potassium–Argon dating $^{40}K – ^{40}Ar$ (1277 × 10^6)	Carbon dating $^{14}C – ^{12}C$ ratio (5570)
Age of material which can be dated (years)	older than 10 million	older than 100 000	between 1000 and about 50 000
Source minerals and rocks	minerals: micas, potassium feldspars, glauconite rocks: granites and gneisses	minerals: micas, augite, hornblende, feldspars, glauconite rocks: lavas, granites, some fine-grained metamorphic rocks	carbon-bearing material of organic origin
Geological applications	dates of original cooling and uplift of granite igneous rocks; dates of metamorphic episodes; dates of deposition of glauconite-bearing sediments	dates of original cooling and uplift of volcanic and granitic rocks; dates of deposition of glauconite-bearing sediments	date of organic material, such as shells, peat, wood, bone and ash from archaeological sites

about 50 000 years old. At present, there is no method for establishing reliable radiometric dates for much of the Quaternary System.

When radiometric dates are published, they are usually accompanied by the **standard error** ($\pm$ figure), which reflects the laboratory uncertainty in the measurement, e.g. instrumental error. A radiometric age published as 50 ± 2.5 Ma means that there is a statistically high probability that the age of the sample is between 47.5 and 52.5 Ma in age. The standard error figure does not show geological uncertainties.

Different radiometric dating approaches have to be used for igneous rocks, metamorphic rocks, sedimentary rocks and organic materials. Igneous rocks are dated from the time they crystallised and cooled. Minor intrusions are useful for radiometric dating, since they cool relatively quickly, yet were not exposed to weathering agencies until much later. Since they cut other rocks, such as sedimentary sequences, they must be younger, but the dates they provide may often be used to provide a minimum date for the host rock which they cut. An example is the Waterswallows Sill in Derbyshire, which cuts rocks of the Carboniferous Limestone Series. A K/Ar date of 311 ± 6 Ma has been obtained from the sill, equivalent to the boundary between the Millstone Grit Series and the Coal Measures, showing that the sill was intruded about 25 Ma after the limestones were deposited.

The radiometric dating of larger intrusions poses a different challenge. A major granite batholith may be hundreds of cubic kilometres in size. Like most rocks, granite is a poor conductor of heat, and a large batholith usually takes millions of years to form, cool and crystallise. For example, the Lake District batholith in north west England has more than five separate phases of intrusion. The evidence from gravity surveys and from the mineralogy of the granites themselves suggests that they are all part of one linked structure. Radiometric dating does not contradict this view, but it does demonstrate an age difference of some 45 million years between the oldest outcrop of granite and the youngest. Since the granites are all related to the Caledonian Orogeny, radiometric dating provides convincing evidence of the extended nature of such mountain building movements, in contrast to the 'short, sharp shock' once envisaged.

In the case of a lava, cooling is an extremely quick process by geological timescales, so a value obtained from a lava ought to give the actual date of eruption. In areas where sediments are being deposited, the lava may have flowed over recently laid down sediments and may be buried by more sediments soon afterwards. In such cases, the date from the lava may be applied to the sedimentary deposits lying immediately above and below the lava. If these, in turn, are fossiliferous, the fossils may be used to place the rock sequence in the scale of relative geological time. Knowing the absolute age of the lava thus gives us a means of assigning absolute dates to the geological column, as shown in Appendix 7.

However, such dates can be misleading. For example, some lavas may have been weathered very deeply shortly after they were formed. This might have permitted the release to the atmosphere of daughter elements, so giving an incorrect date. The date would also be incorrect if there had been a large time gap between the deposition of the sediments below and the lava or between the lava and the sediments above.

Metamorphic rocks are formed by the recrystallisation of existing rocks without melting. The conditions may have been sufficiently severe for the daughter element to escape altogether so when the rock recrystallises the radiometric 'clock' becomes 'reset'. The minerals in metamorphic rocks that can be dated in this way usually include the micas, the feldspars and ferromagnesian silicates, such as hornblende (an amphibole) and augite (a pyroxene mineral).

In the K/Ar method, the daughter element, argon, is a gas, and is easily lost by diffusion if a rock is affected by metamorphic processes. Hence, the use of the K/Ar method might give the date of the metamorphism, but evidence of any earlier events may be lost.

Another useful decay series is where radioactive rubidium (^{87}Rb) decays to stable strontium (^{87}Sr). This method is frequently used on metamorphic rocks, especially those derived from an original igneous rock. Measurements are made on both the whole rock, and on minerals separated out from the rock in the laboratory. Diffusion of ^{87}Sr can occur above temperatures of 200–500 °C, but, since it is a solid, it tends to remain in the rock mass itself, rather than escaping into the atmosphere. This means that, if there is a difference between the age determined from the whole rock and that from separate minerals, the older date is taken to be the date of intrusion and the younger one the date of metamorphism.

Most sedimentary rocks are formed by deposition of the eroded remains of earlier rocks. Since these rocks have not been greatly heated, it is unusual for any new radioactive decay series to be started. Thus any measurements made, for example on micas contained in the rock, show the date of formation of the original mica, in an igneous or metamorphic environment, and not the date of deposition of the sediment.

There are, however, some exceptions. For example, glauconite, a green-coloured potassium silicate mineral, is precipitated under warm, shallow marine conditions. As it forms, it 'traps' radioactive potassium, and so a new K/Ar decay series is started. The K/Ar method can be used successfully to date rocks such as the 'greensands' (sandstones containing glauconite) of Cainozoic and Mesozoic age.

All living things contain the element carbon, usually in compounds with other elements. The carbon is acquired from carbon dioxide in the atmosphere during the lifetime of the organism. Most of the atmospheric carbon is in the form of the stable isotope, ^{12}C, but a small proportion consists of the radioactive isotope, ^{14}C. This is continually produced by cosmic ray bombardment, which converts some of the atmospheric nitrogen (^{14}N) to ^{14}C. This then promptly starts to decay back to ^{14}N, which is reabsorbed into the atmosphere. The half life for this decay series is 5570 years. Living things absorb atmospheric carbon, with the same ratio of ^{14}C to ^{12}C as in the atmosphere itself. Once an organism dies, however, it stops taking up carbon, and the ^{14}C which it contains begins to decay. The ratio of ^{14}C to ^{12}C therefore decreases with age, and can provide a means of dating the organic material itself.

This method is sometimes called the **'radiocarbon'** method or **carbon dating**, but as we have seen, it is only applicable to material of up to about 50 000 years old, because of the short half-life. You should therefore be slow to believe the next news report which describes the 'radiocarbon dating' of a spectacular dinosaur discovery!

There are some well-known sources of error, which need to be appreciated when radiometric dates are being interpreted. These are:

- The laboratory measurements themselves have a range of accuracy, expressed as a standard error ($\pm$) figure.
- Leakage of a daughter product of radioactive decay may have occurred, notably in the K/Ar method. If argon has diffused from the sample, the age obtained will be an underestimate of the true age, i.e. you will think that the rock is younger than it really is.
- Contamination of a sample with an excess of a radioactive parent isotope could have the opposite effect, and result in an overestimate of the age, although this is less likely than the above.
- In the ^{14}C method, the $^{14}C/^{12}C$ ratio in the sample is compared with the ratio in the atmosphere today. The ratio is known to have changed in the past 200 years due to the increased burning of fossil fuels. This produces ^{12}C, but no ^{14}C, thus changing the $^{14}C/^{12}C$ ratio. In practice, an adjustment is made to the results to try to allow for this. The method also depends on the assumption that the rate of cosmic ray bombardment has remained constant for several thousands of years.
- The other methods of radioisotopic dating depend on the assumption that the half-lives of the decay series can be reliably determined in the laboratory, and that the decay rate is largely unaffected by pressures and temperatures in the Earth. This may not always be the case.

11.5 The application of dating techniques

This chapter has shown that there is a range of different techniques that are commonly used to date and correlate rocks. Some more specialist techniques can be applied to certain situations. We can see how some of these methods are applied in practice by looking at different dating problems.

11.5.1 DATING THE NORTH AMERICAN CONTINENT

How can the age patterns of the rocks that form the North American continent be determined?

Until radiometric methods became available, little could be done to date the Precambrian rocks that form the core of the continent, apart from using geological principles such as superposition and cross-cutting relationships, to establish relative dates. The strongly metamorphosed Precambrian rocks were broadly assigned to a time (an eon) known as the Archaean (see the Geological Column in Appendix 7). Sedimentary and less strongly metamorphosed strata were grouped in the Proterozoic eon. Younger strata, mostly towards the margins of the continent, were assigned relative dates in the traditional way, using zone fossils.

The application of radiometric methods, such as the K/Ar and Rb/Sr techniques has led to much more detailed understanding of the Precambian 'heart' of North America, as shown in Figure 11.10. This is not quite the same as a normal geological map, since it does not show the rock types themselves, but demonstrates the dates at which each part of the continent became stable, i.e. had finished passing through the igneous and metamorphic events associated with orogenic activity.

Seen in this way, the continent shows a marked concentric pattern. The data shows that the first regions to form through orogenic activity were near the centre, with progressively younger regions towards the edges. The oldest regions, shown in white on the map, seem to have been ancient small areas of continental crust that became joined together in the orogeny that also produced the stippled region. Further periods of orogenic activity formed new areas of continental crust in pale to dark grey, each one causing the continent to grow larger. All these phases of orogenic activity would have been connected with plate tectonic movements, although early plate tectonic processes may have been rather different from those we see today.

Other continents show a similar, although less obvious pattern, which has led some geologists to calculate by how much the continental crust as a whole might be growing. A figure of the order of 1.3 km^3 per year has been suggested.

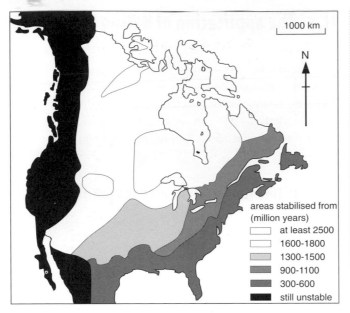

Figure 11.10 *The pattern of ages of the rocks of North America*

11.5.2 CORRELATION BETWEEN TWO SEQUENCES OF JURASSIC ROCKS

How could you carry out a detailed correlation (comparison of dates) between a sequence of Jurassic rocks in Dorset and a sequence of the same age on the Yorkshire coast?

Since the coasts of Dorset and North Yorkshire are about 450 km apart, there is too much variation in the rock types for direct lithological correlation to be made. However, the beds are very fossiliferous, so it has been possible to correlate the rocks by using index fossils, which occur at both localities, but which are of limited time span. This part of the Jurassic has been zoned by ammonites (the same ammonites shown in Figure 11.6),

Figure 11.11 *a) Part of the Lower Jurassic succession of the Dorset coast; b) Part of the Lower Jurassic succession of the North Yorkshire coast. N.B. The successions are drawn to different scales*

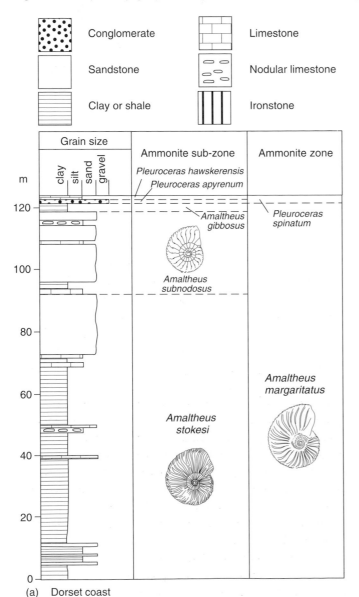

(a) Dorset coast

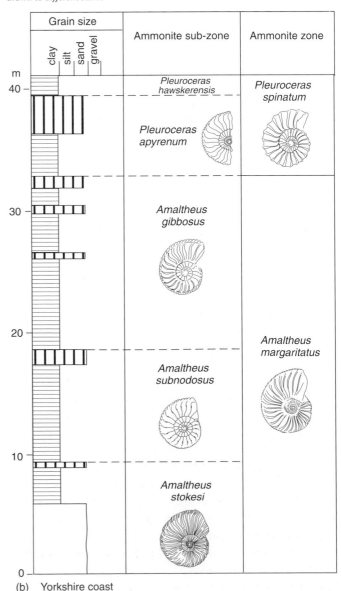

(b) Yorkshire coast

which among other advantages, had a floating or swimming mode of life, resulting in a widespread distribution (see page 196). Figure 11.11 provides comparative sections of both coasts.

The information from the index fossils allows us to correlate the two successions. We can then work out where deposition was fast and where it was slow and then attempt to explain these differences in terms of the palaeogeographical differences between the areas at the time (see Question 3 at the end of this chapter).

11.5.3 DATING CORE SAMPLES FROM THE DEEP OCEAN FLOOR

How can we obtain detailed dating information on a core sample of sediment from the deep ocean floor, when the top of the core is of Recent age, and the bottom, 15 metres below, is of the order of 1 million years old?

This sample would have been obtained by one of the two main methods of sea floor coring. One involves using a specially adapted ship, to obtain long cores by drilling. These boreholes may even penetrate the basalts under the sea floor sediment. The sediments are mostly dated by microfossils, while the basalts are dated by radiometric methods. The results have been of great importance to the theory of plate tectonics, since it has demonstrated that the age of the sea floor increases with distance from the oceanic ridges, as predicted by the theory.

The second method is much simpler: a piston corer is simply dropped from a ship, to penetrate the top few metres of unconsolidated sea floor sediment. Much of this type of coring has been directed at unravelling the history of the Quaternary 'Ice Age'. It has long been realised that the record of the 'Ice Age' preserved on land in areas such as Britain is fragmentary, because any readvance of an ice sheet tends to destroy the evidence of the earlier interglacial deposits. In the deep ocean, however, the very slow sedimentation of material from the surface of the sea continues all the time, preserving an undisturbed sediment sequence.

These deep ocean sequences contain evidence of ice advance and retreat in the **oxygen isotope data** trapped in the calcium carbonate skeletons of marine fossils. Oxygen contains two isotopes, the more common ^{16}O and the less abundant ^{18}O. As an ice sheet expands, the processes involved extract more ^{16}O than ^{18}O from the atmosphere and, in turn, from the sea. This increases the relative amount of ^{18}O in the sea water, so the ratio of the two isotopes changes and these changes are preserved in shells after the death of the organisms.

Measurements of the $^{16}O/^{18}O$ ratio have been made in fossils from the deep-sea cores, and an example is shown in the left hand column of Figure 11.12.

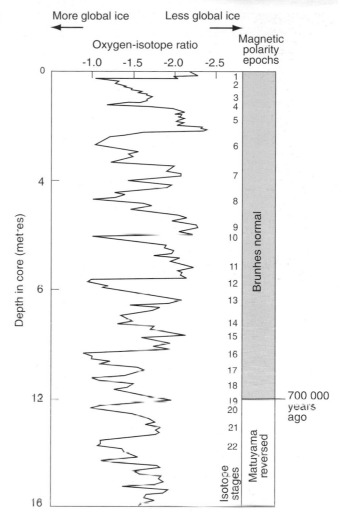

Figure 11.12 *Measurements of the oxygen isotope ratios and palaeomagnetism in a deep-sea core from the Pacific Ocean*

The oxygen isotope measurements show a clear cyclic swing, which reflects the growth and decline of many successive glaciations on the continents. The absolute dating of these events has proved to be more difficult. ^{14}C dating can be used on the topmost metre or so of the core, but deeper than this, the age is too great for the short half-life of ^{14}C. Evolution of fossils in the core is too slow for detailed zoning, and cannot provide an absolute date for any part of the column.

A date was finally achieved, in the 1970s, when geomagnetic data were obtained from a long core in the Pacific Ocean (page 62). Although very weak, the magnetisation of the sediments was measurable, and showed that at a depth of 12 metres below the sea bed, it became reversed. By comparison with many other results, this was found to be the most recent reversal. The date at which this happened was already well known at 700 000 years ago, from measurements made on lavas in Iceland.

This date has provided an important yardstick against which to correlate much of the Quaternary 'Ice Age' on land, and has shown that it is far more complex than the four 'advances' of the ice which had originally been thought. It has also enabled Milankovitch's theory, that the cyclicity of cooling and warming of the Earth is due to variations in the amount of solar radiation that the Earth receives, to be put to the test. Much of the data from the cores supports his theory (see page 228).

11.6 Summary

1 The relative dating of rock sequences can be carried out by applying a series of stratigraphic principles and laws.

2 Fossils are used in the relative dating and correlation of rocks and in the best situations can be used to identify zones with time spans of less than 0.5 Ma.

3 The geological column is the time framework used worldwide for the dating of rocks; it was constructed using relative dating methods; the absolute ages of the different sections in Ma were added later.

4 The most commonly used methods of absolute dating are radiometric dating methods; these are based on the decay of radioactive isotopes.

5 Other methods of dating and correlation can be applied to certain situations; some of these methods have only been developed over the past few years.

11.7 Questions

1 Copy the stratigraphic column shown in the key to Figure 11.2. On your column:
   a) show where you would expect to find an unconformity, (i.e. a break in the deposition of sediment, accompanied by erosion);
   b) alongside the column, state the probable environment in which each of the beds might have been deposited;
   c) suggest the possible climatic conditions at these times.

2 Use a copy of a geological map of the British Isles to answer the following questions, to enable you to become more familiar with the geological column.
   a) Roughly, what percentage of the surface area of the British Isles has Precambrian rocks at outcrop?
   b) In which parts of Britain are Precambrian outcrops most common?
   c) Where are the main outcrops of Palaeozoic rocks found?
   d) What is the compass trend of the major fold structures in rocks of i) Lower Palaeozoic, ii) Upper Palaeozoic age?
   e) The trend of the folds of Alpine origin, in the South of England is parallel to that of the Upper Palaeozoic rocks of Devon and Cornwall. What evidence from the map shows that the two sets of folds must be of different date?
   f) Why are igneous intrusive rocks shown separately at the base of the column?

3 Use Figure 11.11 to answer the following (NB. the Figures are drawn to different scales):
   a) Assuming that the sub-zones represent an even interval of time in both places, in which place was deposition generally more rapid?
   b) Try to explain why the strata near the top of the succession in Dorset are so thin.
   c) Suggest one possible economic use of being able to correlate rock sequences like this across large distances.

CHAPTER 12

Studying geological change: the Devonian Period

Introduction

How are geological periods defined? First a characteristic combination of rock types, fauna and flora needs to be identified and then a zone of marked change at the base and at the top of the sequences being studied have to be found. Such zones, that mark the beginning and end of periods, may be due to sudden relative rises or falls in sea level or major extinction events recorded in the rocks.

A study of the Devonian in Britain illustrates the stratigraphic techniques used in the 1800s to define periods and how the features identified can now be understood in terms of plate tectonic processes today.

From the Carboniferous upwards, the geological column is a regular series of fossiliferous sediments easily recognised all over Britain. How the Devonian System, just beneath the Carboniferous, was first defined and mapped illustrates many of the problems geologists still face today when working with unfamiliar rocks in a new area. This chapter shows how three famous 19th-century geologists working in the 1830s set about extending the column down to older rocks, below the Carboniferous. The problems were severe, because the types of rock vary across the country; in some places Carboniferous lies conformably on red sandy sediments, but elsewhere it lies unconformably on metamorphic rocks. At the time the work was done, there was still uncertainty about using fossils for correlating strata and it was long before radiometric dating. Today, we use the concepts of plate tectonics to relate the different geological processes going on at the same time to develop an overall picture of past environments, but most basic stratigraphy was worked out long before plate tectonics was 'invented'.

12.1 Case Study: Devonian rocks of Britain

Figure 12.1 shows the UK distribution of rocks now known to be of Devonian age, together with some examples of rocks and fossils (all about 400 Ma old) from different localities.

It is clear from this Figure that conditions for rock formation varied very widely across Britain about 400 million years ago!

Figure 12.1 (over the page) *Devonian rocks of Britain 417–354 Ma. Scotland–north east England: Old Red Sandstone continental sediments, sandstones, conglomerates and fresh water lake sediments, and volcanics. North-west England is land with the Devonian represented by an unconformity; plutonic rocks forming at depth. South-west England was covered by marine sediments, with near shore sediments in the south Wales to north Devon area: a) Coccosteus decipiens, primitive armoured fish, with the front of the body covered with external skeletal plates. Caithness N.E. Scotland: in dark grey, almost black, very fine grained finely laminated fresh water sandstones, called 'flagstones' which formed in a quiet land-locked lake; b) Old Red Sandstone conglomerate, near Stirling, Midland Valley, Scotland. Well rounded pebbles of lava, with no fossils. High energy environment where Devonian lavas were eroding to form pebble beds in the desert. (Phenocryst vesicles and flow banding inside some pebbles); c) Granite, Shap, Cumbria. Coarse-grained plutonic rock with large phenocrysts intruded several km below the Earth's surface; d) Unconformity, Horton in Ribblesdale, Yorkshire: Pale grey Carboniferous limestone lies unconformably on Lower Palaeozoic slates. The unconformity here represents all the Devonian, which is missing completely; e) Heliolites porosus, a coral, from Torquay Limestone, South Devon. This is a pale grey compact limestone with abundant shallow water fossils; f) Folded and cleaved shales and limestones, South Devon. The thick beds of pale grey limestone are full of calcite veins, and the red shales are strongly cleaved; g) Folded and strongly cleaved slates of the Meadfoot beds, South Cornwall*

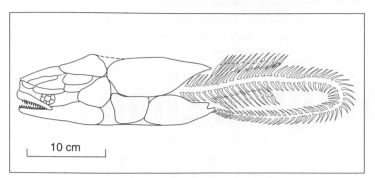

(a) *Coccosteus decipiens*. Caithness Flags, Caithness

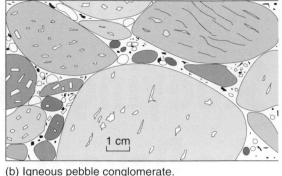

(b) Igneous pebble conglomerate.
Near Dunblane, Stirling

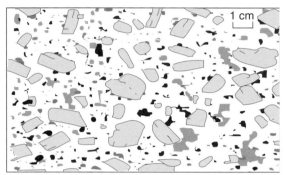

(c) Granite. Shap Fell, Cumbria

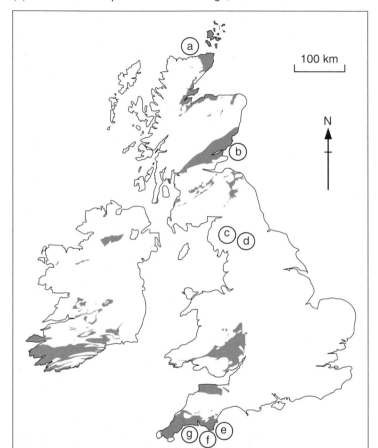

Distribution of Devonian rocks in the British Isles

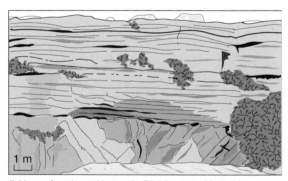

d) Unconformity at Horton in Ribblesdale, Yorkshire

(g) Folded and cleaved slate (marine)
Meadfoot Beds, S.Cornwall

(f) Folded and cleaved shales and
limestone, S.Devon

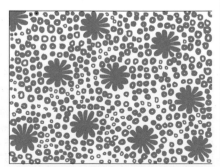

(e) *Heliolites porosus*, marine limestone
with corals. Torquay S.Devon, (mag 8x)

12.2 The Geological Column and the Devonian Period

The geological map and the geological column for Britain (Appendix 7) have been built up by the work of hundreds of geologists over the past 200 years. The principles of making a geological map and geological column have changed little since William Smith first correlated strata using their general appearance and the fossils they contained to produce his large map of England, Wales and part of Scotland in 1815. It is clear from the geological column on Smith's map that he understood that a regular sequence of strata, from the coal-bearing rocks of the Carboniferous, up to the distinctive thick white Chalk (Cretaceous), outcrop across much of England and dip away gently to the south east. Smith said in his homely way that they were arranged 'rather like slices of bread' dipping towards London. At a stroke he not only produced the first geological map of Britain, but also sorted out the sequence of strata of more than half of the geological column, not bad for a land surveyor, who had no geological training at all.

Most of the younger rocks found in England were laid down in the sea, and so contain distinctive marine fossils which are easily recognised as coming from a particular horizon, or zone, in the geological column. For example, during the Carboniferous, evidence from fossils and sedimentary sequences both point to environments of warm seas where thick limestones were laid down, full of life such as corals (Figure 6.8). Later, tropical conditions of deltaic sediments with richly vegetated swamps gave rise to the Coal Measures (Figure 9.4).

In Chapter 5, details of sedimentary rocks were used to interpret the depositional environment of sediments above the Carboniferous, the Permian and Triassic rocks of the Cheshire plain, some of which were formed on land in an arid climate.

Higher up the column, it is possible to do very detailed correlation across the country using ammonite zones in Jurassic strata, even though the lithology varies considerably (page 200). Similarly, the Chalk (Cretaceous) and beds above and below it are easily correlated by their distinctive lithologies and fossils. Chapter 6 showed how the mode of life of some marine fossils can be used to work out features of the environment such as the depth of water or water temperature (Section 6.7.2).

The geological column in Appendix 7 looks straightforward, with a clear sequence of Periods from Cambrian upwards. But Periods are entirely 'synthetic', human creations, that are a convenient way of splitting the history of the Earth into manageable chunks. Periods were defined in the first half of the 19th century, when many geologists believed that Earth history was punctuated by a series of more or less catastrophic events, which might be expected to leave behind a simple sequence of different strata. The representation of the geological column is often incomplete in the rocks below the Carboniferous in Britain, and major unconformities that form 'natural' breaks in the geological column were obvious places to mark the top or bottom of Periods in the column.

Remember, too, that the time represented by the bedding planes *between* the strata is often much longer than the time taken for the material of the beds themselves to accumulate. So, unconformities between groups of strata may represent many millions of years for which no sedimentary rocks are preserved, but elsewhere these 'missing' rocks may be found. This is clearly shown in the Case Study where all the Devonian is missing entirely from Horton in Ribblesdale (Figure 12.1d).

Over the past 150 years, hundreds of geologists have mapped parts of Britain. Most of them have collected fossils for accurate correlation, and with the benefit of more than 50 years of absolute (radiometric) dates, you might think that mapping the rest of the country, and sorting out the remaining bits of the geological column would have been easily completed. Not so: recent work has 'moved' the base of one Period, the Devonian up in the past few years, so that areas shown on many geological maps as Devonian are in fact now thought to lie in the Silurian! Even the radiometric dates are still 'settling down'; within the last 30 years the base of the Cambrian has 'moved' from 590 to 570 to its present value of 545 Ma.

This may strike you as a pretty poor state of affairs, what have these geologists been doing all this time? In this chapter you will see just how tricky it can be to correlate and date rocks older than Carboniferous in Britain. By following the work of the early geologists we shall see some of the problems of working with older rocks.

Why has the Devonian been so difficult? Basically, because the geological column is not complete; there are major unconformities present. Also quite different rock types (facies) were being laid down in different places at the same time. Some of these rocks have also been folded and metamorphosed.

12.3 Unravelling the Devonian and the lower Palaeozoic in the 1830s

With hindsight, scientific developments often look straightforward; it's easy to look back and say: 'Of course, it's obvious, why did it take them so long to work that out?' But at the time, when no-one fully understands a problem, and the scientists concerned are often studying slightly different aspects, the situation can be fraught. Geologists can have definite views about the work of other geologists, especially when they are working over the same ground. This was the situation in the 1830s when three of the most famous British geologists began to struggle with the strata below the Carboniferous, and, as you will see, with each other.

The Carboniferous had already been explored intensively, because the best way for a landowner to become rich was by finding coal to fuel the booming industrialisation of Britain. At this time, there were thought to be four layers to the Carboniferous, from the top downwards: Coal Measures; Millstone Grit; Carboniferous Limestone; Old Red Sandstone. The best English and Welsh coal had been found in the Coal Measures, but in the north some had also been found in the two layers below. It was generally accepted that once a trial borehole reached red sandy rocks called the 'Old Red Sandstone' there was no chance of further coal.

Productive coalfields occured patchily across Britain, and in the 1830s there was considerable doubt over their boundaries, and the sequence of rocks below. Smith's map shows these older rocks as 'killas and slates' covering most of Wales and the Welsh borders, most of Devon and Cornwall, and much of Scotland. These rocks were all thought to be old, metamorphosed, folded and to contain no reliable fossils for correlation.

Meanwhile, across the channel, the French realised the usefulness of a complete geological map of the country, and, by starting in 1825, had almost finished mapping France with an official survey team. In England a

government survey was just beginning; surveyors of the army Board of Ordnance were preparing the first official geographical maps of the whole country. This work began in Devon in the 1830s and continued into Cornwall. So, following their work, a geologist was needed to 'colour in the geology' on the new maps, and publish geological maps at his own expense.

12.3.1 THE THREE MAJOR GEOLOGISTS IN THE DRAMA

1 **Thomas Henry De la Beche** was the person hired to follow the Board of Ordnance surveyors and add geology to their maps. His family estates in the West Indies had fallen on bad times, he needed a job and geological mapping suited, although the pay at £300 a year did not put him in the same class as many of his fellow 'gentleman scientists' in the London Geological Society. The work began on the strata in south west England, where the rocks proved to be very difficult to map because they were metamorphosed, and very heavily folded and faulted.

2 **Adam Sedgwick** was Professor of Geology at Cambridge University, the only geology professor in the country, and was to become President of the Geological Society 1828–30. He decided that he would start mapping the lowest strata that contained some fossils. These he called the Cambrian, after Wales, and began to work *up* the geological column. Cambrian rocks became well known when quarries for domestic roofing slate were opened in North Wales. Sedgwick also held a post with the church, and was clearly an important and fairly well-off establishment figure, who initially worked closely with Murchison, our third character.

3 **Roderick Murchison** was a wealthy Victorian gentleman scientist, fond of hunting and shooting, hard working and hugely ambitious; he was President of the Geological Society 1830–32 and 1840–42, and vice-president through much of the 1830s. Murchison chose to start his mapping in the Welsh borders, working *down* the geological column from the Old Red Sandstone, then regarded as the lowest part of the Carboniferous.

12.3.2 THE STRATA BELOW THE CARBONIFEROUS: IN THE WELSH BORDERS MURCHISON BECOMES 'KING OF SILURIA'

Murchison was successful in working out the rock succession in the Welsh Borders where he found several distinctive new marine lithologies with fossils, which

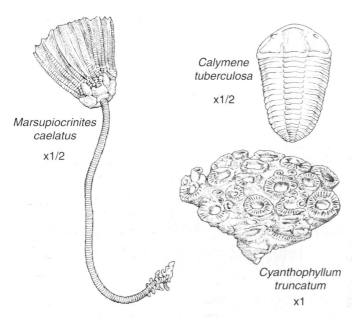

Calymene tuberculosa

x1/2

Marsupiocrinites caelatus

x1/2

Cyanthophyllum truncatum

x1

Figure 12.2 *Wenlock Limestone fossils: crinoid: Marsupiocrinites caelatus; trilobite: Calymene tubercolosa; coral: Cyanthophyllum truncatum*

contained trilobites, crinoids and corals, like those in the Wenlock Limestone, shown in Figure 12.2.

He used these fossils to establish a new geological Period, which he called the Silurian, after an ancient Welsh border tribe, the Silures. These Silurian strata passed up conformably into the sandstones, conglomerates and shales of the Old Red Sandstone, which here were found to contain some fossil fish. Murchison published a full description of these rocks of south and east Wales and the Welsh Borders, as an impressive book (*The Silurian System, 1839*) with a large geological map, numerous cross sections, and lavish plates of fossil illustrations. Then he travelled in Europe, distributing his book to the leading continental geologists, where he also found large areas of similar excellent Silurian strata. Murchison became one of the most successful geologists of all time. Throughout this period, he worked closely on fieldwork with Sedgwick, whose less spectacularly fossiliferous Cambrian strata were thought to lie well beneath the Silurian. They visited many places in Britain and abroad, writing up their work together.

12.3.3 SEDGWICK AND THE CAMBRIAN IN NORTH WALES

Adam Sedgwick was less fortunate than Murchison because he had to spend time giving lectures at Cambridge, and attending to his ecclesiastical duties at Norwich. He was also much less wealthy than Murchison. His contribution was careful fieldwork and description of the rocks and their fossils in the lowest Palaeozoic strata in North Wales, where he established the Cambrian system, based largely on trilobite fossil zones.

Initially there was no conflict with Murchison as Sedgwick's Cambrian lay below Murchison's Silurian. But as Sedgwick worked up the geological column and Murchison worked down, 'their' two sets of strata overlapped in the middle, and neither would yield any of 'his' strata to the other. The two became fierce opponents both working on rocks of the same age, with the same fossils, but putting them into two different Periods in the geological column. It was not until 1879 that a solution was found by a neutral geologist, Charles Lapworth, of Birmingham. He resolved the dispute by taking the bottom of Murchison's Silurian and the top of Sedgwick's Cambrian, and creating from the two a new Period, which he called the Ordovician, after another ancient Celtic tribe, the Ordovices in North Wales. This story hardly supports the stereotype of scientists being reasonable, rational 'seekers after truth'.

12.3.4 DE LA BECHE STARTS THE GEOLOGICAL SURVEY IN THE SOUTH-WEST

But what was going on in the South West? De la Beche began his mapping in a county where the rocks were heavily cleaved, folded and faulted, as shown in Figure 12.3. In Devon and Cornwall it was not always clear which 'way up' the strata were!

Also, Murchison and Sedgwick were ready to interfere. When De la Beche began the task it was felt that the rocks in Devon must be the same age as the Welsh Lower Palaeozoics. The first problem was that about two thirds of the way up the apparently conformable strata in Devon De la Beche found poorly preserved fossil plants and thin coal seams, called the 'Culm' strata. This was greeted with enthusiasm as proof that coal could be found in rocks much older than Carboniferous. If this was true it was very good news for many landowners all over the country who had estates on pre-Carboniferous strata.

For De la Beche there was a chance that he, too, could be mapping rocks from a Period new to science, and with commercial potential. This was a golden opportunity to get his position firmly established as the head of a new and important government agency: the Geological Survey. There was much lobbying of senior politicians on his behalf, including the Chancellor of the Exchequer, to get the funds agreed to start the Geological Survey. (When De la Beche was asked how long it would take him to complete the geological map of Britain, if such plans were carried through, he estimated 21 years if he had to do it himself, but only 10 with the help of 2 or 3 assistants. Over 150 years later, the Geological Survey is still mapping Britain!)

Murchison disagreed with De la Beche's ideas about the age of the rocks in Devon, without even visiting the outcrops. He told De la Beche firmly that the fossil plants

Figure 12.3 *Folded strata at Crackington Haven. Regular alternation of sandy and shaley beds, folded into angular folds with almost horizontal axial planes*

from the Culm strata were so similar to Carboniferous ones (see Figure 12.4a) that these rocks *must* be Carboniferous in age. He also said that if this was so, then there *must* be an unconformity (which De la Beche must have missed) at their base, separating them from the rest of the strata that everyone knew were some sort of much older Lower Palaeozoics. Murchison implied that if De la Beche could make two such obvious mistakes, was he really the man to be doing this most important job, and aiming to be head of a new government agency? De la Beche feared for his future because Murchison was a man with powerful influence in both geological and political circles.

While De la Beche worried about this attack, Murchison intervened again to say that perhaps, after all, De la Beche was correct about the Culm being conformable on the rocks below. In that case, these lower rocks must be of the same age as the Old Red Sandstone that he, Murchison, had found below the Carboniferous and above the Silurian in Wales.

Soon afterwards, good fossiliferous limestones were found near Torquay in Devon. They contained a rich marine fauna with some corals, similar to Carboniferous Limestone species, and others that resembled the corals that Murchison had found in his new Silurian Period strata in the Welsh borders. So, again with almost no work on the rocks in Devon himself, Murchison decided that these strata near Torquay must belong to a new Period for which he coined the name 'Devonian' in 1836. He was able to do this because there was the good fauna of marine fossils (e.g. in Figure 12.4b) on which a new Period could safely be based.

Murchison said that these Devonian rocks must be the same age as the Old Red Sandstone rocks in Wales, so adding a second new Period to the geological column, by correlating De la Beche's Devon strata with the Old Red Sandstones of the Welsh Borders. These two rather different strata he put together into the new Devonian Period.

If Murchison was right, then there was little chance of further Cambrian strata being found in the south west, which did not please Sedgwick, the Cambrian expert. Neither did Murchison's theory please De la Beche who was still hoping to establish himself a new Period of pre-Silurian age in the rocks of Devon.

Murchison was, however, soon able to show that he was correct as he found similar rocks in continental Europe, underneath the Carboniferous strata in the coalfields of Belgium and Germany, containing the same marine fossils. The Devonian became accepted as a new Period name for strata below the Carboniferous and above the Silurian. Not only were the rocks that De la Beche had been mapping in Devon difficult to understand because they were very folded and faulted, but also they had been laid down along the Devonian shoreline, and so contained a mixture of continental and marine deposits.

So, by 1840, Murchison and Sedgwick had mapped the Lower Palaeozoic in much of Wales, using marine fossils to distinguish a lower Cambrian and an upper Silurian Period, with Old Red Sandstone above the Silurian and below the Carboniferous. However, in Devon and Cornwall below the Culm (Carboniferous) strata was a new marine sequence, now recognised as the Devonian Period, the same age as the Old Red Sandstone of Wales.

12.3.5 THE ACTORS DEPART

The three geologists finally accepted these new divisions. De la Beche continued mapping, and eventually persuaded the government to establish the British Geological Survey, with him as its first Director (1835–55). Sedgwick continued as geology professor at Cambridge and with his ecclesiastical post at Norwich. Murchison dominated much of British geology, working all over Europe on the two great Periods he had been responsible for establishing: the Silurian, and the Devonian. Later, he added a third Period, the Permian, based on work he did in Russia. He was knighted and succeeded De la Beche as the Director of the Geological Survey in 1855. He died in harness in 1871 at the age of 79.

Today, the BGS still does mapping in Britain, and is the national storehouse of geological information, with many geological responsibilities across the country.

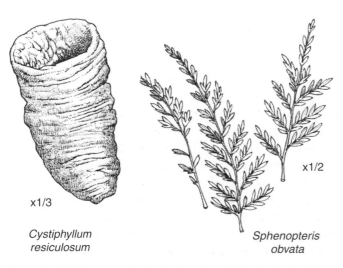

x1/3

x1/2

Cystiphyllum resiculosum

Sphenopteris obvata

Figure 12.4 *Fossil corals from the Torquay limestone:* Cystiphyllum vesiculosum; *Fossil plants from the Carboniferous,* Sphenopteris obovata

12.4 Old Red Sandstone and the geography of Devonian times

Why had it been so difficult to work out the sequences of Devonian strata in England and Wales? A much more complete sequence of marine Devonian facies rocks is developed in Europe, whereas a good continental facies, the Old Red Sandstone, is present further north in Britain, especially in Scotland. Both of these were relatively easy to interpret. Devon itself was a very difficult place for the Victorian geologists to try to define the new Devonian Period, as it contains both facies, so it involved correlation between two sets of rocks of the same age, one containing marine and the other containing non-marine fossils. Examples of the fossils were shown in Figure 12.1a and 12.1e.

Geologists have argued about the details ever since. For example, in Wales the lowest unit of the Old Red Sandstone facies, the Downtonian, was a convenient place to put the base of the Devonian Period. We now know that these rocks correlate with the uppermost Silurian strata, but on many maps, parts of south Wales are coloured Devonian rather than their true Silurian age. Similarly, in Scotland the top of the Old Red Sandstone facies rocks is known to be of Lower Carboniferous in age.

There are often correlation problems with major unconformities, as non-deposition in one area has to be correlated with continuous sedimentation elsewhere. This may happen because of a local or regional change in sea level with land emerging when the sea level falls, called **marine regression**. Land represents conditions when a continent is being eroded, a time of non-deposition, when sediments are removed. When sea level rises (**marine transgression**), and marine conditions return to 'drown' an old continent it is a gradual process, and so the lowest marine strata above the unconformity will become progressively younger away from the invading sea. These are called diachronous strata, where the same lithologies are being laid down at different times across an area.

The Old Red Sandstone is spectacularly developed in Scotland, especially in the Midland Valley, where huge thicknesses of conglomerates and red sandstones abound. These sediments were laid down by large braided and meandering rivers, similar to the Trias streams shown in Figure 5.7, and there are also sediments representing mudflows, and calcite-rich fossil soils. All of these are typical of rapidly eroding mountainous areas under oxidising conditions such as those found today in hot desert areas. There are also thick lava flows, and lavas are found as volcanic rock pebbles in many conglomerates, shown in Figure 12.1b.

In north east Scotland, around the Moray Firth, up to 5 km of Old Red Sandstone continental river-borne sediments are to be found. They contain great thicknesses of fine-grained lake sediments, with abundant and varied fauna of large primitive fishes, which have much of their skeleton as external plates, especially on their heads, shown in Figure 12.1a.

These Scottish Old Red Sandstone rocks differ considerably from Murchison's Old Red in the Welsh borders because they contain no marine strata at all. Scotland is far from the south Devon shoreline; it was at that time an area of rugged mountains where fast streams and flash floods brought coarse sediments from the mountains to inland plains, and the finer material was deposited in landlocked lakes, with their non-marine fauna.

Look at the stratigraphic logs of the strata of Devonian age in Figure 12.5, which go from Cornwall in the SW to Caithness in NE Britain during the Devonian Period. They show:

- in south Cornwall and south Devon, clear water limestones (with reefs) alternating with deep water muds; these are the shallow shelf marine sediments of the Rheic Ocean that continued eastwards through Belgium into eastern Europe;
- in north Devon an alternating sequence of marine sediments with a variety of Old Red Sandstone (ORS) sediments brought in by flash floods from the north;
- in South Wales a non-marine sequence formed on the southern margin of the large continental landmass to the north;
- further north, a large mountain belt containing some deep sedimentary basins in which huge thicknesses of entirely continental rocks were preserved.

But what was the palaeoclimate like in the Devonian? What evidence is there in the rocks themselves?

Many of the Old Red Sandstones are red, some have large-scale cross bedding, and some have rounded grains; all these features point to similarities with sediments forming today in hot deserts like Death Valley in California, Saudi Arabia or the Sahara. The coral reefs seen in the **Rheic Ocean**, which stretched from Torquay to Belgium, point to clear marine water again in sub-tropical seas, like the Great Barrier Reef today.

One hypothesis that might explain this, could be that 400 Ma ago the whole Earth had a much hotter climate than today, and so hot deserts reached to Britain's latitude of 50°N. Alternatively, could it be that during Devonian times Britain was at the latitude on the globe where subtropical (desert) conditions exist today, such as the Sahara, or the Kalahari? On the evidence so far this is merely another hypothesis, so we need other lines of evidence to choose between these two ideas.

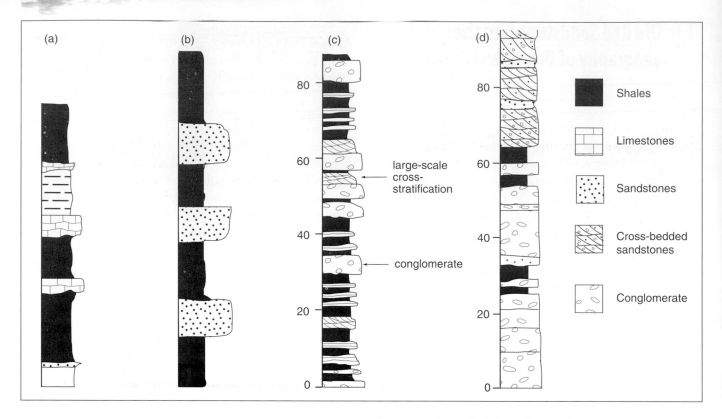

(a)   (b)   (c)   (d)

large-scale cross-stratification

conglomerate

Shales

Limestones

Sandstones

Cross-bedded sandstones

Conglomerate

Figure 12.5 *Columns of typical Devonian strata from Cornwall to Caithness: a) South Cornwall, marine conditions: shale, with some limestones; b) North Devon, near shore conditions: marine shales with non-marine sandstone lenses; c) Welsh borders, Old Red Sandstone meandering river: shales, sandstones, and occasional conglomerates; d) Midland Valley, Scotland, Old Red Sandstone braided river: largely coarse sandstones and conglomerates*

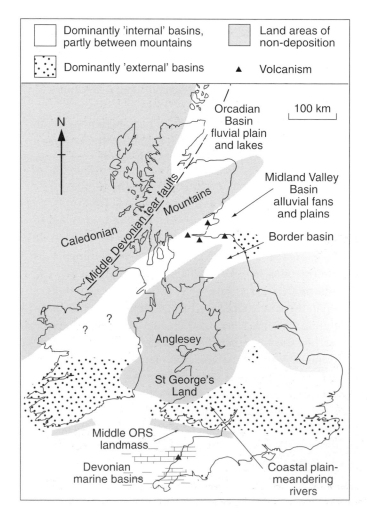

Dominantly 'internal' basins, partly between mountains

Dominantly 'external' basins

Land areas of non-deposition

▲ Volcanism

N

100 km

Orcadian Basin fluvial plain and lakes

Midland Valley Basin alluvial fans and plains

Border basin

Caledonian Mountains

Middle Devonian tear faults

Anglesey

St George's Land

Middle ORS landmass

Devonian marine basins

Coastal plain-meandering rivers

Figure 12.6 *Devonian geography of Britain. Rivers brought coarse sediment from the highlands into land-locked basins in the north. The Great Glen Fault (Figure 8.24) has just brought the northernmost part of Scotland to join the Grampians from the north-east. From the south Wales coastline sediment was washed across a coastal plain into the Devonian marine basin which stretched eastwards from Cornwall*

Looking just at Devonian strata, it is difficult to choose between the hypotheses, or even to consider either a serious possibility since both seem equally improbable. To get more evidence, we need to look at the rocks older and younger than the Devonian, to see what they can tell us.

12.5 Above and below the Devonian

You have already met Walther's Law (Chapter 5, page 90): conditions following each other vertically up the geological column should represent environments which can exist next to each other at the same time. On a larger scale, Walther's Law can be applied to whole Periods in the geological column. This is just another way of saying that, generally, the global processes which shape the planet do not suddenly change. By looking at what we know about conditions during Lower Palaeozoic and Carboniferous times, it will be easier to interpret the environments of the Devonian strata.

Look back in the geological column, (Appendix 7), at the Lower Palaeozoic rocks below the Devonian. In most of Britain these are marine sediments, deep and shallower water deposits, as well as the volcanics of North Wales and volcaniclastics of the English Lake District.

Figure 12.7 summarises the palaeogeography in the Lower Palaeozoic, during the 170 Ma before the Devonian. It shows the opening and then closing of the Iapetus Ocean. Sediments were carried into Iapetus from continents along the north and south of the ocean, to be laid down on the continental shelves, and some swept down over the continental slope to the deeper water beyond. To the north, sediments accumulated off the southern shore of a major continent of what is now Norway-Scotland-Greenland-North America. To the south, there was another vast continent.

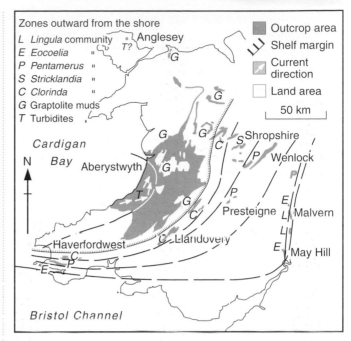

Figure 12.8 *Coastlines and sediments on and off the continental shelf mapped using fossils communities and sediment type, in lower Silurian times. Shallow-water fossils, mainly brachiopods, enable the ancient shelf to be mapped from shore to deeper water. Off the shelf deep water shales with graptolites show turbidites coming in from the south west*

Modern brachiopods are all marine and the indications are that they have always been marine animals. The only exception is the genus *Lingula* which can exist in brackish estuaries. Detailed examination of Silurian brachiopods from Wales has shown that various brachiopod communities lived in different water depths, and so they can be used to map out the Silurian coastline and deeper water on the continental shelf that forms the southern margin of Iapetus. Figure 12.8 shows these zones, and also the deeper water facies beyond the continental edge: muds with graptolites, and incoming turbidites.

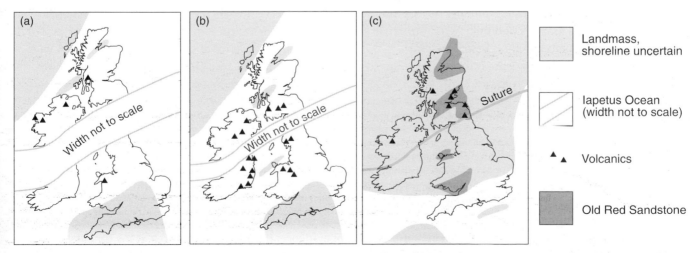

Figure 12.7 *Evolving geography in the Palaeozoic: the closure of the Iapetus ocean: a) Cambrian, 550 Ma, Iapetus still opening; b) Ordovician 450 Ma, Iapetus has started to close; c) Early Devonian, 400 Ma, Iapetus completely closed; the British Isles as a crustal unit has been established by the fusion of the two continental plates either side of Iapetus*

The two sides of this ancient Iapetus Ocean may have been as much as 1000 km apart at its maximum width after a prolonged period of sea floor spreading during the Ordovician. Because of this wide separation, the shelf faunas on the north and south of Iapetus developed quite different species. This is seen in the trilobites found in the Cambrian and Ordovician rocks of north west Scotland, which are very similar to those found in North America, but completely different from those found in the rest of the British Isles. These two faunal provinces are separated today by a line that can be drawn across the reconstructed supercontinent formed when North America and Europe came together (Figure 12.9). The line represents the site of the former Iapetus Ocean, that once separated the two shelf sea areas. The two fossil communities would have evolved completely separately on either side of the ocean.

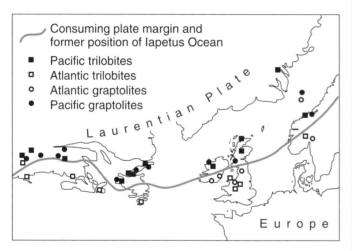

Figure 12.9 *Line of Iapetus; suture drawn where north and south shelf faunas of Iapetus are found adjacent to each other today*

However, during the Ordovician and Silurian Periods the Iapetus Ocean began to shrink gradually (we say the ocean was 'closing') as first one and then two destructive plate margins formed, subducting oceanic crust. As a result of this subduction, volcanism occurred along the destructive margins, resulting in the andesitic volcanism of the Lake District and North Wales. By the start of the Devonian, Iapetus had disappeared completely, shown in Figure 12.7c.

But what can the sediments and their fossils tell us about the latitude of Iapetus? There are no signs in these old shelf sediments of tropical or polar conditions. They were probably laid down in conditions associated with temperate latitudes.

So what about the strata above the Devonian?

Lower Carboniferous limestones were introduced in Chapter 6. They contain the remains of animals of similar types to those found in today's coral reefs, although the actual animals building the reef were of different species from those found today. Does this give any clues as to the likely latitude of Britain in Lower Carboniferous times? Abundant reef formation points to tropical conditions.

In the Coal Measures of the Upper Carboniferous, the plant fossils preserved indicate that conditions were similar to those found today in equatorial mangrove swamps, with very luxurious plant growth. This indicates similarities with tropical rainforests or swamps, typical of the Equator today.

Does this help us to choose between the desert belts north or south of the Equator for the Devonian? If we were near or on the Equator in the Carboniferous, and we are now in the northern hemisphere, this is consistent with a northward drift. So, it is likely that during the Devonian we also were drifting north, from the southern desert belt to reach the Equator in the Carboniferous.

There is a very useful confirmation of this idea when we look at the strata lying immediately above the Carboniferous, the Permian, which is remarkably similar in facies to the Old Red Sandstone of northern Britain. It is so similar that it was called the New Red Sandstone by early geologists (Case Study Chapter 5). it appears that Britain passed through desert conditions again, presumably this time the northern desert latitudes. So the overall sequence of the rocks from the Silurian to the Permian is entirely consistent with a steady drift northwards over some 200 Ma.

12.6 Devonian igneous rocks and plate tectonics

Each time an igneous rock is given an exact (radiometric) age in millions of years it helps to date the sediments which it touches accurately, as shown in Chapter 11. For example, in a sequence of sediments containing a lava flow, the sediments must have the *same age* as the flow itself, and any sediments cut by an intrusion must be *older* than that rock. In this way, the stratigraphic column can now be given precise geological ages in millions of years.

The fact that lavas can become magnetised on cooling has already been introduced in Chapter 4 (Figure 4.13) to calculate the present rate of sea floor spreading, from the repeated north–south reversals of the Earth's magnetic field. Some much older lava flows and sills which formed in horizontal sheets, also can supply another crucial piece of evidence: the *latitude* of the area at the time they formed. As an igneous rock such as a lava cools through its Curie temperature some of the iron-bearing minerals

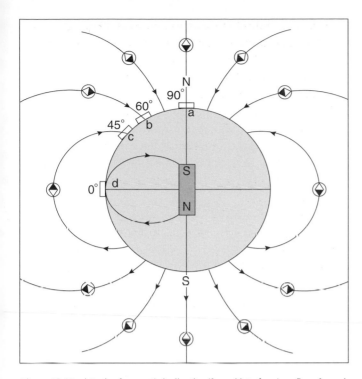

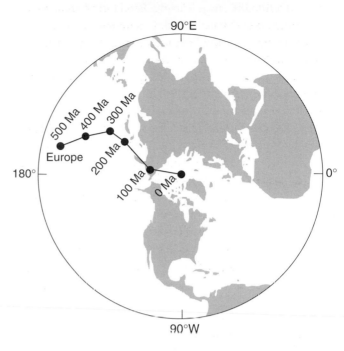

Figure 12.10 *a) Angle of magnetic inclination 'frozen' into four lava flows formed at different latititudes today. (a) 90° at N Pole (b) 73° at 60° N (c) 63° at 45° N (d) 0° at the equator. By measuring the inclination of the magnetic field 'frozen in' to an ancient lava the 'palaeolatitude' where it formed can be calculated, assuming that the Earth's magnetic field has remained the same*

b) Simplified apparent polar wandering curve for Europe for the last 550 million years, the northern hemisphere of the Earth 'viewed' from above the north pole. If the north pole has not moved, then Europe has drifted almost 90° northwards during this time

'line up' in the Earth's magnetic field. They take up the inclination of the Earth's magnetic field, which varies from 90° (vertical) at the poles to 0° (horizontal) at the Equator (Figure 12.10a). The inclination (dip) of the magnetic field of the latitude is 'frozen in' at the time of cooling. To work out this 'palaeolatitude' a sample of an ancient lava is collected, carefully noting its dip in the field, and then the direction of the 'fossil' magnetic field in the rock is measured in the laboratory. From these measurements it is possible to work out the palaeolatitude of the lava when it formed, by matching it with the latitude for that magnetic inclination now.

Conventionally, palaeolatitudes are shown as the apparent position of the north pole, relative to the position of the lava in the field. When a series of palaeolatitudes measured for rocks of different ages in a country are plotted out on the globe in chronological order, they will show a gradual movement of these ancient north pole positions with time, forming an 'apparent polar wandering curve'. Since we can assume that the magnetic pole has stayed fixed, it is the continent which must have moved over the Earth's surface. This means that the path of the wandering continent can be plotted out (in terms of latitude) if the north pole is kept in a fixed position, see Figure 12.10b.

Note that as the Earth's magnetic field is roughly the same inclination all around a line of latitude, it is not

possible to tell anything about the longitude of an old lava sample, so we cannot measure palaeolongitude in this way.

Much of our understanding of larger-scale past events comes from absolute dating and palaeomagnetic apparent polar wandering curves of the volcanic and plutonic rocks formed as these events took place. In this way, we have been able to reconstruct major periods of geological history, for example, the closing and opening of oceans, or the formation of fold-mountain belts in terms of the plate tectonic processes similar to those shaping the Earth today.

So what light can palaeomagnetic measurements throw on the Devonian? There are a number of basaltic and other intrusions in the Lower Palaeozoic, Devonian, Carboniferous and Permian rocks which have given good 'magnetic palaeolatitudes'. The palaeolatitudes in Figure 12.10b confirm that Britain has drifted northwards for the past 500 million years. In Silurian times (440 Ma), we were at 20–30°S, in the Devonian (350 Ma) 15°S, Upper Carboniferous (300 Ma) about 5°N, and in the Permian (250 Ma) about 15°N (see Appendix 7).

But can the igneous rocks of Devonian age also tell us anything about the plate tectonic setting of the UK at the time? Some examples will help to fill out the picture we have built up from Devonian sedimentary strata.

- In the Ochil Hills, near Stirling, Scotland, there are up to 1000 metres of basalts and andesites, dated at 410 Ma, while at the Cheviot Hills in Northumberland, andesites give dates of 395 Ma.
- Underneath much of the Lake District there is a huge batholith of granitic rocks, of which the Shap granite (394 ± 3 Ma) is the best known example.
  There are also similar large granite plutons beneath the North Pennines, called the Weardale and Wensleydale granites. All these granites are dated at about 400 Ma and were intruded several kilometres below the land surface.
- There are many large granite intrusions throughout the Scottish Highlands, both the Southern Uplands, and especially in the Grampians, and many of these are of Devonian age. This again shows that the rocks we now see around these granites must have been buried deep in the crust in Devonian times.

Figure 12.11 *Plate tectonics and the history of the Iapetus Ocean a) 540 Ma, early Cambrian. Scotland lies far to the NW of Wales–England and there is a constructive plate margin at centre of the Iapetus Ocean which is forcing the two masses of continental crust further apart. At its maximum, Iapetus may be 500 km wide. On either side of the ocean, shallow seas with different marine fauna collect sediments from the erosion of land. b) 450 Ma, late Ordovician. Iapetus has been closing for some time and volcanics are forming on both sides of the ocean, but especially in Wales and the Lake District where subduction causes crustal melting. The Scottish Grampian highlands are already above sea level. c) 400 Ma early Devonian. Most of Scotland and northern England is now mountainous and fast erosion under arid conditions gives Old Red Sandstone sediments. In the Welsh borders–south Wales area, there are variable shoreline sediments, while Devon and Cornwall have marine conditions with some coral reefs. Remnants of subducted ocean crust and crustal thickening along the suture where continental plates have joined (Iapetus suture) form a zone of intense metamorphism with melting in the lower crust. This results in volcanics in the Cheviots and the Midland Valley of Scotland and the intrusion of granites from northern England to the Grampian highlands*

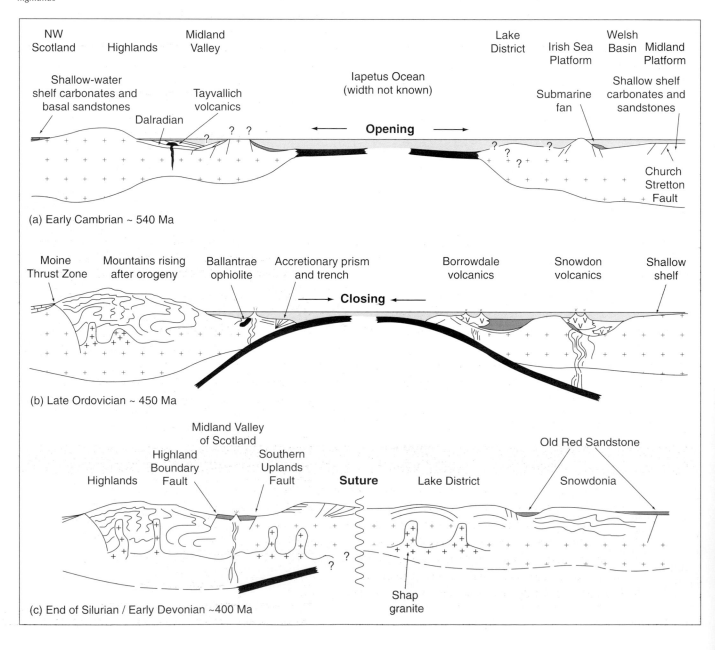

12.7 Putting the evidence together

The easiest way to understand how different types of Devonian rocks are related to each other and to plate tectonic processes is to look at a series of north–south cross sections through the UK at about 540 Ma; 450 Ma and 400 Ma (Devonian), Figure 12.11a–c (these sections correspond to the three palaeogeographical maps Figure 12.7a–c).

For Cambrian, Ordovician and much of Silurian times, the UK was a period of marine sedimentation on both sides of Iapetus, with some igneous activity in North Wales and the Southern Uplands.

Subduction of Iapetus then brought Scotland and England–Wales together at the start of the Devonian when continental collision occurred, Figure 12.11a, b. This subduction and continental crust thickening caused extensive melting, giving rise to volcanics and major granite intrusions, starting in the Ordovician, at about 450 Ma, but increasing into the Devonian. The large volume of granite provided buoyancy to the continental crust, and so caused uplift and formation of huge mountain ranges, especially in Scotland. Erosion of these mountains, and the huge amounts of clastic sediments which resulted meant that during the Devonian much of northern Britain was bare mountains, see Figure 12.11c.

Some deep valleys were formed by huge faults, and here thick Old Red Sandstone facies rocks accumulated. Both normal faults, such as those on both sides of the Midland Valley in Scotland, and huge shear faults, such as the Great Glen fault (Figure 8.24) which brought the Northern Highlands some 100 km from the NE to join the Grampians, broke Britain up into huge crustal blocks or terranes (see page 220), which have dominated geological conditions ever since.

Away from the collision zone in southern Britain, the mountains were smaller, and the shoreline ran more or less between south Wales–Devon, with marine rocks predominating in South Devon and Cornwall.

The closure of Iapetus was the last time that Britain was at a destructive plate boundary, and so subjected to major tectonic deformation. Since then our history has been one of sedimentation, gentle folding, and erosion. From Devonian times onwards, successive marine invasions have tended to come from the south and east, while for much of the time the areas that were land during the Devonian have tended to remain at or above sea level. One reason for this is that the crust here is less dense, and so buoyant, because it contains large granite plutons. Much of the present scenic highland areas of Scotland, Pennines and North Wales owe their present elevation to the crustal melting at the closure of Iapetus, and the consequent intrusion of Devonian granites.

12.8 Summary

1. Working out the sequence of strata in what was to become the new Devonian Period presented huge problems when it was first attempted in the 1830s.
2. Devonian rocks in Britain are of several different facies, from true marine in south Devon through an old shoreline in the Welsh Borders to thick continental Old Red Sandstone deposits in Scotland.
3. Plate tectonic processes brought Scotland to join England–Wales by the subduction of the Iapetus Ocean at the beginning of the Devonian.
4. Collision of two major plates caused much melting, resulting in volcanism and abundant granitic intrusion and uplift during the Devonian. As a result of this, much of Wales and Scotland has been largely above sea level since the Devonian.
5. Lithologies and fossils found in pre- and post-Devonian strata indicate that Britain has steadily drifted northwards across the Equator over the last 400 Ma.
6. Palaeomagnetic studies provide more evidence for this northward drift.

12.9 Questions

1. Why is it much more difficult to work out the sequence of strata in the geological column for rocks *older* than the Carboniferous, than for ones *younger* than the Carboniferous?
2. Why was much more fieldwork required to establish the Silurian and Cambrian strata than that needed for Ordovician?
3. What is the evidence for Britain lying south of the Equator during the Devonian Period.
4. If you were asked to make a geological map in an area where nothing was known about the ages of the sedimentary rocks, why is preparing a stratigraphic column so important?
5. How does a knowledge of plate tectonics help us to interpret the geological past?

Chapter 13

Past and future Earth: geoscience and humanity

Introduction

Throughout time the processes of geology have interacted through physical, chemical and biological activity, resulting in the form of the Earth and its surface features that we see today. Some of the largest scale Earth cycles, such as those involved in plate tectonics, take place over hundreds or thousands of millions of years so that, in human terms, changes are almost imperceptible. The forces involved are enormous and relentless. It is likely that humans can have little effect on them, other than monitoring the resulting earthquakes and volcanoes in an attempt to predict future events.

However, other Earth processes cycle quickly, over days or weeks, such as weather patterns and parts of the carbon and water cycle. Here there is a new geological force at work that has begun to overwhelm some of the natural effects: humans and human activity. We can study how past climates responded to changes in atmospheric composition and energy levels through evidence in the rock record. This may help us to understand how inputs of greenhouse gases such as carbon dioxide (CO_2) and methane (CH_4) may alter geological processes like weathering, through changes in climate.

We can also study how the environmental pressures on the Earth's surface from excavation, agriculture and the growth of built-up areas have begun to disrupt the natural rock cycle. Geoscience has a fundamental role to play in such issues, for example, as the excavation of huge amounts of bulk materials for the construction and minerals industries; or in agriculture with concerns of soil stability, use of mineral fertilisers, and water for irrigation.

This chapter reviews how the Earth arrived at its present state, building on the cycles briefly introduced in Chapter 1 and some of the detail of later chapters. It then speculates on future development of geological processes with the added human dimension.

13.1 Case Study: Earth now

The familiar form of the surface of the Earth is presented to us daily, through satellite images on television and in books. Most people have seen pictures that show such detail that ocean ridges and trenches can be clearly identified.

Two thirds of the Earth is covered by oceans but they are not evenly distributed since most of the large continental areas are in the northern hemisphere. There is permanent ice in the polar regions, on land in Antarctica, but mostly as sea-ice in the Arctic. The distribution of the continents and the oceanic circulation patterns (Figure 1.8a) affects the atmospheric circulation (Figure 1.8b) and climatic zones. This, in turn, is the main driving force behind the hydrological cycle (Figure 1.9) and the weathering, transport and deposition part of the rock cycle

(Figure 1.11 and Appendix 1).

Previous chapters have explained how the ages of the rocks forming the ocean basins were dated and mapped. A summary of the age of rocks on the continents and ocean basins is shown in Figure 13.1.

At present there is an expanding ocean, the Atlantic, that extends from northern to southern latitudes, separating the American plate from the European-African ones (Figure 1.5 and Figure 13.1 a).

A major feature is the mid-Atlantic ridge, a spreading (divergent) plate boundary. The Atlantic began to form 100-200 Ma ago (13.4.1 onwards), so all the oceanic crust is less than 200 Ma and most is less than 135 Ma (Figure 13.1a).

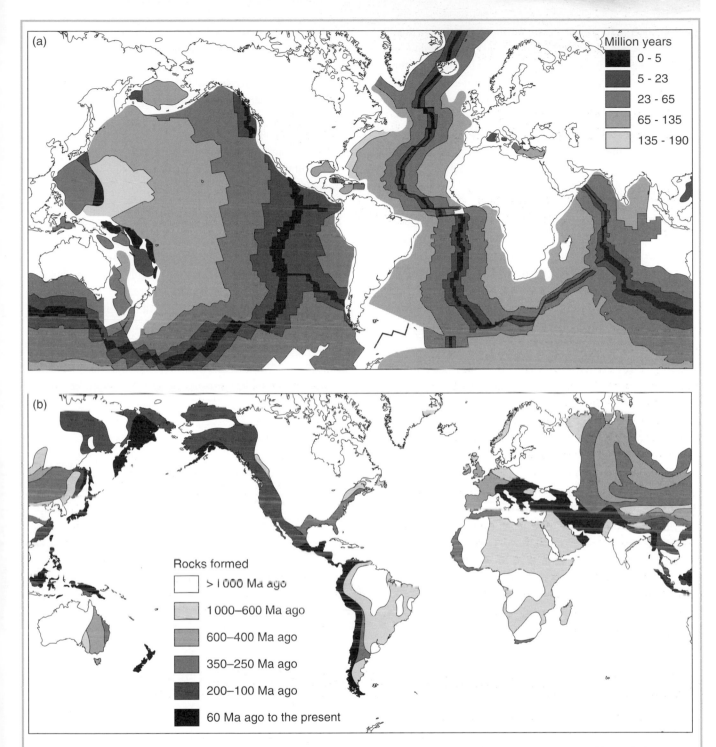

Figure 13.1 *Age of rocks at the surface of the Earth: a) The age of rocks forming the floor of the ocean basins, determined by palaeomagnetic evidence. Blank ocean areas are those where there are insufficient data to support the interpretation of ocean floor ages; b) The distribution of ages of continental rocks, formed during past phases of mountain building. Rocks formed more than 1000 Ma ago: these regions, called cratons, have remained unaffected by Earth movements for long periods, and form the stable core of the continents. They usually have low relief in contrast with the 'young' mountain belts of the Andes, Alps and Himalaya. There are gaps between the intervals of mountain building*

Similarly in the Pacific Ocean, which is larger in area than the Atlantic and where the spreading ridges are not 'mid-ocean', none of the crust is older than 200 Ma. This ocean is probably getting smaller, as it is edged by most of the zones of subduction on Earth. If all the present oceanic crust is relatively young, it means that more ancient ocean floor has been recycled down subduction zones (Chapter 4) and that the size and shape of the oceans has undergone major changes through time.

The continents are generally much older; all have rocks older than 1000 Ma in regions called cratons (Figure 13.1b). These form the stable cores of continents (Chapter 11), and are usually composed of crystalline rocks, comprising igneous and metamorphosed sedimentary sequences. Cratonic areas often show relatively subdued relief and may have a surface covering of sedimentary rocks.

The younger continental rocks (less than 200 Ma) are usually high and rugged; they are associated with convergent plate margins, which are of two main types:

- Fold mountains such as the Alps-Himalaya were formed by continent-continent collision: the metamorphic and tectonic processes involved were described in Chapters 7 and 8. Africa and India moved north to collide with Europe and Asia, resulting in hundred of kilometres of crust being crumpled and folded upwards.
- Volcanic mountain chains associated with oceanic subduction beneath continents (destructive plate margins). Typical of these are the circum-Pacific mountains, such as the Andes (Chapter 4).

How did the familiar pattern of continents and oceans develop? What caused the continents to grow? How could the pattern of the ages of the oceans have developed? To answer these questions we must look at the geological history of the whole Earth which is preserved in the rock record.

The next sections show how the continents moved, joined together, then broke apart several times during Earth history and how the area we now call Britain fits into this global pattern.

13.2 Early Earth history

The study of continental rocks has enabled geologists to reconstruct the configuration and location of the continents from the Precambrian to present. For example, the mineral zircon can be used to date ancient rocks, and palaeomagnetism can give a latitude. Studies of the rocks themselves and the fossils they contain also give clues about their formation, including their plate tectonic setting. Some of these techniques were illustrated for the Devonian in Chapter 12.

13.2.1 EARLY EARTH: WHAT DO WE KNOW?

Informally all geological time before the Cambrian, 4600 – 545 Ma, is called the Precambrian. It is subdivided into Eons: the Hadean, the Archaean and the Proterozoic, shown in Appendix 7.

Most Precambrian rocks have been recycled since that time, so the evidence is sparse. However, some of the oldest areas of rock on Earth, from Isua in Greenland (3.8×10^9 years) show evidence of life, and, since they are metamorphosed sediments, they represent a second 'turn' of the rock cycle. Of the original igneous rocks from which the sediments were formed there is no trace, except where the zircons that they contained persist. In Northern Australia rocks containing zircons give dates of original igneous formation of 4.2×10^9 years.

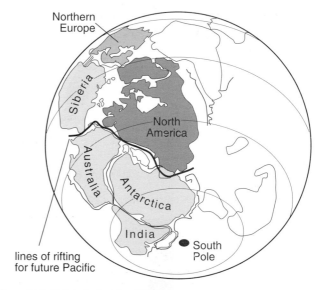

Figure 13.2 *Plate tectonic picture 750 Ma ago*

When continental rocks are exposed to weathering, dissolved material from the crust is taken into seawater. Isotopes of strontium in carbonates give evidence of sea-water chemistry and so, indirectly of continental growth. This indicates that there was a large increase in the area of continent exposed to weathering at the end of the Archaean, at around 2500 Ma and a slowing down since then of continental growth. Evidence from isotope studies of basalts indicates that significant continental growth began about 4000 Ma ago, and was at a peak by the end of the Archaean. Perhaps 50 per cent of the present continental crust was formed during the Archaean.

Where Archaean and Proterozoic rocks are found they often contain banded iron formations (BIFs, Chapter 10), sometimes forming 15 per cent of the sediments deposited. These are rich in iron oxides, that indicate general reducing (i.e. non-oxidising) conditions on Earth, with little oxygen in the atmosphere. BIFs disappeared from the rock record at 1.7×10^9 years and so provide useful evidence for the increase of oxygen in the atmosphere at that time. It is thought that by 1.9×10^9 years atmospheric oxygen had reached some 15 per cent of present levels (Appendix 7).

Around 1000 Ma ago all the continents were part of a large landmass called **Rodinia** in the southern hemisphere. Later, around 750 Ma towards the end of the Proterozoic, part of the North American craton ('**Laurentia**') separated from Antarctica and Australia, by rifting, shown in Figure 13.2. This rifting began a 'shuffling' of the plate material, with collisions resulting in the assembly of a supercontinent called Gondwana at the beginning of the Cambrian.

Late in the Proterozoic, between 900 – 600 Ma there were intense glaciations that affected the whole Earth. The regions where evidence for these glaciations has been found are shown in Figure 13.3. The causes of the glaciations may have been reduced volcanic activity at spreading ridges, so lowering the amount of CO_2 in the atmosphere. Also, the Sun was radiating less energy at this time, which was relatively early in its life.

Figure 13.3 *Ice ages in the early geological record*

Age Ma	Evidence from
600	Scandinavia, Scotland, Greenland, China, Africa. This is thought to be the most extensive glaciation experienced by the Earth, with ice to tropical latitudes.
740	Australia, China and South West Africa.
900	Greenland, Scandinavia and Spitzbergen

13.2.2   THE PRECAMBRIAN IN BRITAIN (4600-545 MA)

In Britain the rock record of the time before the Cambrian is patchy; rocks of Precambrian age are found fairly extensively in Ireland and northern Scotland but in the rest of Britain only isolated outcrops exist: for example, in Anglesey and north Wales, the Malvern Hills of Worcestershire and Charnwood Forest in Leicestershire.

The oldest British rocks are in the **Lewisian** Gneiss complex in Scotland, formed during the period 3300 – 1300 Ma Proterozoic and late Archaean (Figure 13.4a), when the rocks that are now Scotland were part of a

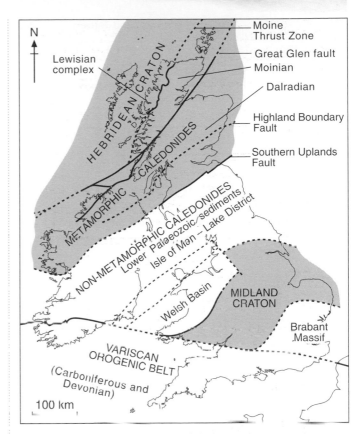

Figure 13.4a *Structural units of Britain, of the Caledonian (Precambrian to Ordovician)*

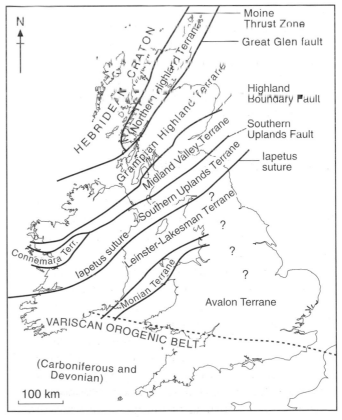

Figure 13.4b *Terranes in Britain (terranes are explained on page 220)*

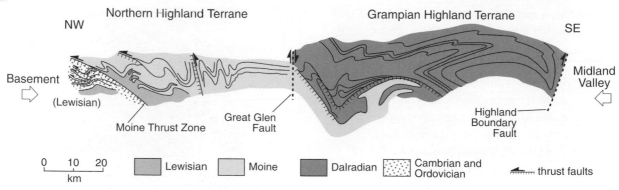

Figure 13.4c *A section from NW–SE across Scotland, showing the oldest rocks in the NW. Most of the units are separated by thrust faults. The rocks each side of the thrust are terranes that have different histories and may have been displaced thousands of kilometres.*

northern continent. The Lewisian complex is overlain by a suite called the **Torridonian**, and separated from them by a marked unconformity. The Torridonian are red-coloured, unmetamorphosed clastic rocks (it is thought that the latitude of the northern continent was tropical at this time). There is a great variety of rock types within the Torridonian series, river and lake deposits and also formations with the characteristics of coastal deltas.

A major tectonic boundary, the Moine Thrust, separates the Torridonian sediments from metamorphosed Moine Series sediments. These are sandstones and mudstones, metamorphosed at around 1050 Ma, so they must have been formed before that date. They must, therefore, have been laid down before the Torridonian sediments, which are younger. They were probably metamorphosed at a location further east and thrust westwards during the Caledonian orogeny (Chapter 7), up and over the younger Torridonian rocks, to their present position. This has produced the fairly unusual situation of unmetamorphosed sediments being overlain by metamorphic rocks, which can only be explained by thrusting. Indeed, thrusting on this scale was first recognised at a Moine Thrust locality.

Figure 13.4b shows the different **terranes** of the British Isles. Terranes have distinct sedimentary, igneous, metamorphic and structural histories that differ from the rocks that border them. They represent slices of crust that have been moved, sometimes by thousands of kilometres, along thrusts or transcurrent faults (Figure 13.4c).

There is a third group of rocks in the highland region of Scotland, called the **Dalradian**, that extends between the Highland Boundary Fault and the Great Glen Fault. This is another terrane, called the Grampian Highland Terrane. The oldest of the Dalradian rocks are around 700 Ma and the youngest extend into the Cambrian, i.e. are younger than 545 Ma. They are all metamorphosed sediments, from a variety of surface environments. Many of the rocks have a greenish colour and phyllite sheen.

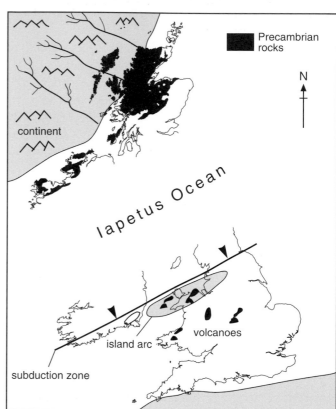

Figure 13.5 *Britain at the end of the Proterozoic. The width of the Iapetus Ocean is unknown. Sedimentation was occuring on the passive margin of the northern continent, while in the late Precambrian, active volcanism was taking place over the subduction zone of the southern continent*

Some groups contain cross-bedding, and fossil algal colonies (stromatolites), indicating coastal and shallow shelf sea conditions. A particularly prominent horizon is a fossil till, a **tillite**. Although the sediment has been metamorphosed, it is still recognisably a glacial deposit and is part of the evidence for a late Precambrian glaciation recorded in Figure 13.3.

Palaeomagnetic evidence indicates that North America and Britain were separated at 550 Ma, by the Iapetus ocean that had formed late in the Precambrian, shown in Figure 13.5.

The Precambrian Avalon terrane that underlies much of England and Wales (Figure 13.4b) is only exposed in a few scattered localities, shown in Figure 13.5. The rocks

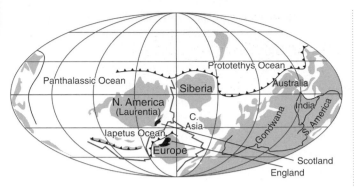

Figure 13.6a *Plate tectonic situation at the beginning of the Cambrian, at around 545 Ma*

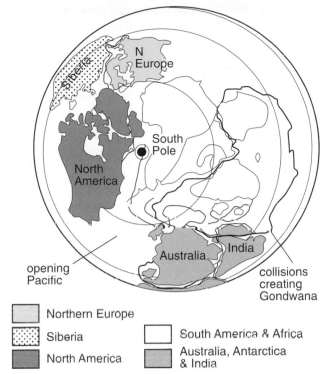

Figure 13.6b *The assembly of today's southern continents to form Gondwana and to show the rift developing into the Pacific Ocean. You are looking at the Earth from 'beneath' with the South Pole near the centre of the map.*

are often volcanic deposits, e.g Charnwood Forest, Anglesey, Pembrokeshire, but some may have been reworked and deposited by rivers.

13.3 The Palaeozoic (545 – 248 Ma)

13.3.1 CAMBRIAN EARTH (545 – 495 MA)

The Cambrian Period marks the start of the Palaeozoic (ancient life) and was the time that fossils first became reasonably abundant. The plate tectonic situation at the start of the Cambrian, around 545 Ma, is shown in Figure 13.6a, which has been pieced together from the fragmentary evidence found on the continents. The supercontinent Rodinia had begun to break up as blocks moved northward.

Africa lay across the south pole, so experiencing glaciation, whereas North America straddled the Equator, as did Siberia, and these areas had abundant rain. Further to the east, was a large landmass including what was to become China, Australia, India, Antarctica and South America. The northern part of this landmass, particularly South America and Australia, was in latitudes that received little or no rain. At the beginning of the Cambrian these land masses came together to form the supercontinent **Gondwana**, shown in Figure 13.6b.

The new system of ocean ridge plate margins that broke Laurasia and Siberia away from Rodinia increased the volume of active ridge systems. So the volume of ocean basins decreased and sea-level rose, to flood what was previously land (marine transgression). The transgression increased throughout the Cambrian, so that sea-level was around 350 m higher than at present by the start of the Ordovician (510 Ma) (Appendix 7). During this time deposits of shales, interspersed with limestones, were laid down in places that were to become the Rocky Mountains of USA and Canada. These shales indicate that the marine transgression was not smoothly continuous; there were stops, starts and short reversals during the overall sea level rise.

Focusing on the situation in Britain, Figure 13.5 shows that the Iapetus Ocean had opened and Scotland was situated on a northern continent with Canada and Greenland. Sedimentation was taking place that was typical of a shallow sea environment.

The rest of Britain lay on the southern shore of Iapetus. As tectonic and volcanic activity reduced, the sea flooded the area from Anglesey to south Wales (marine transgression). In the northern part of this Welsh basin turbidity currents deposited thick sequences of sediments (greywackes). In south Wales there were fewer turbidites, probably indicating shallower water. All Britain lay between 30° – 60° S, and so experienced temperate conditions. Southern Europe, however, at more than 60° S and surrounded by a cold ocean, experienced colder conditions.

In the seas life had changed from the soft bodied organisms of the Ediacaran fauna to a new stage, where organisms had developed limbs, exoskeletons and internal organs. There was a huge expansion in the number of phyla, known as the 'Cambrian explosion'. We know about these organisms largely because of the exceptional preservation of the Burgess Shale fauna of middle-Cambrian age, in Canada. The reconstruction

(Figure 6.12) shows the variety of weird creatures that had evolved; some of which were evolutionary dead ends, with no living relatives.

In the shallow seas of North America, trilobites lived in carbonate sediments just north of the Equator. These sediments became the Rocky Mountains. The trilobites found in Wales contain almost no species in common with those of North America.

13.3.2 FROM ORDOVICIAN TO CARBONIFEROUS (495-354 MA)

Through the Ordovician and Silurian periods plate tectonic activity was moving most of the continental masses closer together. During the last few Ma of the Ordovician a major glaciation affected the southern hemisphere. Sea level fell and extensive inland shallow seas disappeared to be replaced by dry land. Rich marine faunas of the vast, shallow Ordovician oceans were devastated as 50 per cent of genera disappeared. At the beginning of the Silurian the sea advanced inland again, with a rapid radiation of species (Figure 6.18).

The northern continent containing Scotland and much of North America was being driven towards the European plate containing England. The Ordovician and Silurian rocks of Britain preserve evidence of the subduction of the floor of the Iapetus Ocean as the continents moved closer together. The sediments of the ocean floor were becoming steadily squeezed, resulting in folding, faulting and metamorphism. This collision reached its climax at the end of the Silurian Period forming a great mountain range at the junction between the two plates. The newly formed continental rocks of the fold mountains joined the continents together into a new supercontinent called **Laurasia**. This is the Caledonian Orogeny (Chapter 7) in Britain and produced the **Caledonide** mountain range that bound Europe to North America, shown in Figure 13.7.

During the Devonian period that followed the Silurian collision, the area that is now Britain was lying in the tropics south of the Equator, and so was subjected to the subtropical conditions and varied terrain that produced the variety of Old Red Sandstone sedimentary rocks described in Chapter 12. Laurasia continued to move

Figure 13.7 *Plate tectonics in the middle Silurian (430 Ma), showing the Caledonide mountains*

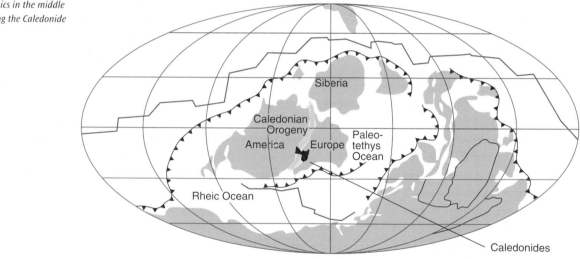

Figure 13.8 *Plate tectonics in the late Devonian (370 Ma), showing the supercontinent Gondwana, the Rheic Ocean, proto-Tethys Ocean and Panthalassa Ocean*

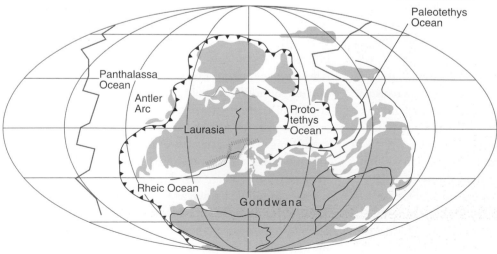

northward, pursued by the southern hemisphere Gondwana. The scene was set for the equatorial sedimentation of the Carboniferous period followed by another grand continental collision.

13.3.3. CARBONIFEROUS EARTH (354 – 290 MA)

The sediments deposited in lower Carboniferous times are so different from those laid down in the upper Carboniferous that in North America the Carboniferous is divided into two different Periods; the lower Carboniferous is called the Mississippian and the upper Carboniferous is the Pennsylvanian Period.

Palaeomagnetic and palaeoclimatic evidence from early Carboniferous times shows that the Laurasian supercontinent was astride the equator. Meanwhile the Gondwana supercontinent was centred over the south pole. The ocean in between, the Rheic Ocean, was slowly closing as Gondwana moved northwards as shown in Figure 13.8.

Many of the rocks of lower Carboniferous age in Britain are limestones containing corals (rugose) characteristic of tropical seas providing evidence for Britain being near the equator at this time (Figure C6.2). The rocks are typical of shallow shelf seas far from any land areas supplying sediment. Britain at this time was dominated by upstanding blocks on which limestones were deposited and deeper, subsiding basins with shale deposition, a pattern that was to repeat itself later in geological time (during the Jurassic). Increasing amounts of sand and mud in northern England and southern Scotland show that sediment was being brought from a landmass that lay across northern Scotland. So the picture

of the lower Carboniferous period is just as complex as that described for the Devonian, but was dominated by marine conditions.

Upper Carboniferous sedimentation in Britain was very different, partly because of a global climatic event. The supercontinent Gondwana (Figure 13.8) was centred over the south pole and a large landmass over a pole is one of the triggers for glaciation. If volcanic activity is also low and other factors combine to reduce the amount of carbon dioxide in the atmosphere, then an ice age can begin. A major glaciation affected the Gondwana continents and sea levels fell globally as the ice locked up a lot of water on land. The melting that occured during interglacials caused the continental shelf to be flooded again. Thus the glaciations made their presence felt far beyond the glaciated areas as sediments recorded series of floodings and drainings (transgressions and regressions) of continental areas. The cyclic deposits are referred to as cyclothems and many were recorded in British Coal Measure deposits at this time.

At the end of the Carboniferous, Gondwana, which had been moving northward, finally caught up with Laurasia in another great collision. The Rheic Ocean closed in an orogeny that formed **Variscan (Hercynian)** fold mountain chains in Europe, Russia and similar mountain ranges in North America and north Africa. These were probably the greatest mountains formed during Earth history. The collision produced the largest supercontinent the Earth has ever known, called **Pangaea**. All the land, except China, was in a continent that reached from pole to pole, surrounded by one global ocean called **Panthalassa**, shown in Figure 13.9. A large embayment on the eastern side between eastern Laurasia and Gondwana, that was to play a significant part later, is called **Tethys**.

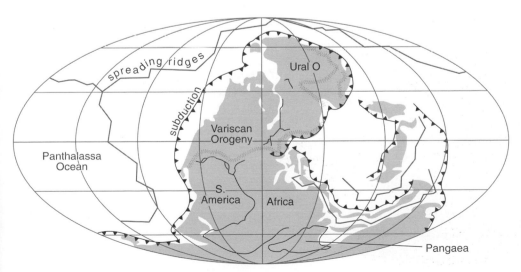

Figure 13.9 *Continental distributions in the late Carboniferous 300 Ma, showing the Variscan Orogeny mountains*

13.3.4. ACROSS THE MESOZOIC BOUNDARY: FROM CARBONIFEROUS TO JURASSIC (290–206 MA)

The collision that formed Pangaea roughly coincided with a greatly expanded glaciation in the polar areas, perhaps as a result of changes to oceanic circulation. The early Permian glaciation in the southern hemisphere (similar to that during the Carboniferous) caused a marked drop in sea-level. There were only intermittent connections between inland seas with strong evaporation when seas were isolated. The interior of the enormous continent was far from the sea and so conditions were very arid resulting in the widespread New Red Sandstone deposits of red sands, silts and evaporites found in Europe and North America. These deposits are characteristic of the Permian and Triassic periods that straddle the geological boundary between the Palaeozoic and the Mesozoic (Chapter 5 Case Study). You might ask why a major boundary in the geological column was placed within rock sequences that are very similar in Europe. The answer lies in the fossils. You will recall that the end of the Permian was a time of major extinction when about 96 per cent of all species on Earth became extinct. It may be that these extinctions were associated with the formation of the pole-to-pole supercontinent disrupting the ocean and atmospheric circulation patterns and causing major climatic changes. Also, the Siberian flood basalts coincide with the Permian–Triassic boundary (Figure 4.24).

13.4 Mesozoic to Recent (248 Ma–present)

The Triassic Period marks the beginning of the Mesozoic (middle life). The Pangaean supercontinent began to rift apart. A number of interconnected rifts would eventually become the constructive margin from which the Atlantic Ocean grew. Meanwhile, the climate and geology on the continental areas remained much the same until the beginning of the Jurassic period.

13.4.1 JURASSIC EARTH (206–142 MA)

As Pangaea separated and new ridges were formed between the new plates, the ocean basin volume decreased. This caused a marine transgression and a worldwide (eustatic) rise in sea level. The flooding that marks the end of the Triassic period is called the Rhaetic transgression in Europe. Much of Europe was covered by an enormous shallow, epicontinental sea in which areas of the sea floor were rising or subsiding at different rates. Shallow water sediments, limestones and sandstones, were being deposited in some areas at the same time as deeper water clays were being laid down elsewhere.

The one remaining major land area in Britain was Scotland and rivers draining southwards began to build deltas in northern England. These deltaic sediments were trapped in one of the basins so that very little sand or mud reached the seas of central and southern England. A clear shallow tropical sea developed, forming thick limestone deposits which were frequently rich in ooids, the tiny carbonate balls formed in shallow tropical sea conditions with active wave and tidal currents. These limestones have become the familiar buff and cream building stones of Cotswold villages and a range of cathedrals and other important buildings in Britain.

Figure 13.10 *Continental distributions in the middle Jurassic, 180 Ma ago.*

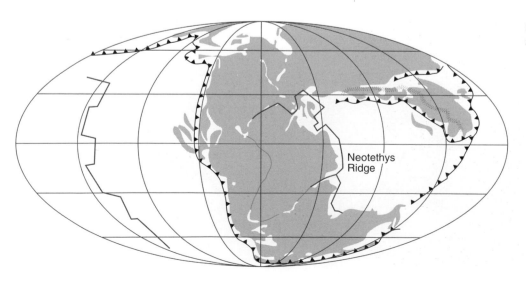

Neotethys Ridge

Meanwhile, in the USA, cross-bedded wind-blown Navajo sandstones were deposited, similar to those of the Triassic.

Sea level continued to rise and reached its peak in the late Jurassic but fluctuations still occurred so that thick sweeps of clay that were deposited during deeper sea conditions alternate with shallower water sediments.

There is no evidence of worldwide glaciation in the Jurassic. Continents were interspersed with wide expanses of sea allowing free oceanic circulation and the Earth generally experienced equable conditions and prolific marine life. Enormous numbers of ammonites are preserved in limestones, and they illustrate accelerated evolution. The dinosaurs dominated the land and the air and marine reptiles populated the seas (Figure C.6.3). Birds evolved, but there were few mammals. A worldwide flora of woody plants and trees had developed.

On a global scale, the new Atlantic ocean was beginning to open and the cordilleran arc system on the west of the Americas became established. The northern part of the Pangaean supercontinent, Laurasia, had almost become detached again from the Gondwana continental masses to form the Tethys embayment to the east and an embayment between north and south America to the west as shown in Figure 13.10. The separation of south America from south Africa is marked by the eruption of the flood basalts of the Karroo and Parana (Figure 4.24).

The Jurassic ended as it began, with a global sea level change. But this time sea level fell and continental areas rose above the waves, becoming subject to erosion again.

13.4.2 CRETACEOUS EARTH (142 – 65 MA)

By the early Cretaceous the 'Straits of Gibraltar' had opened linking up the eastern Tethys with the sea between north and south America, so forming an east-west seaway across the centre of old Pangaea. Meanwhile the early Atlantic was continuing to open, eventually forming a north-south linking seaway there as well (Figure 13.11).

During the lower Cretaceous the area that is now Britain was subjected to varying conditions resulting from worldwide fluctuations in sea level associated with extensive ridge spreading activity. By the middle Cretaceous, ocean anoxia developed below 300m due to a lack of circulation and mixing. There was widespread activity of ocean ridges and a huge marine transgression. Higher global temperatures (6 – 12°C) resulted in great biological productivity on land and the transport of organic material to the oceans led to anoxic conditions and storage of carbon in sediments.

The upper Cretaceous saw sea level rise to heights probably never seen on Earth before. Much of Europe was flooded and the whole of the British Isles may have been under water. When land areas are few and far between, there are no sources of sand and mud and so the upper Cretaceous epicontinental seas were very clear (Figure C8). With the latitude at about 35°N (the latitude of Bermuda and the Mediterranean today), conditions were ideal for the formation of thick limestone deposits, called the Chalk, familiar in many parts of southern and eastern England; an almost unique deposit in the geological record. Scanning electron microscope work at high magnifications has revealed that chalk is formed mainly of coccoliths, tiny carbonate plates found in the cell walls of planktonic algae. The sedimentary and fossil evidence for the depth of the Chalk sea are conflicting but

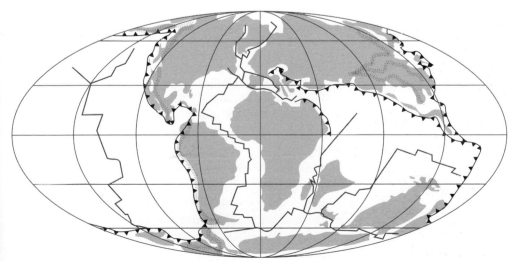

Figure 13.11 *Continental distributions in the late Cretaceous, 80 Ma ago.*

the general view is that it was deposited in very quiet conditions between 100 and 600 m below sea level.

During the Cretaceous, ammonite and dinosaur evolution had continued apace and a wide range of different forms had evolved including highly efficient flying pterosaurs. Mammals continued to develop slowly; modern bony fish developed and modern flowering plants (the angiosperms) evolved. Dramatic changes were ahead however, because the end of the Cretaceous was to see the extinction of the ammonites and the dinosaurs and many changes in other groups of fossils. The reasons for this mass extinction were complex, but may have involved the impact of an asteroid (p120) and global climate change. With many of the reptiles gone, the mammals could begin to flourish as the Tertiary began.

At the end of the Cretaceous the opening of the new Atlantic Ocean was accompanied by the closure of the Tethys. Africa had separated from the other southern continents and the northward movement of the African plate had been faster than that of the European plate. Tethys steadily closed causing some folding, uplift and erosion of the Chalk sequence in Britain.

13.4.3   FROM CRETACEOUS TO QUATERNARY (65 MA–1.5 MA)

During the Tertiary period, between the Cretaceous and the Quaternary, the southern hemisphere continents continued to move apart. The opening of the north Atlantic was accompanied by large scale igneous activity that affected Scotland and the northern part of Ireland. This activity was of the constructive margin type and gabbros associated with central igneous complexes, dolerite dykes and thick sequences of basalts were the major igneous rocks produced. The Iceland hotspot dates from this time.

Meanwhile the African plate had been pursuing the European plate on its northward path and the collision reached its climax in the Alpine Orogeny during the mid-Tertiary. The Alps and Pyrenees were formed through large scale folding, nappe formation, thrusting and metamorphism. The effects of the Alpine orogeny were felt as far as Britain where the Mesozoic and Tertiary sediments of southern England were deformed into open folds, while faults in other parts of Britain were reactivated.

It was at this time that the Indian Plate collided with Asia producing the Himalaya and welding India to the Asian continent.

13.4.4   QUATERNARY EARTH (1.64 MA – TODAY)

By the start of the Quaternary, the continents and oceans were positioned as we see them today and the coastlines were in similar places too. But unusual climatic instability was about to stamp its effect on the broader climatic and depth changes caused by plate tectonic movement. The Ice Age was about to begin.

In common with other glaciations in the geological past, this was a series of ice ages separated by interglacials. During the interglacials, the climate was much warmer than it is today in Britain and elsewhere. Since the Quaternary ice age is so geologically recent, it has left a lot of evidence of its effects on the Earth's surface, both on the land and under the sea. On land we see the effects of the huge ice sheets, possibly a kilometre or more in thickness that covered areas as far south as the Great Lakes in North America and London in Europe. The features produced on land have been described on p 94. Meanwhile, almost complete records of sedimentation were accumulating in the deep oceans and it is their microfossil evidence that now provides us with a detailed record of global temperature changes at that time (p120).

What caused this climatic instability? Has it ended or could ice return? What might be triggered by 'global warming'?

13.4.5   A PLATE TECTONIC FUTURE (+50MA)

What of the future? What will the surface configuration of the Earth look like in, say, 50 Ma time? To answer questions like these we need to make some assumptions, based on the way the plates have been moving:

- the Atlantic will continue to expand, at the expense of the Pacific Ocean;
- the transform fault (conservative margin) along the coast of California will carry the Los Angeles area to the north-west;
- the Yellowstone hotspot may enlarge, beginning the fracturing of mainland USA;
- the East African Rift will open to form a new proto-ocean and this rift will continue northwards, through the Red Sea, and through Israel/Jordan;
- Australia will move northwards, and begin to collide with Indonesia;
- the Mediterranean will continue to close;
- the land bridge in Central America will disappear because of rifting, changing the ocean circulation pattern.

Will all of these happen? They are simple, logical extrapolations of present plate movements and the possible results are shown in Figure 13.12.

There may, additionally, be changes of sea-level which are unpredictable:

- if the Earth climate moves from the present interglacial condition back to a glacial state, sea-level will fall, joining Britain to Europe in ways not envisaged by the European Union and making the Channel tunnel redundant;
- if global warming is established and continues, sea-level will rise, because warm water occupies more volume than cold. Also the Antarctic land-ice will begin to melt, adding to the volume of water. This scenario implies that many cities that are currently near sea-level will disappear, as will many Pacific islands and about one-third of the area of countries such as Bangladesh and the Netherlands.

13.5 External influences

It is clear from our brief study of Earth history that conditions on Earth have changed through time. Many scientists have tried to calculate whether there is any pattern, or cyclicity, in the variation, and if there is, what factors might be involved. The scales and timescales on which some geological processes occur are plotted on Figure 13.13.

13.5.1 MILANKOVICH CYCLES

During Earth history there have been many climate changes recorded in rocks. Some of these can be explained by plate tectonic movement, for example that Britain has drifted northwards through climatic belts, as explained in Chapter 12 and shown above. However, other world-scale features cannot be so conveniently

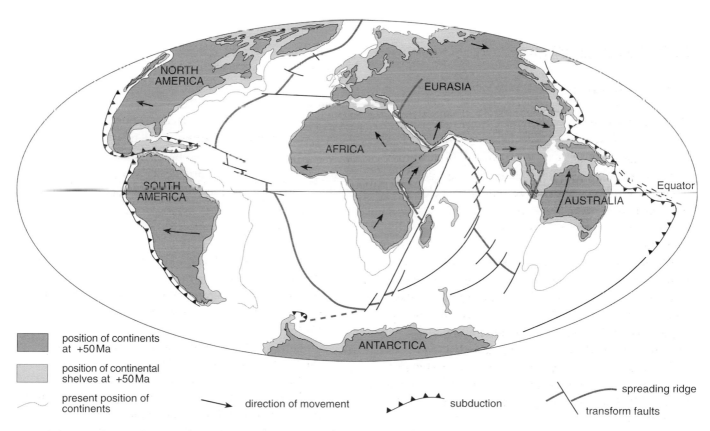

position of continents at +50 Ma

position of continental shelves at +50 Ma

present position of continents

direction of movement

subduction

spreading ridge

transform faults

Figure 13.12 *The Earth's surface assuming a further 50 Ma of plate tectonic movement. This diagram does not take account of any sea-level changes that might take place during that time*

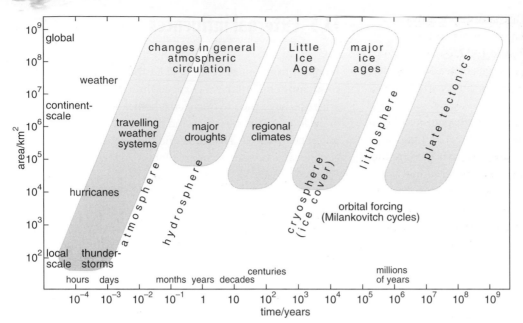

Figure 13.13 *The timescales over which processes occur. Short-term variations are mostly limited to the atmosphere. Long-term variations involve more components of the Earth-system*

explained, for example, during the Cretaceous Period, the climates on Earth were globally warmer. More recently, during the Quaternary, climates were colder (the Ice Age). There seems to have been a cyclicity with a major glaciation every 100 000 years and smaller ones 41 000, 23 000 and 19 000 years apart.

There are cyclical variations in the shape (eccentricity) of the Earth's orbit around the Sun and also in its angle of orientation (obliquity) towards the Sun. The Earth also wobbles slightly on its axis of rotation. As the distribution of the continents varies through time as well, all of these factors can combine to cause the amount of solar radiation received to vary considerably.

The eccentricity cycle varies by 6 percent with a 100 000 year period; the obliquity varies by up to 3° with a period of 41 000 years. The collective name for these cycles (and there are many we have not mentioned) is the **Milankovitch cycles**, after the astronomer/geophysicist who first suggested that they might affect climate, and in particular the Quaternary glaciations. Milankovitch cycles, influence for example, the intensity of seasons in each hemisphere. The present Earth's orbit causes the Earth to be closest to the Sun in January and furthest away in June. So the northern hemisphere has slightly warmer winters and cooler summers than was the case 11 000 years ago when Earth was furthest from the Sun in January. This might help to 'explain' the glaciation in the northern hemisphere at that time. Climate models have been constructed for 6000 – 120 000 years ago and their results are close to the observed geological record in, for example, North Africa. During that period there was an

increased temperature difference between land and sea, triggering stronger summer rain and high lake levels in what is now the Sahara Desert.

Oscillations in the glacial/interglacial pattern are related to the levels of CO_2 in the atmosphere, being low during glacial periods and rising rapidly as the ice melted and the climate warmed. The changes in CO_2 (which were entirely natural and have no connection with recently rising levels through burning fossil fuels) are due to the interaction between atmosphere and ocean and through the take-up of CO_2 by marine organisms. Whether the change in CO_2 *caused* the climate change or vice versa (the change in climate resulted in a CO_2 change) is not known because the dating of the events is not so precise that this can be determined.

Milankovitch cycles correlate well with climate for the past 2 Ma in the northern hemisphere, but cannot, at present, explain all the climatic changes, including the start of the Quaternary glaciations. One suggestion for the trigger of glacial periods is the disposition of the continents. If the poles are located in oceans, currents circulate to exchange heat more evenly from poles to equator. If continents are close to or over polar regions the difference in temperature between the poles and equator is increased. Ice and snow reflect sunlight, so the poles get colder, especially if there is snow and ice that lasts all year. Antarctica moved over the south pole about 100 Ma ago and 30 Ma ago Drake's Passage opened between Antarctica and South America, allowing the circumpolar circulation to be established. The Earth's climate started to cool from 70 Ma ago.

13.5.2   SHORT CYCLES: SUNSPOT ACTIVITY AND EL NIÑO

The stream of ionised (charged) particles that flows from the sun is called the solar wind, and this increases with increases in sun spot activity. This activity has, on average, an eleven year cycle, between a quiet phase and maximum activity when huge plumes of gas and ionised particles flare off from the surface of the sun. During manned space missions there is some danger to spacecraft and astronauts when they encounter the particles. The solar wind is deflected towards the polar regions by the Earth's magnetic field, where the particles ionise atmospheric gases. They can cause intense disruption to radio communication and have been blamed for massive power failures in North America. They also result in the natural light show – the 'aurora borealis' or 'aurora australis' (Northern or Southern Lights) – in polar regions. Quite recently scientists have begun to believe that sunspot activity and the solar wind may have an effect on climate, but the mechanisms are not well understood. If this is true, then it is another cyclic phenomenon that has affected the Earth since its formation. Evidence from banded iron formations (BIFs) and sediments in Australia dating to 680 Ma ago demonstrate cycles of 11–22 years, implying that sunspot activity may have had a regular periodicity through geological time.

It has been suggested that increased sunspot activity causes increases in ultraviolet radiation, which can interact with oxygen causing ozone formation and increased stratospheric temperatures. In the 1980s Danish meteorologists noticed that sunspot cycles with high activity tend to be shorter than lower activity ones. Plotting the average length of cycle on the same graph as an 'average' Earth temperature showed a very strong correlation, shown in Figure 13.14. Stratospheric ozone has been observed to rise by 2 per cent during high sunspot activity, enough to cause shifts in the pattern of winter storms by about 500 km, close to observed shifts in weather patterns. This suggests that there are feedback loops acting on incoming radiation that are fast enough to magnify the increase in activity and result in a significant effect on climate.

The sunspot cycle has a similar timescale to the cycles of the phenomena called El Niño (called 'the boy child' because it often arrives at Christmas). The El Niño effect is caused by a combination of factors: lessening of the South East Trade winds and heating of the ocean off Peru reducing the effect of normal cold upwelling water (see Figure 1.8a). The ocean surface circulation reverses and this in turn has major effects on local weather patterns (Figure 13.15). These events happen when the air pressure difference between the high pressure in the south eastern Pacific and the low pressure over Indonesia is at a minimum. This pressure difference rises and falls in cycles over several years, hence the scientific name for El Niño, El Niño-Southern Oscillation (ENSO).

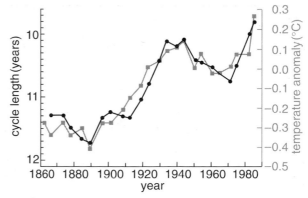

Figure 13.14 *Patterns of sun spot activity, showing the relation of the cycle ('black' line) with the average air temperature ('grey' line), expressed as departures from the average 1950–1980. (Plots of sea-surface temperature show similar correlations with the sunspot cycle)*

The El Niño phenomenon illustrates a close interaction between the tropical ocean and atmosphere, and a positive feedback loop that magnifies the effects. This sort of relationship is well known by those that study tropical storms (hurricanes and typhoons), where the energy comes from the release of latent heat as the rising air condenses to form clouds and rain. The rising air draws in further moisture from the sea surface and the system gains more and more energy until the feedback loop is broken by the storm drifting over land.

El Niño results in some freak weather. In Peru, for example, 400 mm of rain has fallen in a matter of days over an area where 4 mm was normal for one year! Similarly unseasonal storms can soak California, while the usual heavy rain over Indonesia moves southwards and South-east Asia experiences drought. All these changes from 'normal' weather can be linked to the El Niño conditions and these put strain on natural ecosystems. Strong El Niño effects occurred in 1972, 1977, 1982 and 1997-8; at the time the 1982 event was the most extreme, but the most recent episode (1997-8) has been the strongest so far.

El Niño also has distant effects. In Zimbabwe, for example, it has been found that the yield of maize can be more reliably predicted from the state of the Southern Oscillation in the Pacific than it can from local weather forecasts.

Similar effects have been measured in the Indian Ocean and the Atlantic. When the air pressure difference between the Icelandic low pressure and the high pressure of the Azores is high, westerlies blow stronger in the Atlantic, so the Gulf Stream and North Atlantic Drift flow more strongly than usual. When the pressure difference is low the winds and currents are weaker than usual. These differences oscillate in a similar way to ENSO.

Although oscillations in ocean currents and winds are natural, the increasingly strong El Niño over recent decades is being linked by some scientists to overall

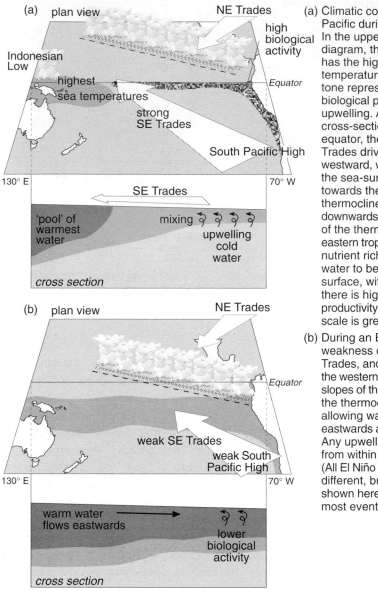

Figure 13.15 *Formation of El Niño-Southern Oscillation*

(a) Climatic conditions in the Pacific during a normal year. In the upper plan-view diagram, the dark grey area has the highest sea-surface temperatures; the patterned tone represents high biological productivity due to upwelling. As shown in the cross-section along the equator, the South-East Trades drive surface waters westward, with the result that the sea-surface slopes up towards the west and the thermocline slopes downwards. The shallowness of the thermocline in the eastern tropical Pacific allows nutrient rich subthermocline water to be mixed up to the surface, with the result that there is high biological productivity here. The vertical scale is greatly exaggerated.

(b) During an El Niño event, the weakness of the South-East Trades, and the westerlies in the western Pacific, cause the slopes of the sea-surface and the thermocline to collapse, allowing warm warter to flow eastwards along the Equator. Any upwelling now occurs from within the surface layer. (All El Niño events are slightly different, but the features shown here seem to occur in most events.)

global warming. In Northern Europe, if this is associated with a reduction of the North Atlantic Drift, it might mean a local *cooling* of the climate.

13.5.3 ASTEROIDS AND COMETS

During the history of the development of Earth sciences, many revolutionary ideas have been put forward, to be met by ridicule. When Wegener proposed the idea of 'continental drift', physicists assured him that there could not possibly be a mechanism for continents to plough through the solid, ancient ocean basins. Of course, we now know that the ocean basins are not old and act as a conveyor belt for the continents, like your purchases on a supermarket conveyor to the checkout.

The first Earth-crossing asteroid was discovered in the 1930s. Nowadays tens of near-Earth asteroids (called Near Earth Objects or NEOs) are discovered every year. When, in 1980, **Louis Alvarez** suggested that an asteroid hit the Earth around 65 Ma ago, to cause the mass extinctions at the end-Cretaceous, his idea had a mixed reception. Since then more evidence has been found to support the idea that there was an impact (p120) and scientific argument centres on whether or not it *caused* the extinctions. Advances in satellite photography have enabled the structures of some 150 impact craters to be identified, at scales from hundreds of kilometres in diameter to 5 km across, shown in Figure 13.16. Some had been known as impact structures for years, for example the Ries crater in South Germany, where astronauts trained in 1970 in order to recognise rocks that they might find on the cratered

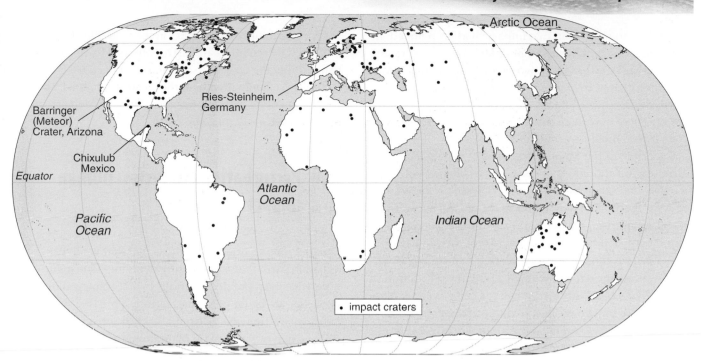

Figure 13.16 *Identified impact structures*

lunar surface. Some had originally been classified as volcanoes (for example, Meteor Crater, Arizona, USA), until **Gene Shoemaker** found quartz grains that had been subjected to extreme pressures ('shocked' quartz), characteristic of an impact, not cooling from a magma. The types of rocks and mineral deformations formed only by extreme shock pressures are: conical shatter cones; microscopic deformation of silicate minerals (planar deformation in quartz); formation of glasses and high pressure minerals (stishovite is the high pressure version of quartz); and rock melting. Further from the impact, glassy spherules and fragments called **tektites** can be found. All these can be used as evidence for impact cratering.

Rarely are asteroid or meteorite remains found in an impact crater. The heating during their passage through the oxygenated atmosphere causes most objects to burn up before reaching the ground, especially comets which are mainly ice, not rock. The pressures and temperatures on impact are sufficient to melt or vaporise the impactor and the target rocks, too. Even without an impact, devastation can still result; a strange area of flattened trees in a remote area of Siberia was once thought to be an early nuclear experiment that went wrong. More recently this Tunguska event has been interpreted as an asteroid that exploded at an altitude of 10 km before impact, causing a huge pressure wave that flattened the trees.

The record of collisions is fragmentary, like the geological column itself. Many impacts must have been into the ocean, where the evidence has not been preserved. Others may be lying undiscovered beneath the ice of Antarctica or Greenland, or have been infilled by subsequent sediments and will only be discovered by

geophysical techniques. The Chixulub crater in Yucatan was discovered using geophysics as it had previously been explored as a potential source of oil.

In 1994 the planet Jupiter was hit by a series of impacts from Shoemaker-Levy 9, a comet discovered at the same time but at different observatories by **Caroline Shoemaker** and **David Levy**. The comet broke up into string of smaller parts during its approach to the planet, resulting in around twenty collisions over several days. Astronomers and geologists wondered whether impacts on the Earth could be similar. The 25 km Ries crater in Germany has a tiny (5 km diameter) subsidiary crater 50 km away known to be the same age, shown in Figure 13.17. Other 'doublets' are

Figure 13.17 *Steinheim crater, South Germany, a secondary impact associated with the larger Ries Crater, 50 km to the north-east. The feature is approximately 5 km across, with a central raised dome caused by rebound after the impact*

known but no more than two impacts had been linked. In 1998 a paper was published that linked two major craters in France and Canada with two smaller craters that may have been caused by pieces breaking off when approaching our planet, as with Shoemaker-Levy on Jupiter. These may have circled the globe for a few more orbits before finally crashing to Earth.

The origin of the Moon has long been debated. Currently it is thought that there was a collision between an object the size of Mars (around 6000 km diameter) and the proto-Earth, 4.5 – 4.6 billion years ago. As a result material vaporised from the surface of the Earth and also from the impacting object. This was shot up into Earth orbit, where it condensed and accreted to form the Moon. If this was so, the site of the impact will never be found, as the Earth had barely formed when the collision took place and all traces must have been removed by subsequent geological events. Craters on the Moon are larger than equivalent impacts on Earth, because there is less gravity to constrain the ejecta; you may have seen pictures of astronauts leaping huge distances on the surface of the Moon because of the low gravity.

There is a finite, but small, possibility of an asteroid crossing the orbit of the Earth in the next century or so. Around once every 100 years the Earth is struck by a NEO between 10 m – 100 m across. This would cause a regional disaster if it were to hit a populated area. Every several thousand years Earth is struck by an object 100 m – 1 km in size, likely to cause greater damage, on the scale of the greatest known natural disasters. When the size of the asteroid is larger than 1–2 km, the results could envelop whole countries and there is a high probability of global consequences from changes to atmospheric chemistry and cooling by atmospheric dust, in the same way as after major volcanic eruptions. The relationship between the frequency of impacts and the size of craters can be seen in Figure 13.18.

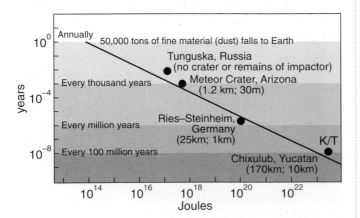

Figure 13.18 *Frequency of impacts with the Earth and energy liberated. The figures in brackets refer to (crater size; impactor size)*

The possibility of an impact in the year 2006 has been discussed by scientists and astronomers. However, it was realised that the object 'discovered' had been observed before and examination of earlier records enabled a better calculation of its path to be made. We have been assured that this object will miss the Earth.

13.6 Perturbations to cycles: human impact

The previous sections have illustrated that we live on a dynamic Earth that is constantly evolving. One main difference from previous periods is that some geological processes are being perturbed (affected by) one species, *Homo sapiens*, in ways as dramatic as the effects of the colonisation of the land by plants some 400 Ma ago, with accompanying soil and atmospheric changes.

13.6.1 CARBON, CARBON DIOXIDE AND GLOBAL WARMING

The carbon cycle was briefly introduced in Chapter 1; it is one of the fundamental cycles that integrates geological and biological processes. Carbon plays a unique role because:

- it can form compounds that dissolve in water (such as carbon dioxide), as well as compounds that are insoluble;
- it combines with other elements to make more compounds than any other element and these may be solid, liquid or gaseous. These compounds are constantly cycled through the inorganic and living components of the Earth;
- carbon compounds of various types are the store and source of energy for organisms; in the form of RNA and DNA these are the way of passing on genetic information from generation to generation.

The carbon cycle is, in fact, a number of cycles that link together and that act over different timescales. These are indicated on Figure 13.19 and include:

- the terrestrial-biological cycle (involving plants, animals, soil and atmosphere) that acts over short timescales, of months to decades;
- the inorganic, marine carbon cycle which acts over intermediate timescales (hundreds to thousands of years);
- the longest timescales, where 'leakage' from the cycles described above causes carbon to accumulate in sediments, so being removed from the shorter term cycles.

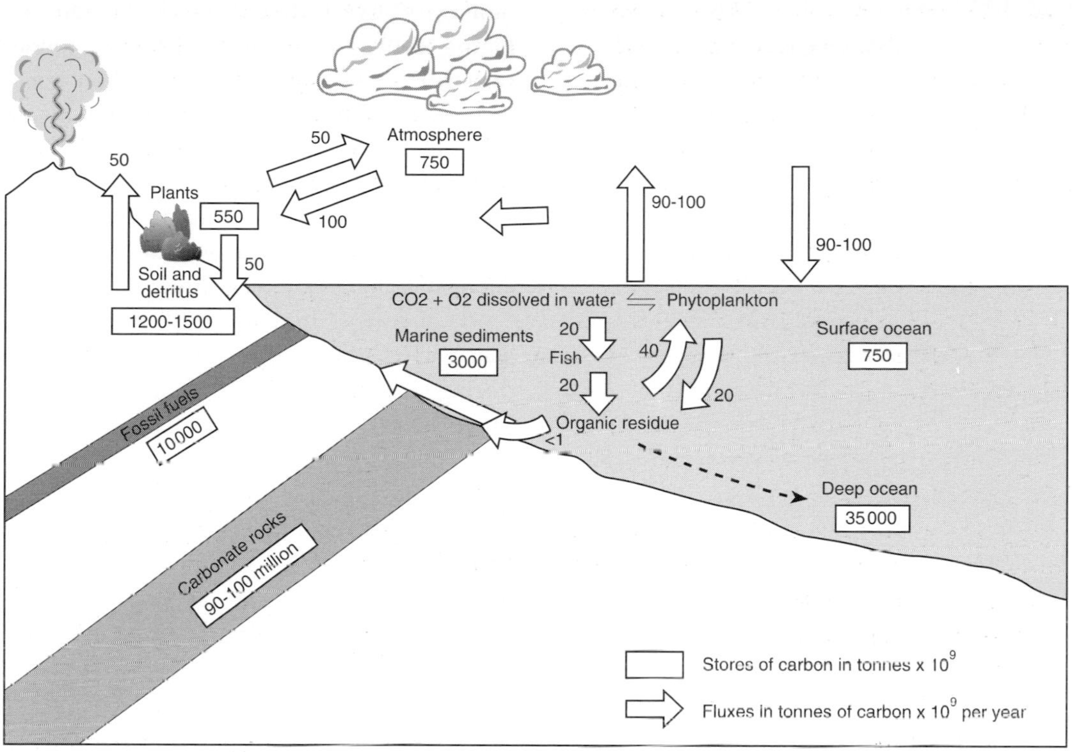

Figure 13.19 *The carbon cycle*

The amounts of carbon that are exchanged between the different parts of the cycles (fluxes) are shown in Figure 13.19, as are the amounts of carbon held in the different parts of the cycle (reservoirs).

The terrestrial part of the carbon cycle is dominated by the recycling of organic carbon, mainly plant material, through interaction of CO_2 in the air and the soil with the water cycle. Plants photosynthesise, taking CO_2 from the atmosphere and using energy from sunlight to convert it to carbohydrate, so releasing oxygen. Some CO_2 is returned to the atmosphere by the reverse reaction, to provide energy for the plant to sustain itself. Animals respire, eating plants to provide themselves with energy, giving out CO_2 and water as by-products. However, in comparison with plants, animals form a tiny fraction of the biomass. The stores and fluxes of carbon for this part of the cycle are shown in the top left-hand part of Figure 13.19.

CO_2 is one of the *greenhouse gases*, that is, it allows radiation from the sun to heat the Earth, but absorbs the long-wave radiation from the Earth and re-radiates some of it back towards Earth, thus keeping the temperature of the Earth's surface warmer than it would otherwise be. Other greenhouse gases are methane (given off by animals, and paddy fields), water vapour, ozone and nitrous oxide. As a result of these gases, the Earth's surface averages about +15 °C in temperature, instead of −18 °C. So, without the blanket of greenhouse gases the Earth would be a frozen globe. The estimated temperature

variation through geological time is shown in Appendix 7. This is one of the factors that has been essential for the development of life through geological time; the maintenance of surface temperatures favourable to liquid water and life. The surface conditions, the carbon cycle and CO_2 content of the atmosphere, oceans and life itself are interdependent; they are said to be 'tightly coupled'. It has been estimated that marine algae that give off a cloud-seeding substance called DMS (dimethylsulphide) cool the global temperature by about 4 °C. Some scientists believe that the feedback loops involving the activities of organisms contribute to maintaining temperatures within a range suitable for life; this is a central part of the **'Gaia hypothesis'**.

Changes in atmospheric CO_2 over time can be detected by measuring 'fossil atmosphere' that is trapped in bubbles of air in the ice of Greenland and Antarctica (Figure 13.20a). These show a steep rise associated with with the ice retreat over thousands of years. During the past 200 years CO_2 in the atmosphere has increased rapidly, probably due to fossil fuel burning by a greatly expanding world population. Figure 13.20b shows the increase in CO_2 measured in Hawaii, between 1958, when the average value was about 315 ppm and 1992, when it had risen to 350 ppm. The increase over this 34 year period is about one hundred times the natural rate of increase at the end of the Pleistocene.

A key question for those studying climate change is: how and why did CO_2 naturally increase during the

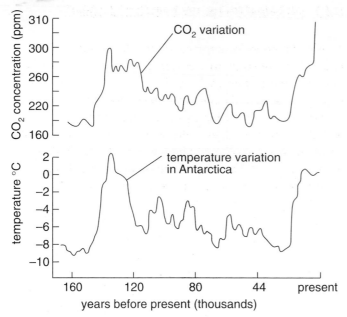

Figure 13.20a *CO₂ and temperature variation for Antarctica for the past 160 000 years*

deglaciation from 18 000 – 10 000 BP? How did the environment react over this time? By studying this system we may gain insights into the effects of the addition of greenhouse gases to our atmosphere. We can use 'the past as the key to the present'. Study of carbon isotopes in the shells of organisms in sediments and documented in ice cores and sediment records suggest that a very large amount of carbon was transferred from the oceans, via the atmosphere, to plants, soils and nearshore organic sediments during the deglaciation. If we are to understand this cycle we have to account for this transfer, and the increase in atmospheric CO_2 at that time, as well. It is clear that CO_2 has not been an inert participant in the post-glacial period; its feedback contribution to the greenhouse effect has led to further warming, linked to a rise in sea-level, changes in ocean circulation, plant growth and other factors in the global carbon cycle.

In surface waters phytoplankton are eaten by zooplankton, which are food for larger animals, and the carbon involved is cycled quickly. At the same time, faecal pellets and small particles, such as dead algae, clump together to form 'marine snow' and fall to the bottom, where they are the food source for bottom-dwellers. This transfer of carbon, from the surface to the deep waters, is called the biological pump.

The 'hard parts' of organisms accumulate on the sea floor within marine sediments (3×10^{12} tonnes shown in Figure 13.19), although some $CaCO_3$ is dissolved during the journey, or at the sea bed. During times of high surface productivity (algal blooms), enough marine snow falls for carbonate to accumulate on the sea bed, while nearshore, in clear tropical waters, substantial reefs are

built up. $CaCO_3$ is the main sink of carbon, shown in Figure 13.19 as the huge $90 - 100 \times 10^{15}$ tonnes of carbonate rocks. A great deal of carbon (as soluble carbonate and bicarbonate) is stored in the deep ocean (35×10^{12} tonnes) and much less (7.5×10^{11} tonnes) in surface waters. We may need to consider ways of 'storing' the excess CO_2 that is produced by human activity in the waters of the deep ocean, or in the rocks beneath, to avoid enhancing the greenhouse effect.

The marine sediment record shows climate-related changes in $CaCO_3$ production and dissolution, especially during switches between glacial and interglacial periods. There are complex feedbacks with atmospheric CO_2, through to land plants and soils, where the CO_2 concentration is up to 100 times that of the air. It is this plant root/soil acid interaction that is vitally important in rock weathering. Rock weathering supplies dissolved bicarbonate to the oceans via rivers and a change in this source, or in the amount of $CaCO_3$ buried in sediments, can alter the amount of $CaCO_3$ stored in the whole ocean. The sediment record of deep-sea $CaCO_3$ burial and dissolution is one of the most important keys to understanding the past history and the probable future balance of atmospheric CO_2.

Overall, rocks are the largest reservoir of carbon on Earth. Buried organic carbon (including fossil fuels) is about one quarter of the mass of that in limestones, including chalk. The residence time for carbon in these stores is in the order of 100-200 million years. Recycling occurs when deeply buried sediments are brought to the surface, especially through plate tectonic (mountain building) episodes. The carbon compounds can then be weathered, eroded and dissolved into streams and rivers and carried to the oceans and the atmosphere to be cycled again.

A key question is: Is the carbon cycle a system in balance? This is an extremely complex question because of

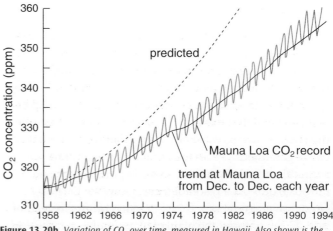

Figure 13.20b *Variation of CO₂ over time, measured in Hawaii. Also shown is the estimated increase predicted on the basis of fossil fuel combustion*

the varying timescales and the different forms that carbon may take. Figure 13.19 shows that the atmosphere contains 750×10^9 tonnes of carbon, and is one of the smaller stores, compared with the deep ocean, or soils. The atmosphere has connections with all the short, intermediate and long-term cycles of carbon. Changes to equilibrium are likely to have the largest effects on the atmosphere, with knock-on effects through plants and soil, to rock weathering and through direct exchange with the oceans. Volcanic emissions and rock weathering are tiny in comparison to the ocean-atmosphere flux, where more CO_2 results in huge algal blooms and ocean anoxia. At present, although all details of the interacting carbon cycles have not been quantified, it is clear that there have been imbalances between the stores and fluxes in the past and from which surface conditions have recovered. However, the input of CO_2 into the atmosphere by humans over the past two centuries has been huge and if it continues at the same rate, within a geologically short time it may be impossible for the carbon cycle to maintain surface conditions suitable for life.

The International Panel on Climate Change (IPCC) consists of 2000 scientists who have reported that:

- temperature is at its highest since *Homo sapiens* first appeared 100,000 years ago and will increase a further 1- 5 degrees by the year 2100.
- land glaciers are retreating rapidly everywhere except Norway, where they are growing because of increased rainfall. The glaciers of Glacier National Park, Montana have decreased by 73% since 1873 and they may totally disappear by 2030 due to lack of snowfall. There will be an increase in rainfall, causing floods, erosion and lack of water in summer, because of higher evaporation and the lack of a 'snow-bank' to give water in hotter months.
- sea-level has risen 10-20 cm during the past 100 years and will continue to rise, probably up to 50 cm by 2100.
- there is a broadening of latitudinal range of tropical insects, leading to an increase in diseases such as malaria in temperate zones.

There are also forecast changes in oceanic circulation and cloud cover that IPCC admit are difficult to quantify.

Most, but not all, scientists studying the Earth's atmosphere believe that the increased quantity of greenhouse gases in the atmosphere is resulting in global warming and that this may in the future have some of the dramatic effects listed above. Nevertheless, argument and discussion continues on the detail of the processes and timescales involved and the effectiveness of attempts to reduce greenhouse gas emissions. However, since the effects could eventually be so catastrophic for the world's population and life on Earth, many scientists continue to argue strongly for reduction in these harmful emissions.

13.6.2. FRESH WATER: THE MOST PRECIOUS RESOURCE?

A United Nations conference has concluded that '... all people have the right to access to drinking water and of a quality equal to their basic needs ...'. The importance of this can be seen in the relationship between the percentage of population that have access to safe drinking water and child mortality rates which shows the close link between unclean water and high death rates in children. In many parts of the world, groundwater is the cheapest, most reliable and cleanest source of water, but is also often being over-exploited.

One idea that might provide a solution to some of these problems but which has not yet been seriously considered is artificial recharge of aquifers, where water is pumped into aquifers during the wet season. The water is then available for use during the dry season and cannot be lost by draining away through rivers or by evaporation. This method would involve careful treatment of the water before recharging, to avoid pollution of the aquifer, but may well become a cost-effective method of enhancing fresh water supplies. In countries like India, where even moderate predictions of population growth indicate significant water shortages beyond the year 2025, and where monsoons produce marked wet and dry seasons, such methods may become vitally important. So in the future, artificial recharge may replace the building of surface reservoirs as the most effective method of storing fresh water. Whatever methods are used in the future, the job of the hydrogeologist will continue to be vitally important in finding and maintaining water supplies.

13.6.3. EXCAVATION, RECLAMATION AND CULTIVATION

Currently some 40% of the derelict land in Britain, the so called 'brownfield sites' being considered for new building, is mining- and quarry- related. These sites include the holes in the ground themselves, tips of waste and areas of subsidence. Whilst metal and coal mining in the UK may be declining, the demand for the industrial minerals used primarily in the construction industry continues to grow, although subject to periodic declines in times of recession. Present demand is around 5 tonnes per head of population per annum. Extraction of these materials must be very carefully managed if it is not to lead to more dereliction and loss of land.

Nowadays, there are tight controls on the reclamation of land subject to quarrying and much of it is put to good use in waste disposal. There is also government pressure to use brownfield sites for new buildings rather than the cheaper 'greenfield sites' on the margins of towns and cities. Similar issues affect many of the better developed countries, but in developing countries not subjected to such strict planning controls, loss of good building land to extraction-related dereliction is likely to become more of an issue in the future. In areas of derelict land, geoscientists are needed to assess and map the potential hazards before measures can be recommended to deal with them.

Not only is loss of land a problem in urban areas, but loss of agricultural land is affecting the world's food supplies. Some 13% of the land surface is used for crop-growing and around 15% of this cultivated area is subjected to major erosion by water, wind and chemical and physical degradation. Of this, around 6% is due to salinisation caused by poorly-conceived irrigation schemes and the use of poor land clearance methods or inappropriate crops. Soils have complex ecosystems that, once destroyed, are difficult or impossible to replace. Part of the future role of the geoscientist will be to improve understanding of soil processes as a vital contribution to sustainable agricultural practices.

Some 2% of the Earth's land surface is irrigated and irrigation needs reliable water supplies, particularly in drier seasons. Increased crop production needs increased use of fertilisers. In both these cases, geoscientists have a vital part to play in providing the water supplies and identifying mineral reserves from which fertilisers can be produced.

13.6.4 EXTINCTIONS AND POPULATION GROWTH

The most recent mass extinction event began around 50 000 years ago and is continuing at an accelerating rate. More than 200 genera of large animals have been exterminated together with countless species of small animals and insects, some of which had not yet been discovered and classified by scientists. It is human activities which are causing this devastation. For example, humans clear tropical forests and move into the habitats previously occupied by these animals and plants. The tropical rain forests are extremely effective and efficient photosynthesising areas; their destruction means the biosphere cannot absorb as much CO_2. If paddy fields replace rainforest the situation is even worse, as they generate methane, a potent greenhouse gas. In temperate areas, extensive cultivation and 'agribusiness' uses weedkillers (herbicides) and insecticides that have effects on natural flora and fauna. Since the publication of Rachel Carson's book *Silent Spring* in 1963 there have been many voices raised in concern at the damage to our environment through pesticides that persist in the food

chain and, more recently, fertilisers that can pollute our underground water supplies and consequently our drinking water. Many recent developments, for example in market garden and glasshouse crops, have concentrated on disease and pest control by more 'natural' means, such as the use of natural predators. Not only does agriculture remove the natural vegetation cover which is important to the CO_2 balance, but it also releases more CO_2 into the atmosphere.

One scientist described this situation as the 'people plague'. On geological timescales, humans have not been around long enough to be called a 'successful' species (only 3 Ma, compared to the dinosaurs' 30 Ma) but their effects on other organisms, the surface of the Earth and, increasingly, on the climate and evolution of the planet itself, have been profound. What is more, these effects may accelerate with increasing population growth and technological development.

13.7 Geoscientists' input

Geoscientists have a key role to play not only in monitoring but in suggesting ways of dealing with the problems involved. In 1997 the retiring Director of the British Geological Survey (BGS) stated that 'the earth sciences are needed to determine global physical and chemical fluxes, reservoirs, pathways and sinks; to consider these on timescales ranging from decades to millennia and on scales of magnitude from the micro to the macro and global, and to separate out anthropogenic from 'natural' or pre-anthropogenic rates and processes. But more than this the earth sciences can also provide some of the answers to many of the sustainability issues now facing us. Whilst there are many serious issues impacting upon the sustainable use of the earth's resources, there is every reason to believe that solutions will be found, not least by the earth scientists'.

The director went on to stress the interplay of the many factors affecting the availability of important resources, water, air, soils, land, energy and materials. He pointed out that geoscience 'is a key to this understanding and this will require better documenting, surveying, monitoring, modelling and understanding the system as a whole'.

Understanding environmental concerns in order to maintain a healthy planet were the focus of the Earth Summit meetings at Rio (1992) and Kyoto (1997). Topics such as limiting CO_2 emissions and protecting the rain forest were discussed and this led to the development of new policy.

There is a realisation that **sustainable development** must be a goal, that is, current development should not jeopardise the ability to meet the needs of future generations. This means using resources efficiently, with recycling and the minimising of environmental impacts of extraction, processing, manufacture and disposal. We also need to maintain diversity of life and the biosphere on which our lives depend.

13.7.1 MONITORING PLATE TECTONIC HAZARDS

Britain is not a tectonically active area. Earthquakes in the UK are generally small, often resulting from mining in the past, and there are no active volcanoes. However, British people still living in Montserrat in the Caribbean have a hazardous existence on the side of a volcano (Figure 4.1b). Many of the visiting scientists monitoring the volcano in attempts to predict future eruptions are also British.

One of the problems they face is of timescale. This volcano previously erupted in the 1600s, before 'scientific' records; the population had forgotten that Montserrat was volcanic! There is nothing to compare the present eruption with, to know whether it is behaving 'normally' or not. But by measuring and monitoring the effects of volcanic activity such as ground deformation, seismicity, the width of opening cracks, gas emissions and gas content of ash, scientists hope to model and predict when magma is moving higher in the vent, which would precede an eruption. This type of monitoring is particularly important in island arc and subduction-related volcanoes, which can be highly explosive, such as those in Montserrat and Central America.

Similar monitoring takes place routinely in the USA, and also in Europe, on volcanoes such as Etna and Mount Vesuvius in Italy, because of the proximity of centres of population.

In a similar way, zones of known tectonic stress, such as major transform faults are monitored for earthquake prediction. Laser ranging devices are used to measure ground deformation such as the creep along the San Andreas Fault in California. As with volcanoes, the database of information is building only slowly, over human timescales, whereas these processes have been taking place over 4600 Ma of Earth history.

The enormous forces involved mean that, at best, some measure of prediction might be successful; we will never be able to stop the widening of the Atlantic, or the Pacific Plate from diving beneath Japan, and so prevent hazards like eruptions, earthquakes and landslides.

13.7.2 GEOCHEMICAL MONITORING

The environmental pollution issue has given rise to ideas such as 'the polluter pays' and the '**precautionary principle**'. This says that 'Government will be prepared to take precautionary action to limit the use of potentially dangerous materials... even when the scientific knowledge is not conclusive, if the balance of likely costs and benefits justify it'. In other words, it is better to be safe than sorry when dealing with materials that might damage the environment; an example is the CFC gases now known to destroy the protective ozone layer. These had been used for years as refrigerant gases and were thought to be harmless and inert.

A major growth area of employment for geoscientists is in geochemical monitoring in the fields of:

- the safe disposal of domestic and industrial wastes, to ensure that, for example, aquifers are not polluted;
- water supply standards; sources (e.g. rivers and aquifers) are monitored for pollutants;
- the safe storage of radioactive waste (low and medium-level waste from hospitals and industry, high-level waste from nuclear power stations);
- monitoring the environment, for example beaches and seawater quality;
- recording atmospheric pollution, from power stations and industrial complexes.

13.7.3 INFORMATION STORAGE AND RETRIEVAL

Geological mapping has been one of the key tools of the geologist ever since William Smith produced some of the world's first geological maps in the late 1700s. Some mapping techniques have changed little since then, but others would have astounded Smith. For example, not only do we have many more sources of information than were available in the 1700s, including geophysical, borehole logging and remote sensing methods, but modern technology allows us to record the information in much more flexible ways. Modern mapping techniques are digital, allowing a record to be kept for each point on the ground. The topographic mapping of the Ordnance Survey in Britain records a whole host of features, including altitude, land use, constructions from iron age hill forts to modern motorways, etc. Field geologists of the British Geological Survey in Britain add many more observations to the topographic records. These include: rock and soil type and glacial deposits; slope stability; areas of mining; quarrying, subsidence, etc; areas of potential foundation problems or of potential reserves of useful materials; aquifer locations and any other feature related to the geology or ground conditions. The sites at which observations are made are also noted, including rock exposures, borehole, mine and quarry locations, cuttings and temporary exposures due to foundation excavation. Old mining, canal and tunnel excavation records are incorporated where they are available and likely to be accurate.

The result is an enormous and growing database of information from which information can be drawn for particular purposes. Chapter 8 (page 146), explained how, rather than producing single geological maps, the BGS now publish sets of 'thematic maps' (Figure C.8.1–8.3) that cover a range of these features. Commercial organisations can request maps of specified areas showing certain features and the digital information can be manipulated and printed out on demand to meet their requests. Such maps are expensive, but are cheaper than the mistakes that have been made in the construction industry in the past, when good geological advice has not been sought.

Modern information storage techniques integrate geological and other information in ways that were previously not possible and they highlight the value of collecting information on a holistic basis (methods that study all the factors that can be involved and so consider the issue as a whole).

13.7.4 HOLISTIC OR INTEGRATED APPROACHES

Study of our planet has become fragmented into many disciplines: Earth science encompasses 'traditional' subject areas such as mineralogy, palaeontology and geophysics and also newer, more interdisciplinary areas such as oceanography and biogeochemistry. Most British universities structure degree courses around these traditional subject areas, though increasingly they are introducing 'environmental' aspects to programmes.

Another approach, more common in the USA, is to study the Earth through a 'systems approach', considering the lithosphere, biosphere, atmosphere, hydrosphere and cryosphere (frozen water) as interacting dynamic systems. Study is not only of the spheres themselves, but also the inputs, outputs, the flows between the parts, and the interconnections of cause and effect between them. In particular there is a search for links between the Earth's physical, chemical and biological processes to understand past and future global change. This may appear to be a new way of studying Earth science, but it is not, since concepts such as 'the present is the key to the past' use the idea that Earth systems work in the same way now as they did in the geological past.

Studying the interconnections of the dynamic Earth highlights their importance to the world today. Earth processes and their effects commonly hit the headlines. Not only do topics such as deforestation, landslides, earthquakes, volcanic eruptions, flooding, mining and mineral extraction, pollution, global warming, asteroid impacts and others fascinate many people, but they have had, or may have, crucial effects at all scales from small village communities to the whole human race. Geoscience understanding will help those with an interest in these issues to gain a better understanding of the many factors involved and the importance of their interactions.

Holistic approaches are also beginning to influence research in Earth sciences, which often involves large interdisciplinary teams with international collaboration becoming more commonplace. This is particularly the case when investigating the 'big issues' of Earth science, such as climate change, the effects of increased greenhouse gases on rock weathering and the interface with the oceans and atmosphere. The authors hope that readers will find this book a useful introduction to the geological aspects of geoscience and to the complex systems and processes that influence all aspects of the planet on which we live.

13.8 Questions

1 What are your predictions on how the area we call Britain will change in the geological future? These predictions should be supported by scientific evidence.
2 It is predicted that a one metre rise in sea level would cause the loss of 17.5% of the area of Bangladesh, a low-lying country on the Indian subcontinent. What effects might such a sea-level rise have on Britain? Consider such factors as the towns and cities, transport and communication, supplies of raw materials, energy and water and the impact on agricultural areas.
3 What role do you think geoscientists will play in the future of our planet? What is the balance between monitoring problems and suggesting solutions to them likely to be?

APPENDIX 1   The Rock Cycle

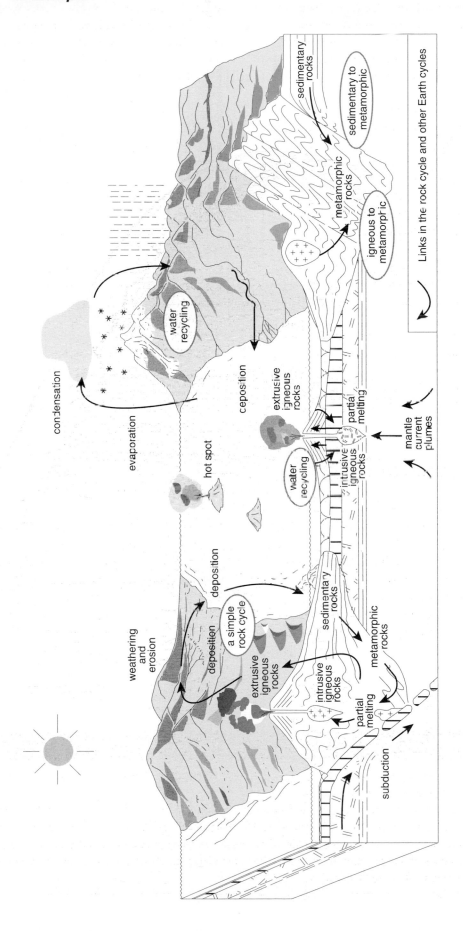

Appendix 2 *Minerals and the key features used in identification*

Name	Composition	Crystal system	Hardness	Relative Density	Colour	Lustre	Streak	Cleavage	Fracture	Other features	Occurrence
Amphibole group Hornblende	Complex silicate	monoclinic	5–6	3–3.5	black, often greenish	vitreous (glassy)	white	two, nearly at 60°	SC to uneven	bladed crystals	intermediate and some silicic ign rocks; common in meta rocks
Aragonite	$CaCO_3$	orthorhombic	3.5–4	4	colourless white or grey	vitreous (glassy)	white	poor	SC	reacts with dilute hydrochloric acid (HCl)	sedi rocks (limestones). Shells and corals
Calcite	$CaCO_3$	trigonal	3	2.7	white or colourless	vitreous (glassy)	white	three, rhombic	rarely seen	reacts with cold dilute HCl; 6-sided crystals ending in pyramids common	sedi rocks (limestones); meta rocks (marble); gangue mineral
Chalcopyrite	$CuFeS_2$	tetragonal	3.5–4	4.2	brassy yellow	metallic	greenish black	none	uneven	more golden coloured than pyrite	copper ore mineral
Dolomite	$CaMg(CO_3)_2$	trigonal	3.5–4	2.86	honey colour, colourless or white	vitreous or pearly	white	as calcite, above	SC or uneven	reacts with hot dilute HCl; rhombic crystals with curved faces common	sedi rocks (limestones)
Feldspar group Orthoclase	$KAlSi_3O_8$	monoclinic	6–6.5	2.6	white, grey or pink	vitreous to pearly	white	two, almost at 90°	C	rectangular crystals; twinning common	common in silicic ign rocks and meta rocks; in some sedi rocks
Feldspar group Plagioclase	$NaAlSi_3O_8$ to $CaAl_2Si_2O_8$	triclinic	6–6.5	2.6–2.8	white or grey	vitreous to pearly	white	two, almost at 90°	C to uneven	small long thin rectangular crystals	in many ign and meta and some sedi rocks
Fluorite (fluorspar)	CaF_2	cubic	4	3.2	variable: blue, colourless, yellow, purple, pink, green	vitreous (glassy)	white	four, across corners of cube	C to uneven	often forms good cubic crystals; twinning common	gangue mineral; source of fluorine
Galena	PbS	cubic	2.5	7.5	lead grey	metallic	grey	three at 90° (cubic)	SC	feels very heavy. Reacts with HCl to produce hydrogen sulphide gas	lead ore mineral
Garnet	$Fe_3Al_2Si_3O_{12}$	cubic	6–7.5	3.6–4.2	usually red or brown	vitreous to resinous	white	none	SC to uneven	near spherical crystals common	meta rocks; rarely in other types of rock
Haematite	Fe_2O_3	trigonal	6	5	red-brown or black	metallic or dull	red-brown	none	uneven	forms rounded masses called kidney iron ore; magnetic on heating	iron ore mineral; cement in some sedi rocks
Halite	NaCl	cubic	2–2.5	2.2	usually colourless to white	vitreous (glassy)	white	three at 90° (cubic)	C	soluble; cubic crystals common	sedi rocks; evaporite mineral
Magnetite	Fe_3O_4	cubic	6	5.2	black	metallic	black	poor	uneven	strongly magnetic; crystals often octahedral	iron ore mineral; mafic ign rocks
Mica group Muscovite	Complex silicate	monoclinic	2.5–3	2.8–2.9	colourless white, silvery	vitreous to pearly	white	one	–	splits into thin flexible transparent sheets	silicic ign rocks, many meta rocks and some sedi rocks
Mica group Biotite	Complex silicate	monoclinic	2.5–3	2.8–2.9	black or dark brown	vitreous to pearly	white	one	–	splits into thin flexible sheets	silicic and intermediate ign rocks, meta rocks, sometimes in sedi rocks
Olivine group Fayalite Forsterite	$(MgFe)_2SiO_4$	orthorhombic	6.5–7	3.2–4.4	green, yellow or brown	vitreous (glassy)	colourless	poor	C	often altered to green serpentine	mafic ign rocks
Pyrite (iron pyrites)	FeS_2	cubic	6–6.5	5.0	brassy yellow	metallic	greenish black	none	uneven	cube faces often striated	common in mineral veins (but not an ore of iron); found in black shales
Pyroxene group Augite	Complex silicate	monoclinic	6	3.4	black or greenish black	vitreous (glassy)	white	two, nearly at 90°	uneven to SC	stumpy crystals	mafic and intermediate ign rocks
Quartz	SiO_2	trigonal	7	2.65	variable: usually white or colourless	vitreous (glassy)	white	none	C	six-sided crystals terminated by pyramids common	ign, sedi and meta rocks; gangue mineral
Sphalerite	ZnS	cubic	3.5–4	4.1	usually brown or black	resinous to adamantine	white or brown	six at 60°	C	metal ore with non-metallic lustre	zinc ore mineral

Key   C = conchoidal; SC = subconchoidal; ign = igneous; meta = metamorphic; sedi = sedimentary

Appendix 3 *Common rock types*

Formation process	Name	Texture and grain size	Composition and minerals	Formation details
Igneous				
extrusive	andesite	fine <1 mm, volcanic	intermediate: feldspar (plagioclase, orthoclase), quartz	fast cooling of volcanic lava resulting from partial melting beneath island arcs or mountain zones
	ash/tuff	fine volcanic fragments	variable, usually intermediate or felsic/silicic	explosive volcanic activity, usually at island arcs or mountain zones
	basalt	fine <1 mm extrusive or intrusive, volcanic	mafic: pyroxene, feldspar (plagioclase), occasional olivine	fast cooling of magma from partial melting of mantle at ocean ridges; extrusive lava flows, intrusive dykes
	dacite	very fine/glassy extrusive lava or volcanic glass	felsic/silicic: similar to granite but plagioclase feldspar > orthoclase	fast cooling of explosive, gas-rich, silica-rich magma forming volcanoes of destructive plate margin
	pumice	vesicular, extrusive volcanic glass	felsic/silicic: volcanic glass no mineral crystals	very fast cooling; explosive, gas-rich, silica-rich magma forming volcanoes of destructive plate margins
	rhyolite	very fine/glassy extrusive lava or volcanic glass	felsic/silicic volcanic glass, occasionally feldspar crystals	fast cooling of silicate-rich lava at destructive plate margin beneath continent
intrusive, shallow depths	dolerite	medium 1–5 mm, intrusive	mafic: pyroxene, feldspar (plagioclase)	slower cooling than basalt e.g. sills
	microgranite	medium-grained, <1.5 mm, intrusive	felsic/silicic: feldspar (albite, orthoclase), mica (biotite, muscovite) quartz	fast cooling of silicic granitic magma in dykes/sills
	pegmatite	very coarse-grained, often extremely large crystals	felsic/silicic: feldspar (albite, orthoclase), mica (biotite, muscovite), quartz, tourmaline	late stage crystallisation of fluids in fractures around major batholiths
	porphyry	large crystals >5 mm in finer-grained groundmass	large crystals are usually well-shaped pyroxene and/or feldspar (mafic magma) or quartz crystals (silicic magma)	slow cooling to form large crystals, followed by rapid cooling, which may be extrusive
intrusive, deep	diorite	coarse >5 mm intrusive, plutonic	intermediate: feldspar (plagioclase), biotite or hornblende or pyroxene	slow cooling in magma chamber at depth above destructive plate margin within continent
	gabbro	coarse >5 mm intrusive, plutonic	mafic: pyroxene, feldspar (plagioclase), occasional olivine	slow cooling in magma chamber beneath ocean ridge; ring complexes; plutonic equivalent of basalt
	granite	coarse >5 mm, intrusive, plutonic	felsic/silicic: feldspar (albite orthoclase), mica (biotite, muscovite) quartz	slow cooling in magma chamber above destructive plate margin, within continent; plutonic
	granodiorite	coarse >5 mm intrusive, plutonic	felsic/silicic: similar to granite but plagioclase feldspar > orthoclase	slow cooling in magma chamber above destructive plate margin, within continent; intrusive equivalent of dacite
mantle	peridotite	coarse >5 mm plutonic	ultramafic: olivine, occasional pyroxene	mantle
Sedimentary				
clastic	arkose sandstone	medium-grained, 2–0.0625 (2–16th) mm	sandstone with more than 25% feldspar	immature sandstone; fairly short transport distance
	breccia	coarse, angular fragments	variable	debris below rock face; very near source; also fault zones
	clay	fine <0.0039 (256th) mm	clay minerals and quartz	very low energy conditions
	conglomerate	coarse, >2 mm, rounded fragments	variable	high energy conditions
	greywacke sandstone	medium-grained 2–0.0625 (2–16th) mm	sandstone with more than 15% mud matrix	turbidity current deposits
	mudstone	fine, massive (not well-layered)	mainly clay minerals and quartz	low energy conditions
	orthoquartzite sandstone	medium-grained, 2–0.0625 (2–16th) mm	sandstone with more than 95% quartz	mature sandstone; long transport history
	sandstone	medium-grained, 2–0.0625 (2–16th) mm	variable (includes arkose, greywacke and orthoquartzite)	moderate to high energy conditions; by water or wind
	shale	fine, fissile (splits easily)	many clay minerals and quartz	low energy conditions
	siltstone	fine, 0.625–0.0039 (16th–256th) mm	many clay minerals and quartz	fairly low energy conditions
	till	very coarse to very fine	variable	ice melt deposit

Appendix 3 *Continued*

Formation process	Name	Texture and grain size	Composition and minerals	Formation details
Sedimentary (continued)				
carbonate	chalk	fine	primarily calcite	platelets from marine algae deposited in very low energy conditions
	dolomite	variable	more than 90% dolomite	altered from limestone during diagenesis
	limestone	variable	more than 50% calcite and aragonite	mostly the remains of organisms; deposited mainly in warm seas
chemical	chert (flint in chalk)	very fine (microcrystalline)	silica	nodules grow in limestones during diagenesis
	rock salt	variable	halite	salt water evaporation deposit
organic	coal	fine	carbon and hydrocarbons	swamp deposit
Metamorphic				
high T, low P (thermal/ contact metamorphism)	hornfels	granoblastic also 'splintery', randomly oriented crystals	equidimensional interlocking crystals of andalusite, cordierite, quartz and micas	high T, low P, contact metamorphism
	marble	saccharoidal ('sugary')	calcite and aragonite	recrystallised limestone by contact or regional metamorphism
	metaquartzite	saccharoidal ('sugary')	quartz	recrystallised sandstone by contact or regional metamorphism
	spotted rock	maculose	fine-grained recrystallised micas with dark 'spotting'	first signs of metamorphism in country rocks near an intrusion (aureole)
low to high T, low to high P (regional metamorphism)	eclogite	granulose, coarse-grained	pyroxene and garnet	basalt recrystallised at very high P (subduction)
	gneiss	gneissose banding, usually fairly coarse-grained	segregation of quartz and feldspar (pale) from biotite and garnet (darker) into distinct bands	high grade (high T and P) regional metamorphism
	granulite	may be foliated, variable	pyroxene, garnet, kyanite or sillimanite	extremely high temperature, high T, moderate P
	greenschist	variable	contains chlorite	basalt recrystallised at low T and low P
	marble	saccharoidal ('sugary')	calcite and aragonite	recrystallised limestone by contact or regional metamorphism
	metaquartzite	saccharoidal ('sugary')	quartz	recrystallised sandstone by contact or regional metamorphism
	migmatite	contorted gneissose banding	'swirly' bands of felsic and mafic minerals	degree of partial melting – intermediate between metamorphic and igneous rock
	phyllite	foliated, slight crenulation; coarser than slate	aligned muscovite and chlorite	higher grade (med T and P) regional metamorphism of slate
	schist	wavy foliation, usually medium-coarse grained	bands of minerals >1 mm, e.g. of biotite; growth of metamorphic minerals e.g. garnet	higher grade (med T and P) regional metamorphism of phyllite
	slate	parallel foliation (cleavage) fine grained	fine-grained quartz and micas	lowest grade regional metamorphism of mud/shale (low T, low P)
low T, high P	blueschist	variable	contains glaucophane (dark blue)	low T, high P metamorphism (subduction)
shearing (dynamic)	mylonite	lens-shaped fragments in fine-grained matrix	sheared rock particles, often with rough foliation; matrix may show recrystallisation	shattering and gouge along major faults and overthrusts
metasomatic	skarn	variable	may contain oxides or sulphides	limestones altered by hydrothermal fluids (metasomatism)

Key

T = temperature

P = pressure

APPENDIX 4   Classification of Life

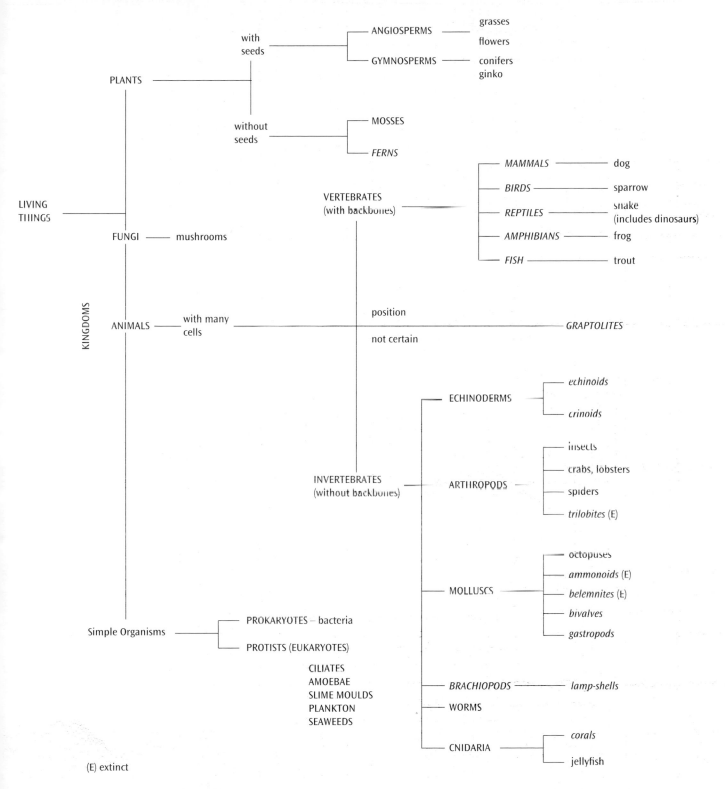

Appendix 4 *The biological classification of life forms, concentrating on plants and animals. Most life, however, is microscopic and one-celled, contained in the microbes and protists of this diagram. Life forms that are important geologically are in italics.*

Appendix 5 *Fossils*

Common name	Group name	Modern examples	Description	Living environment	Value	Geological range Max. no. of families
Molluscs	**Phylum Mollusca Bivalves** Class Bivalvia	Cockles, mussels, oysters, scallops razor shells	Bivalves have two valves or shells which are hinged together and are usually mirror images of each other. On death the muscles relax, the shell opens and the valves separate. Scallop (*Pecten*), oyster (*Ostrea*) and devil's toenail (*Gryphaea*, extinct) do not have bilateral symmetry and have shells of calcite that are more likely to be preserved.	Most are marine; some freshwater. Most shells are aragonite. Mode of life mostly benthic. Active, fixed and burrowing forms. Can tolerate wide range of environments and water depths.	Indicates salinity, energy levels, etc. of the environment. Bivalves are only rarely used to date rocks (slow evolution until Tertiary, then rapid)	Cambrian – present **Max** – today
	Gastropods Class Gastropoda	Snails, whelks, periwinkles and limpets	All gastropod shells are coiled in a conical spiral though the coiling is not obvious in the limpet's shell.	Marine and fresh water, mostly benthic, diverse facies associations	slow evolution until Tertiary, then rapid	late Cambrian to present **Max** – today
	Cephalopods Class Cephalopoda Nautiloids	*Nautilus*	Shells coiled in one plane. Divided into chambers filled with gas, which can be compressed by the animal. This allows movement up and down in the water. Earliest nautiloid shells were straight. Straight nautiloids became extinct; only the smaller coiled variety has survived.	*Nautilus* – marine. Nautiloids more widely spread. Swimming/floating. Widespread across facies. Best preserved in limestones and shales. The most efficient predators in the sea (before fish); some grew to 5 m long.	Interpretation of the lifestyles of extinct cephalopods, ammonoids.	mid-Cambrian onwards **Max** – Ordovician
	Ammonoids Subclass Ammonoidea	None, except *Nautilus*	Goniatites developed into the ceratites which later evolved into ammonites; all are now extinct. Ammonoids were coiled in a flat spiral and the shell was subdivided into chambers by the septa. Predator – movement as *Nautilus* (see above)	Marine, active swimmers, particularly abundant in Jurassic and Cretaceous seas.	Evolved very rapidly, are relatively abundant and common and therefore useful for dating rocks	mid Devonian – Cretaceous **Max** – Triassic
	Belemnites	None – extinct	Bullet-shaped hard part is not a shell but an internal skeleton similar to that of the present day cuttlefish. Occasionally the soft parts are preserved as a carbonised film.	Marine, active swimmers, particularly abundant in Jurassic and Cretaceous seas		early Carboniferous to Tertiary **Max** – Jurassic
	Phylum Brachiopoda	In Pacific and Indian Oceans	Valves nearly always of different sizes and shapes. The left side of each valve is a mirror image of the right side, i.e. bilateral symmetry down the centre of the shell. Sometimes called lamp shells.	Shallow water marine, benthic; adapted to fixed and burrowing lifestyles; some found in shales and sands	Used for dating the Silurian	early Cambrian onwards **Max** – Devonian
Echinoderms	**Phylum Echinodermata** Echinoids Class Echinoidea	Sea urchins	Sub-spherical shapes formed of a series of calcite plates. Two types: regular echinoids – pentagonal shape; irregular echinoids bilateral symmetry.	Marine benthic epifaunal and infaunal in mostly shallow water environments; best preserved in limestones. Move by using muscles which are attached to spines and by using their tube feet, operated by a hydraulic system.	Irregular echinoids are used as zonal fossils to date Cretaceous rocks.	late Ordovician onwards **Max** – Tertiary
	Crinoids Class Crinoidea	Feather stars	Plant-like animals usually sessile (fixed in position). In life the skeleton was covered by flesh; when the animal died the flesh usually rotted and the skeleton broke into many disc or rod like segments.	Shallow marine reefs away from sediment. Most sessile, some floaters		mid-Cambrian to present **Max** – Ordovician
Trilobites	**Phylum Arthropoda, Subphylum Trilobita**	None (extinct) – but related to insects, crabs, and wood lice.	Hard exoskeleton consisted of a head, a thorax or body and a tail. The thorax was flexible as it was made of many separate segments. Largest trilobite 60 cm long; smallest less than 5 mm; majority about 10 cm long. Most had eyes and some could swim, though the majority probably crawled along the sea bottom.	Epifaunal marine benthic, active crawling /swimming mostly in shallow water; widespread; best preserved in low energy shales	Zonal fossils for dating the Cambrian.	early Cambrian to end Permian **Max** – Cambrian
Graptolites	**Phylum Hemichordata.** Class Graptolithina Dendroids	None (extinct)	Thin 'saw blade' appearance. Colonial – each graptolite skeleton housed many individual animals, each living in a separate tiny cup attached to the main skeleton. The animals were all attached to each other by a canal similar to a spinal cord.	Floating in sea, widespread across facies but best preserved in low energy shales		late Cambrian to early Carboniferous **Max** – Ordovician
	Graptolites Class Graptolithina	None (extinct)	Graptoloids with two or more branches (stipes) common in the Ordovician; single-stiped forms confined to the Silurian and early Devonian. Skeletons very fragile.	Lived floating in sea. Found in deep, but not in shallow marine sediments, where they were broken up	Used for detailed correlation of Ordovician and Silurian sequences.	early Ordovician to early Devonian **Max** – Ordovician

Appendix 5 *Continued*

Common name	Group name	Modern examples	Description	Living environment	Value	Geological range / Max. no. of families
Corals	Phylum Cnidaria Class Anthozoa Scleractinian corals Order Scleractinia	Corals – related to sea anemones and jelly fish	Colonial: many individual animals living in the same skeleton. Polygonal pattern or series of cylinders, each with a radiating structure. Solitary: one animal lives in the coral cup, usually cone shaped with a radiating pattern in cross section. Tabulate and Rugose earliest types, replaced by Scleractinia at end of Permian.	Reef – shallow marine (very few freshwater). Fixed to substrate. Modern colonial corals only live in clear turbulent water, confined to warm seas of tropics and sub-tropics	Correlating Lower Carboniferous rocks. Palaeoenvironmental interpretation	Scleractinian early Triassic to present; **Max** – Cretaceous
	Rugose corals Order Rugosa	None (extinct)	Rugose corals have radiating septa. Both solitary and colonial varieties are common.	Warm shallow, well-lit seas which are free of mud.	as above	late Ordovician to end Permian; **Max** – Devonian
	Tabulate corals Order Tabulata	None (extinct)	Tabulate corals have series of horizontal plates (tabulae). Earliest corals, all colonial.	Warm, shallow, well-lit seas which are free of mud.	as above	late Ordovician to end Permian; **Max** – Silurian
Microfossils		Plankton, Foraminifera, Radiolaria, Coccoliths, Pollen and Spores	Fossils normally too small to be seen with the naked eye. Foraminifera (shells of calcium carbonate) Radiolaria (made of silica). Conodonts (tiny tooth-shaped parts of an extinct eel-like animal). Ostracods (micro-crustaceans). Coccoliths (calcite scales or marine algae). Pollen and spores (from plants)	Planktonic – floating in seas and oceans	Used for correlation by oil companies; abundant in rock chippings obtained from boreholes and in drill cores. Give evidence for depth, salinity and water temperature	early Cambrian to present; **Max** – today
Vertebrates	Phylum Chordata, Fish	Fish	First animals with backbones (vertebrates) to appear. Early types jawless (not common today). Several types evolved including sharks, and all bony fish.	Marine and freshwater	Exceptional preservation sites give insights into evolution	late Cambrian – present; **Max** – Tertiary
	Amphibians Class Amphibia	Frogs, newts and toads.	Fully able to live on dry land – they breathe air and more quickly/enough to catch prey. Cold blooded and returned to water to lay eggs. Some forms reached more than a metre in length, but the common living forms today are much smaller.	Land and fresh water – but water for reproduction	Amphibian fossils are rare, but they give insights into the evolution of life.	late Devonian – present; **Max** – Carboniferous
	Reptiles Class Reptilia (4 groups)	Crocodiles, lizards, etc.	Cold-blooded but able to lay their eggs on land. Anapsids earliest group gave rise to the tortoises; including Mesosaurus, found fossilised in both Africa and South America. Synapsids gave rise to the mammals, before becoming extinct. Diapsids developed into the dinosaurs and crocodiles. Euryapsids gave rise to the marine reptiles – all of which later became extinct.	Land, marine reptiles in sea, flying reptiles in air	Fossils rare, but examples can be found of 'dinosaur graveyards' where many bones are preserved. Reptile fossils give evidence for continental drift (plate tectonics).	mid Carboniferous to present; **Max** – Jurassic
	Mammals Class Mammalia	Humans, cats, dogs	Warm-blooded with fur or hair as insulation. Give birth to live young and produce milk to feed the young. Early forms small (mouse to cat size) but evolved into the wide range of mammals seen today. Some forms adapted to marine conditions (whales, etc.) and some to the air (bats). Homo sapiens is a mammal.	Land, sea, air	Mammal fossils also give insights into the evolution of life. Fossils rare.	Late Triassic to present; **Max** – present
Land Plants	Kingdom Plantae	Grasses, trees, flowering plants	Fragments of the stems, leaves and roots are often found and preserved as a carbon film in sandstones and shales. Flowering plants developed in Cretaceous. Spores and pollen derived from plants are important microfossils.	Land. Abundant well preserved plant fossils indicate fresh water conditions.	Produce oxygen and support food chain. Give information about climate, temperature	late Silurian to present; **Max** – today
Trace fossils		Footprints, droppings, burrows	Any sign of life, such as borings, teeth marks, faecal pellets, etc. Important indicators of the lifestyle of the animal that made them, e.g. many trails are feeding trails. Faecal pellets give clues on what the animal ate. Footprints can give information on the weight and speed of animals and the ways they moved. They give clues to animal habits, e.g. some dinosaur footprints indicate that the animals travelled in herds.	Land or water – most common in fine sediments	Environmental interpretation. Footprints are only found on land or in very shallow water whilst some tracks, trails and burrows are characteristic of shallow or deep water.	Pre Cambrian, 1000 Ma to present

Appendix 6 *Economic minerals*

Mineral name	Chemical formula	Major occurrence	Property(ies) used	Major uses
Barite (Barytes)	$BaSO_4$	Gangue mineral in hydro-thermal veins	Relatively high density (RD 4.5)	Drilling muds; writing paper
Bauxite	$Al_2O_3.2H_2O$	Tropical weathering	Aluminium content	Ore of aluminium (30%)
Cassiterite	SnO_2	Hydrothermal veins, placer deposits	Tin content (RD around 7, H around 7)	Ore of tin (0.5%)
Chalcopyrite	$CuFeS_2$	Hydrothermal veins	Copper content	Ore of copper (0.5%); electrical wire
Chromite	$FeCr_2O_4$	Magmatic segregation; placers	Chromium content (RD 4.6, H 5.5)	Furnace linings, steel plating; ore of chromium (30%–45%)
Diamond	C	'Pipes' of kimberlite; placer deposits	Hardness; gem qualities lustre, rarity; (RD 3.5, H 10)	Industrial cutting and abrasive tools; gemstones
Fluorite (Fluorspar)	CaF_2	Gangue mineral, hydro-thermal veins	Fluorine content	Main source of fluorine – tooth care; refrigeration; aerosols
Galena	PbS	Hydrothermal veins	Lead content	Ore of lead (5%); batteries
Graphite	C	Metamorphism of carbon-rich rocks	'Softness' (H 1–2); electrical conductivity; heat resistance	Lubricant and pencil 'leads'; carbon electrodes; heat resistant materials
Gold (native)	Au	Hydrothermal veins; mainly in placer deposits	Electrical conductivity, untarnishable (RD 19.3)	Electrical and electronics, jewellery (0.0004%)
Gypsum	$CaSO_4.2H_2O$	Evaporating sea water deposit	Converted to plaster of Paris $CaSO_4.\frac{1}{2}H_2O$ by heating	Plaster is used for plastering walls and broken limbs
Haematite	Fe_2O_3	Precambrian sedimentary deposits; vein deposits	Iron content	Ore of iron (55%)
Halite	NaCl	Evaporating sea water deposit	Sodium and chlorine content; depresses freezing point of water	Chemical industry; food seasoning and preserving; salting icy roads
Ilmenite	$FeO.TiO_2$	Magmatic segregation; placer deposits	Titanium content (RD around 5, H 5–6)	Ore of titanium; steel additive, high temp alloys; paint pigment
Kaolinite	$Al_4Si_4O_{10}(OH)_8$	In and near granite batholiths (breakdown of feldspar)	White colour, fine texture	Ceramics, coating for paper, 'filler' in pharmaceuticals
Magnetite	Fe_3O_4	Magmatic segregation; placer deposits	Iron content (RD 5.2, H 6)	Ore of iron
Muscovite mica	$KAl_2(AlSi_3)O_{10}(OH)_2$	Large crystals in pegmatites	Insulating properties	Electrical insulation
Quartz	SiO_2	Pure in vein quartz; fairly pure in quartz-rich sands and metaquartzites	Transparent when fused (H 7); silicon content; piezoelectric effect	Glass-making; abrasive; source of silicon compounds; electrical apparatus (silicon chips)
Sphalerite	ZnS	Hydrothermal mineral	Zinc content	Ore of zinc (3%); batteries
Talc	$Mg_6Si_4O_{10}(OH)_2$	Alteration of Mg-bearing rocks	'Softness' (H 1) Lack of reactivity	Talcum powder; filler in paints, paper, rubber

RD = relative density; H = hardness. Percentage in brackets in 'uses' e.g. (3%) is the average cut off grade.

APPENDIX 7   Geological Time

Appendix 7A *The divisions of geological time and major events since 570 million years ago (Phanerozoic time*

Eon	Era	Period *Duration Ma* **Start Ma**	Key stages in the evolution of life and common life forms	The diversity of life (variation in number of families)	Key events	Global sea level change	UK latitude (approx.)
Phanerozoic	Cenozoic	**Quaternary** *1.64*	Early humans	⇐ Inc. Dec. ⇒	• Major glaciation • Linking of N & S America • Alpine Orogeny in UK; Alps formed as Tethys closed • Widespread igneous activity in northern UK • Collision of India with Asia • Separation of Australia & Antarc.	High Low	55°N
		Tertiary *63*	Increase in mammals Horses, cows, elephants, pigs, apes, dogs, bears, etc. appear and increase Flowering plants in full development				40°N
		— 65 —				Present day	
	Mesozoic	**Cretaceous** *77*	Extinction of dinosaurs and ammonites Primates evolve Mammals and flowering plants (angiosperms) appear		• Opening of North Atlantic began		35°N
		— 142 —					
		Jurassic *64*	Dinosaurs and ammonites abundant Birds and mammals appear				30°N
		— 206 —					
		Triassic *42*	Mammals evolve Flying dinosaurs and reptiles appear First modern corals Ammonites evolve		• Opening of S Atlantic Ocean began		
		— 248 —					
	Upper Palaeozoic	**Permian** *42*	Mass extinction Rise of reptiles and amphibians Conifers and beetles appear		• Formation of Pangea supercontinent		10°N
		— 290 —			• Major glaciation • Hercynian/Variscan Orogeny in Europe – closing of the Rheic Ocean		
		Carboniferous *64*	Coal forest plants First reptiles and winged insects Seed-bearing plants (gymnosperms)				0°
		— 354 —					
		Devonian *63*	First amphibians and ammonoids Earliest trees and spiders Rise of fishes Graptolites become extinct				20°S
		— 417 —			• Climax of Caledonian Orogeny – closing of Iapetus. Laurentian plate joined to European plate		
	Lower Palaeozoic	**Silurian** *26*	First spore-bearing land plants; first soils Earliest known coral reefs				
		— 443 —					
		Ordovician *52*	First fish-like vertebrates Trilobites and graptolites abundant Corals appear		• Major glaciation	Present day	30°S
		— 495 —	⇐ increasing				
		Cambrian *50*	Trilobites, graptolites, brachiopods, molluscs, crinoids, radiolaria and foraminifera The 'Cambrian explosion' – complex marine organisms evolve with $CaCO_3$ shells – abundant fossils first appear				
		— 545 —					

Appendix 7B *The divisions of geological time and major events since the formation of the Earth*

Eon *Duration Ma* **Start, Ma**	Key stages in the evolution of life	Key events	Oxygen content of the atmosphere	Global temperture change
Phanerozoic *545*	See Phanerozoic geological column	See Phanerozoic geological column (Appendix 7A) for more details • Frequency of fires in Carb. coal forests indicates oxygen levels similar to or even higher than today • Land animals appear – need oxygen levels about present values		Ice Ice Ice
545				
Proterozoic *1930*	• Ediacaran faunas in Aust., Russia, China. Soft bodied animals • Silica skeletons in single celled algae • Stromatolites decline (grazers) • Stromatolites at their maximum; eukaryote diversification • Multicellular marine organisms evolve – Eukaryotes with nucleus and cytoplasm – needing oxygen above 0.1% • Size of cell doubles • Gunflint Chert (Canada/US) stromatolite • Single celled eukaryotes	• Break-up of early supercontinent • Orogeny in Scottish rocks • Soft bodied metazoan fossils first appear – need oxygen levels above 2% • Glaciation – Scotland, Greenland, Africa, China • Glaciation – Australia, China, S Africa • Glaciation – Greenland, Scandinavia • Formation of early supercontinent • Orogeny in Scottish rocks • End of major banded ironstone deposition (iron deposited in Fe^{2+} state, indicating low oxygen levels) • First red beds deposited, iron in Fe^{3+} state – must have been significant amount of oxygen in atmosphere	Present day	Major ice age Present day Ice age
2500		• Continental cores of most major continents formed by this time • Orogeny in Scottish rocks	30% 20% 10%	Cold Warm
Archean *1300*			None	
	• Stromatolites • Prokaryotes – bacteria and photosynthesising blue green bacteria (algae)	• Oxygen produced by early life forms • Earliest banded ironstones deposited (iron deposited in Fe^{2+} state, indicating little or no oxygen present) • First sedimentary rocks formed (Greenland) • Greenstone belts in India, Australia, S Africa, Canada		
3800	None	• First oceans probably formed • Volcanic outgassing and contributions from asteroids, etc. produced secondary atmosphere • Volcanic activity widespread on cooling Earth. Radioactive decay at higher rate than now • Zircon dates from igneous source rocks in NW Australia • Continued bombardment by asteroid-like bodies caused Earth to become very hot – probably a few thousand degrees • Formation of Earth and growth through collision of many asteroid-like bodies		
Hadean *800*			None	
4600				

(Left margin vertical label spanning Proterozoic/Archean/Hadean: **Precambrian**)

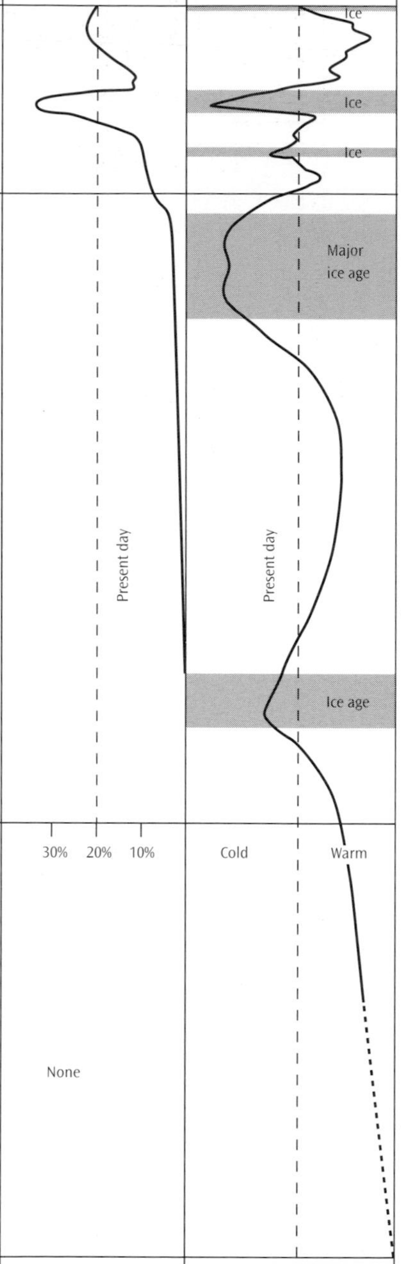

Note; All Geological Periods are subdivided into Epochs, as:

Period	Epoch	Start, Ma
Quaternary	Holocene or Recent	0.01
	Pleisocene	1.64
Tertiary	Pilocene	5.2
	Milocene	25.5
	Oligocene	35
	Eocene	56.5
	Palaeocene	65

Appendix 8 *Stratigraphic log plotting sheet*

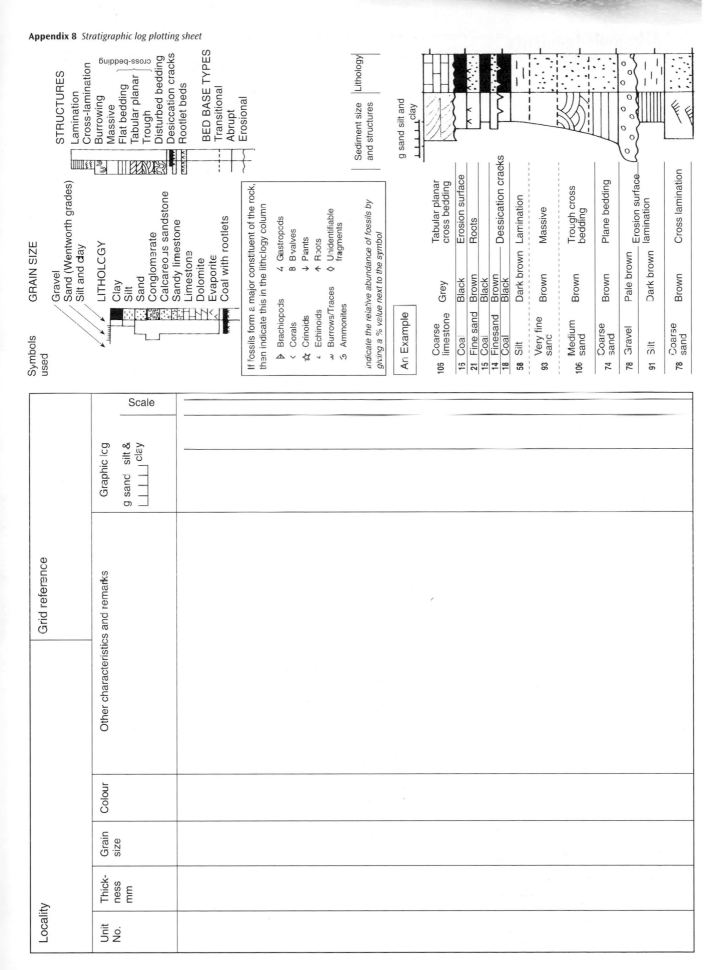

Acknowledgements

The authors and the publishers would like to thank the following for permission to reproduce copyright photographs in this book:
Life File, Figure 2.2, Figure 5.14a,b; Axiom, Figure 2.4; Landform Slides, Figure 2.16, Figure 8.2, Figure 8.15; Maggie Williams, Figure 8.6; Corbis, Figure 3.1a; Andrew Lambert, Open University, Figure 3.1b; Mark Davies, Open University, Figure 4.1; Sandra Smith, Open University, Figure 4.10; Peter Francis, Open University, Figure 4.15; Dee Edwards, Open University, Figure 4.19b, Figure 4.21b, Figure 6.2b,c, Figure C2.1, Figure C3.1, Figure C3.2, Figure C3.3, Figure C3.4, Figure C4.2, Figure C4.3, Figure C4.4, Figure C6.27a,b,c,d,e,f, Figure C7.2a,b, Figure C10.1; Michael Jay, Figure 4.20, Figure 12.3; British Geological Society, Figure 5.2; National Museums and Galleries on Merseyside, Figure 5.5; Poroperm Laboratories, Figure 5.6, Figure 5.7; Tony Shelton, Stoke 6th Form College, Figure 7.7; Geoscience features picture library, Figure 8.1a, Figure 8.22, Figure 10.9; Science Photo Library, Figure 8.1b, Figure 8.11; Skyscan, Figure 8.20; Still Moving Picture Company, Figure 8.24; Fotofachlabo Schnepf, Stuttgart, Figure 13.17.

The publishers would like to thank Tony Wilkins and Associates, John Taylor and Associates and Bill Donahoe for producing the illustrations herein.

The Department of Earth Sciences, Open University would like to thank:

Crystalmaker™, and David Palmer, for Figure 3.2a,b, Figure 3.4a; John Watson, for Figure 6.12 and Figures C6.1–C6.5; Andy Tindle, Earth Sciences, and KMI, Open University for Figures C3.5a,b, C3.6a,b, C4.1, C7.1.

Figures 5.1, 5.3, 5.8, 5.9 are from "Aeolian and mixed aeolian – aqueous sedimentation in modern and ancient sub-tropical desert basins. Examples from the Sahara and the Permo-Traissic of NW Europe", unpublished PhD thesis, Irgens Øxnevad, I.E., 1991.

Figure 5.4 from "Sedimentation of the Triassic (Scythian) red Pebbly Sandstones in the Cheshire Basin and its margins", Thomas, D.B., Geol. Vol. 7, 1970.

Every effort has been made to contact the holders of copyright material used in this book, but if any have been overlooked the publishers will be pleased to make the necessary alterations at the first possible opportunity.

Further reading

Anderton et al (1979) *A dynamic stratigraphy of the British Isles*. London, Allen and Unwin
Battey MH (1981) 2nd edition *Mineralogy for students*. London, Longman
Black RM (1988) *The Elements of Palaeontology* (2nd edition). Cambridge University Press, Cambridge
Brown GC, Hawkesworth CJ and Wilson RCL (Eds) (1992) *Understanding the Earth: a new synthesis.* Cambridge, Cambridge University Press
Clarkson EKN (1979) *Invertebrate Palaeontology and Evolution*. London, Allen and Unwin
Cox K, Price NB and Harte B (1974) *An Introduction to the Practical Study of Crystals, Minerals and Rocks*. London, McGrawHill
Doyle P (1996) *Understanding Fossils*. Chichester, Wiley
Duff D (1993) *Holmes' Principles of Physical Geology* (4th Edition). London, Chapman and Hall
Emiliani C (1992) *Planet Earth*. Cambridge, Cambridge University Press
Fortey R (1997) *Life: An Unauthorised Biography*. London, HarperCollins
Francis PW (1976) *Volcanoes*. Harmondsworth, Penguin Books
Gillen C (1982) *Metamorphic Geology: an introduction to tectonic and metamorphic process*. London, Allen and Unwin
Holland HD and Peterson U (1995) *Living Dangerously: the Earth, its resources and the environment*. Princeton N.J., Princeton University Press
Leeder M (1982) *Sedimentology: process and product*. London, Allen and Unwin
Lovelock, J (1991) *Gaia, the practical science of planetary medicine*. London, Gaia Books
McLane M (1995) *Sedimentology*. Oxford, Oxford University Press
McLeish A (1986) *Geological Science*. Glasgow, Blackie (now unfortunately out of print)
Park RG (1987) *Geological structures and moving plates*. Glasgow, Blackie
Press F and Siever R (1986) *Earth* (4th Edition). W.H. Freeman and Co
Press F and Siever R (1997) *Understanding Earth* (2nd Edition). W.H. Freeman and Co
Rose S (1997) *Lifelines: Biology, Freedom and Determinism*. London, The Penguin Group
ESTA (1994) *Routeway*. Sheffield, GeoSupplies
S269 Course Team (1997) *Earth and Life: Evolving Life and the Earth*. Milton Keynes, The Open University
S269 Course Team (1997) *Earth and Life: Origins of Earth and Life*. Milton Keynes, The Open University
Selley RC (1976) *Introduction to sedimentology*. London, Academic Press
Skinner BJ and Porter SC (1989) *The Dynamic Earth*. Chichester, Wiley
Smith D (Ed) (1989) *Cambridge Encyclopedia of Earth Sciences*. Cambridge, Cambridge University Press
Tucker M (1981) *Sedimentology Petrology: an introduction to sedimentary rocks*. Oxford, Blackwell Scientific
Woodcock NH (1994) *Geology and environment in Britain and Ireland*. London, UCL Press

Index